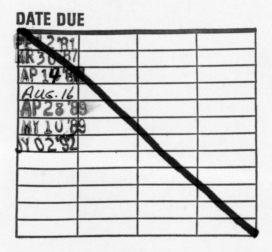

RECREATION AND SPECIAL POPULATIONS

Recreation and Special Populations

Edited by

Thomas A. Stein
H. Douglas Sessoms

University of North Carolina

Boston   Holbrook Press, Inc.

Library of Congress Catalog Number: 72–91546

Contents

FOREWORD   ix

1   INTRODUCTION TO RECREATION
AND SPECIAL POPULATIONS   1

Purpose · Historical Overview of Rehabilitation Services · Recreation Services: A History of Concern · The Present Situation · A Philosophical Base · Objectives to This Book · Planning the Discussion · The Authors

2   PROBLEM SOLVING AND LEADERSHIP TECHNIQUES   27

Problem Solving-Approach to Leadership · Assessing Goals · Planning a Course of Action · Evaluation · Problem Solving and Program Development: A Guide for Action

3   MEETING THE RECREATIONAL NEEDS OF
SPECIAL POPULATIONS IN THE COMMUNITY   43

Eric Errickson

Guidelines for Provision of Recreation Services to Special Populations · Problems and Resources in Delivery of Recreation Service to Special Populations · Toward Leisure Participation for All

4   RECREATION AND THE MENTALLY RETARDED   65

Gene A. Hayes

History · Definition of Mental Retardation · Classification · Etiology · Mongolism · Psychological Factors · Social

Factors · Physical, Social and Mental Traits · Social Dynamics of Recreation · Recreation and Leisure Time Needs · Activities · Community and Institutional Relationship in Programming

5 RECREATION AND YOUTHFUL
AND ADULT OFFENDERS   103

Marion and Carroll Hormachea

Development of Punishment and Correctional Philosophy · Rehabilitation and Corrections · The Role of Recreation in Corrections · Specialized Recreation Programs · Recreation Program Needs · Recreation in Pre-Release and Half-way-House Situations · Conclusion

6 RECREATION AND THE MENTALLY ILL   129

Lee E. Meyer

Mental Illness-Mental Health · Early Perspectives · The Recreation Movement—A Parallel to the Mental Health Movement · The Beginning of Organized Recreation Programs in Hospital Settings · Post World War II Developments in Mental Health Practices · Post World War II Organized Recreation Services in Institutions for the Mentally Ill · Community Mental Health Perspectives of the 1960's · Impact of Mental Health Practices of the 1960's on Recreation and the Recreator · Recreation Program Orientation · New Roles for Recreators

7 RECREATION AND THE ALCOHOLIC
AND DRUG ADDICT   167

H. Douglas Sessoms

The Social Aspects of Drug Use · Basic Definitions · Theories of Addiction · Drugs and Social Relationships ·

Approaches to Treatment and Rehabilitation ·
Recreation's Role

8 RECREATION AND PERSONS WITH
   PHYSICAL DISABILITIES   193

   Thomas A. Stein

   Background of Services · Understanding Terms · Problems of Disability · Environmental Barriers · Program
   Concepts · Sheltered Programs in the Community · Sheltered Outdoor Recreation Programs · Toward Integrated
   Recreation

9 RECREATION AND THE VISUALLY IMPAIRED   227

   Elliott G. Young

   Introduction · Physical Aspects · Population · Causes ·
   The Senses · Psychological and Social Aspects · Recreation · Youth Recreation Program · Adult Recreation Program · Older Adult Recreation Program

10 RECREATION AND THE ECONOMICALLY DEPRIVED   281

    James F. Murphy

    Nature and Extent of Poverty · Etiology · Middle-Class
    Versus Lower-Class Values · Psychological Depression ·
    Psychological Immaturity · Health Factors · Neighbor-
    hood Life: Urban Scene · Neighborhood Life: Rural Scene
    · Leisure Classes · Program Planning Considerations ·
    Needs Index · Organizing Recreation Activities for the
    Poor · Examples of Special Programming · Suggestions
    for Program Improvement and Development · The Future

11 RECREATION AND RACIAL MINORITIES 323

Ira J. Hutchison, Jr.

Introduction · Minorities: A Demographic Perspective · A Social Perspective · A Cultural Perspective · Historical Perspectives · Contemporary Perspectives · Implications for Recreation Services

12 RECREATION AND THE PROBLEMS OF YOUTH 353

Donald A. Pelegrino

Youth and Leisure Today · Physiological Needs of Adolescents · Psychological Aspects · Socialization of Youth · Some Thoughts and Possible Solutions

13 RECREATION AND THE AGING 379

Peter J. Verhoven

Demographic Background · Living Arrangements · Leisure and the Aging · Biological and Medical Considerations · Psychological Factors · Sociological Factors · Post Retirement · Transitional Period · The Later Years · Settings for Recreation Services for the Aging · Purposeful Programs · Principles to Planning · The Future

14 EPILOGUE AND A DESIGN FOR ACTION 409

Objectives and Philosophy: A Restatement · Sequential Planning · Common Programming Trends · A Plan for Action · Summary

INDEX 425

Foreword

Recreation—denoting all types in the broadest concept of the term.

Special Populations—denoting the growing interpretation of particular limitations in one's social, physical, or psychological living pattern.

Community Action—members of the social order, who are finding satisfaction through dynamic therapeutic practices for more abundant and wholesome human relationships for all.

One of the significant social phenomena of the contemporary era is the rapid growth of the place of *recreation* in the amelioration of, adaptation to, and prevention of man's many ills and disabilities. Involved are scenes of marked changes taking place within individuals and groups, social customs, and social institutions.

The numbers and distribution of population, the force of the growth of wealth, the many new contacts and contracts among men, and the gain in the sum of human knowledge are not only applied to all phases of life, but carry with them the possibilities of new and redirected desires; new social ideals; and, in the end, the demand for modified social orders.

Looming large upon the horizon of this scene is the tremendous growth of facts and factors producing the fascinating phenomena of the place of leisure and recreation in the life pattern of our people and its significant acceptance as a way of life.

Therapeutic recreation is perhaps the most rapidly growing and expanding process in the recreation family; only in the last few decades has it been recognized and acknowledged for its value to the individual and the group. As the recreator becomes proficient and perceptive to the needs and desires of special populations, recreation will become accepted as basic in the hierarchy of human needs.

Therapeutic recreation seems to be more indicative of the setting than of the activities provided. It is different somewhat due to those being served and the restrictive nature of some activities. Adaptation is a most important factor in program development due to the physical, mental, emotional, and social status of the participant. The basic activities are not so designated that certain activities are presented for specific conditions, but certain activities may be more appropriate at a given time for a given person.

Leadership is recreation's most important dimension. There is no substitute for a well-trained leader—professional or volunteer. Formulating techniques and promoting a balanced program for all ages, both sexes, and all social and economic strata build for a democracy of choice. The authors of this volume, through their presentations based upon experienced leadership, bid you to join them in having recreation and special populations bring forth telling, fascinating, and creative innovations and practices for the enrichment of individuals and groups in the total democratic process. From its pages may we gain inspiration, knowledge, and enthusiasm for progress in the days and years ahead.

Harold D. Meyer
Chairman Emeritus of the
Curriculum in Recreation Administration
University of North Carolina

1 Introduction to Recreation and Special Populations

Courtesy National Easter Seal Society for Crippled Children & Adults, Inc.

H. DOUGLAS SESSOMS

THOMAS A. STEIN

PURPOSE

There are immediate difficulties in attempting to introduce the broad subject of recreation services for those individuals and groups requiring special attention. This is due to the vast diversity of population segments with which we are concerned. To give some notion of the problem, this book considers the recreation needs of two special age groups—teenage youth and the elderly—and specific disability and disadvantaged groups including youthful and adult offenders, economically disadvantaged, racial minorities, alcoholics and narcotic addicts, mentally ill, mentally retarded, physically disabled, and visually impaired. We are convinced that a common thread tends to tie these special groups together. Simply stated, the overwhelming majority of these people have not been effectively served by society in meeting many of their social, psychological, or physiological needs and aspirations.

The purpose of this chapter is to attempt to briefly transmit some understanding as to how rehabilitation and recreation services have developed, where they are at the present time, and to offer a philosophical base upon which to relate the remainder of the book. Of necessity, the discussion is quite general in order to maintain an all-inclusiveness to all special populations. It will be noted that certain populations, such as those with hearing difficulties, those considered disadvantaged because of sex, or those living in rural environs, are not included. We recognize that these groups may not have received adequate services from our recreation delivery systems. However, it was the contention of the editors that the scope of this text should be limited to those population groups which, in their opinion, have the more critical leisure needs.

HISTORICAL OVERVIEW
OF REHABILITATION SERVICES

Historically, the needs of disadvantaged members of our society have emerged from a past of minimal social concern or, at best, an outmoded but prevailing attitude that isolation from community life offered the appropriate answer to their dilemma.

Too often public reaction included the concept of charity whereby individual dignity was transformed into degrading dependency. Occasionally, such acts of collective charity were accompanied by attitudes of pity, disdain, or overt ridicule. Throughout our history, according to Robert Straus,

> Persons disabled by problems for which little could be done or which appeared only remotely related to the broader social need, have usually been subjected to a variety of harsh and hideous treatments. These have included death, torture, ostracism, imprisonment, slavery, relegation to a caste-like separate society, and, as a minimum, living under a cloud of stigma and chronic awareness of being abhorrent to fellow man.[1]

The concept of institutionalism, for purposes of segregating such persons from the so-called acceptable majority of our population, became the policy of both governmental and nonpublic agencies. The county farm, insane asylum, prison, black town, reservation, poorhouse, and old folks' home were examples of this separating process.

Prior to World War I and, to a lesser degree, until 1940, those public and nonpublic programs geared toward the special problems of disadvantaged individuals were largely directed toward the provision of maintenance—that is, providing the basic necessities for existence and subsistence and, therefore, minimizing the effects of deprivation. Once the individual was isolated, the isolation itself tended to become a permanent condition for many. Having been "put away," societal concern diminished, resulting in inadequate financial support and, as a consequence, oppressive facilities, minimal programs, and poorly trained leadership. Surely, this was not conducive to aiding the person toward a return to productive, satisfying and, where applicable, socially acceptable community living. In cases where the individual was returned to the community, it usually meant the return of an unaltered person to an unaltered environment.

Although prior to the twentieth century there were some federal laws passed which provided a degree of opportunity to physically rehabilitate certain people incapacitated by injury or illness, it was not until 1918 that the first specific legislation was passed. This law was directed toward the vocational restoration of disabled veterans.[2] Funds were to be used for job training; counseling and job placement services; and, where needed, such prosthetic devices as artificial limbs, crutches, wheelchairs, etc. In 1943, again because of the concern for returning disabled military personnel, a new act which was much broader in scope was passed by the Congress. Medical and surgical treatment based on diagnostic or psychological examination, hospitalization, and any services needed to rehabilitate an individual for an appropriate vocation were now included.[3]

In 1945, additional provisions were authorized to train rehabilitation personnel, to construct rehabilitation facilities, and to finance demonstration programs.[4] In 1963 the Vocational Rehabilitation Administration broadened its services to include the mental health and mental retardation of children as well as adults.[5] Later, the potential clientele for rehabilitation services were to include nearly all disadvantaged populations including youthful and adult offenders, the poor, and minority racial groups. By 1968, to accentuate this broadening concern within the Department of Health, Education and Welfare, the Vocational Rehabilitation Administration and the Administration on Aging were administratively placed under a newly created agency called the Social and Rehabilitation Services Administration. No longer was government concerned only for the care, treatment, and vocational needs of special populations, but it also included program opportunities to meet the needs of the total person, including his leisure needs, and to train professional personnel to provide effective leadership.

RECREATION SERVICES:
A HISTORY OF CONCERN

A parallel development to the evolving of rehabilitation services was the development of organized recreation programs in the community, under both public and private auspices, and in some institutional settings.

Recreation in the Community*

The crisis today in America's cities along with the weakening of the nation's moral fiber in the twentieth century parallels a

* The chapter author is grateful to Dr. James F. Murphy for providing much of the background information contained in this section. Dr. Murphy is the author of the chapter on "Recreation and the Economically Disadvantaged."

similar circumstance 100 years earlier in our country's history when the advent of the Industrial Revolution spurred national leaders to take a close look at the problems of technological advancement and its effects upon people. Similarly, much of the current social ferment is related to a rapidly changing society which is outdistancing the level of comprehension and manageability of the poor.

The deprived lack many of the basic advantages afforded the more affluent. With the squalor and despair of the urban and rural slums acting as a constant barrier to change, some deprived people have shed the cloak of complacency and have struck out against society, demanding immediate social reforms. Certain racial minority groups have been at the forefront of this social unrest while other disadvantaged populations, perhaps because they lack leadership, organization, and numbers, have not been able to make their demands felt.

The present condition of society is hauntingly reminiscent of the situation which sparked the initiation of the play movement in this country near the close of the nineteenth century.

> It grew out of a situation of need owing to such factors as technological developments, particularly the introduction of modern machinery of production with its monotonous and nerve-racking work; urbanization, especially the over-crowded living conditions in sections of cities; changing home conditions and family disorganization; the speed of living, including increased mobility and daily rushing about; and the increase of leisure.[6]

The pioneer leaders sensed that there was a need for amelioration of the problem and called attention to the necessity of providing recreation to all citizens, especially the under-privileged groups in urban areas. The play movement eventually matured into the recreation movement with the formation of the Playground Association of America in 1906. It is considered by George Butler as the single most important event in the American recreation movement.

> No single event has had greater significance for the recreation movement than this Washington meeting [a gathering of national leaders in Washington, D.C., in April, 1906, who met to discuss the nation's play needs]. Previously the drive

for playgrounds had received no concerted guidance or support; formation of the Playground Association of America . . . gave it new impetus and competent national leadership.[7]

The attempt by social workers to meet the increasing problems resulting from urban living in the 1880's led to the founding of settlement houses. These institutions, like the publicly and privately sponsored park and playground programs that generally came later, made a great impact on the promotion of play activity in America. Additionally, social settlements attempted to provide for the total health, education, and welfare needs of a needy citizenry. Play and recreation were considered part of the total need of the individual.

The institution which paralleled the growth of recreation is known as the social settlement, commonly called the community center. . . . The first expression of the movement in the United States was in New York in 1887, followed by the opening in Chicago by Jane Addams in 1889. Social settlements grew out of the humanitarian movement to aid the poor. Originally they were located in slum areas where people with means, leisure, and education could meet the needs of the poorer classes on the basis of neighborhood friendliness. They have become centers of education, recreation, and welfare activities.[8]

When attempting to arrive at a conclusion as to which cause was most influential in the development of the recreation movement in America, it is extremely difficult to give more credit to one person or institution than another. It is fairly evident that Hull-House in Chicago had a great deal of influence on the initiation of the recreation movement. Its purpose for operation was a reflection of the times. Jane Addams, founder and director of Hull-House, interpreted the necessity for the social settlement by giving three reasons for its existence:

It aims, in a measure, to develop whatever a social life its neighborhood may afford, to focus and give form to that life, to bring to bear upon it the results of cultivation and training; but it receives in exchange for the music of isolated voices the volume and strength of the chorus. It is quite impossible for me to say in what proportion or degree the subjective necessity which led to the opening of Hull-House combined the three trends: first, the desire to interpret democracy in social terms; second, the impulse beating at the very source of our lives, urging us to aid in the race progress; and thirdly, the Christian movement toward humanitarianism. . . . The Settlement, then, is an experimental effort to aid in the solution of the social and industrial problems which are engendered by the modern conditions of life in a great city.[9]

The mode of living in the congested northern cities in the latter part of the nineteenth century had deteriorated somewhat from its status prior to the Industrial Revolution. The cities were fast becoming centers of crime; sickness was prevalent in the dirty alleys of many of the nation's most prosperous communities; the streets were full of children desiring something to do. The majority of urban workers could not engage in the booming variety of sports and outdoor activities coming into vogue. According to Dulles, "their entertainment was necessarily passive, commercialized, and cheap."[10]

Slums were becoming a reality in overcrowded sections of large cities. Various residential sectors were becoming dilapidated as industry encroached on their boundaries. Many immigrants poured into the areas where housing was cheap and minimally adequate. The propagation of unwholesome and inexpensive forms of entertainment went uncontrolled. Delinquency was rampant in most metropolitan areas, and the slums became centers of crime.

According to Butler, several related issues led to the need for establishing an organized recreation movement.

Bad housing conditions resulting from the growth of tenement slum areas, the great influx of immigrants, the rising tide of juvenile delinquency, the increase in factories accompanied by the evils of child labor and unsanitary and unsafe working conditions, the spread of commercialized amusements which were often associated with vice—all helped create a condition which made the provision of wholesome recreation a necessity.[11]

Park and recreation areas began to be planned at the close of the nineteenth century, largely at the insistence of social workers and influential citizens. The early success and impact of organized recreation are generally attributed to individuals with a human welfare motivation who supported the value of wholesome, supervised recreation as a basic and legitimate function of local government.

David Gray supports this belief and reiterates the fact that the recreation movement was spawned from the hard work and insistent efforts of the settlement house movement, which later gave way to the fostering of youth agencies. Gray states that the "earliest practitioners had a human welfare motivation in which the social ends of human development, curbing juvenile delinquency, informal education, cultural enrichment, health improvement and other objectives were central."[12]

It should be realized that the first efforts in support of the recreation movement were in behalf of the poor and underprivileged. The attempt to bring social services "down" to the neighborhood level was an effort to offer recognizable relief to the isolated and helpless poor people of the crowded northern cities. In 1897, a tract of two acres of land was purchased in New York City by the determined efforts of Jacob Riis. A well-equipped demonstration playground was developed on this site —on land which had been previously covered with five- and six-storied tenements. This successful experiment led to further recreation facility expansion in the city.

> In addition to apparatus, wading pool, and game spaces, a gymnasium with baths was constructed, and seats were provided for spectators. It was intended that the playground should be a "neighborhood affair." So successful was this experiment that the Park Department was induced to provide similar equipment and facilities in other parks in congested sections of the city.[13]

As recreation became a more legitimate function of government and as more affluent citizens recognized its worth, neighborhoods that could articulate their needs pressed for the development of new facilities and play spaces in the suburbs. This development led public recreation departments to concentrate their efforts less with the indigent and more with the advantaged citizens in suburban areas. Gray notes that eventually the "idea grew that any neighborhood which lacked public recreation services was, in a sense, underprivileged, and that centers ought to be provided throughout the city."[14]

Recreation in the Institution

With regard to recreation services in institutional settings, the services offered were principally intended to provide diversion from an otherwise dreary existence. Activities were usually provided on a sporadic basis under the direction of well-intentioned but untrained leaders. In many settings the total recreation bill of fare depended wholly upon the occasional, often rare, visits of altruistic groups during holiday seasons. One need only visit many nursing homes to find that this type of "program" exists today. Where organized activities were offered on a regular basis, organized volunteers or members of an institution's staff, i.e., medical, custodial, or similar personnel, served in a recreation leadership capacity. Such responsibilities were in addition to primary tasks.

The notion that recreation could be an important tool in the total rehabilitation process, particularly in the social development or redevelopment of the individual, was one that began gaining adherents in the late 1940's. This was a result of change in society's view of the patient and a recognition that these persons, who had been effective contributors to society, could in many instances still be productive members of society with proper rehabilitation. Perhaps a major factor in altering community attitudes was the return of veterans with various mental and physical disabilities. However, except for some demonstration efforts at in-service training, it was not until the late 1950's that concentrated formal educational programs were offered to provide specialized training for recreators to work with the disadvantaged.

Recreation Services to
Special Populations Today

As we consider the general state of recreation services in America today, a concern for people and their leisure seems to be emerging as a principal preoccupation of many professionals in the field. In some instances we have been forced into taking a hard look at our objectives and actions by outside influences arising out of crisis. This is especially true of our services to those who are deemed socially, culturally, or economically disadvantaged. Too, there seems to be a growing concern, although perhaps not as yet arising out of crisis, for those who are disadvantaged because of mental or physical limitations. We are groping for ways of effectively extending our community recreation services to such persons. This looking also includes ways of bringing some of them into recreation leadership positions. Yet our efforts are so often sporadic and ineffectual. Why? Undoubtedly there are many reasons which, because of their interdependency, form a complex web of cause-and-effect relationships. Lack of funds, shortage of trained leaders, and inappropriate design and/or location of areas and facilities are some of the reasons given by administrators for not providing viable services to many special populations. However, it is suspected that one overriding factor affecting our general lack of service to these groups is that of misunderstanding or lack of knowledge about the psychological, social, and physiological condition of disadvantaged individuals. Further, where services are offered or where they allow for inclusion of these people, failure to better understand their needs and aspirations sometimes results in activity which is not attuned to such needs. This insensitivity, on occasion, may result in a negative reaction on the part of potential clientele—e.g., the group of black teenaged boys who no longer want any part of a neighborhood recreation center or playground. As one member of this group stated during an interview, "Man, I've spent my life on playgrounds and in centers playing basketball. All they [presumably the city fathers and recreation leaders] want to do is keep us off the streets. I'm graduated from that now and I don't want to set foot in one of those places [public recreation centers] again."

A young woman with a physical disability requiring her to be in a wheelchair expressed it another way: "I know they don't have any signs saying 'Handicapped Not Welcome.' But even if I could get in our community recreation center—which I can't—the people there probably wouldn't know what to do with me. I would only make them and myself uncomfortable."

Of course we are seeing an increase of program demonstrations by a number of public and nonpublic agencies which attempt to circumvent traditional approaches and to find more appropriate ways of serving these people. (Some of these are presented in later chapters.) We must recognize that not all of these attempts to develop viable programming are going to be resounding successes. Mistakes will be made and this can be expected when it is realized that few (if any) precedents exist for much of what we are attempting to do. We do not have the luxury of other people's experiences upon which to build; we cannot look at their mistakes in order to avoid errors in judgment. In a real sense our community recreation services to special populations are a pioneering effort. Our effectiveness will surely increase as we gain experience, become more knowledgeable, and communicate our results to one another. That is really one of the aims of this book.

THE PRESENT SITUATION

The concept of recreation as a change agent, a vehicle for modifying individual behavior, is one that is beginning to be recognized by public officials as well as social service professionals from outside the recreation field. It is becoming increasingly clear that the provision of wholesome opportunities for the satisfaction of leisure needs of special populations is an essential ingredient to good individual and community health. (That this may be true of the total citizenry is not debated.) By way of explanation, some leaders have begun to look to recreation service agencies to help minimize the stresses of boredom which often accrue to a person with a physical disability or to an individual who has retired when vast amounts of unobligated time are void of meaning and are accompanied by a feeling of uselessness. With respect to people who have paid their debt to society through imprisonment, the comment made by a warden of a state prison to the writer seems apropos. He noted that when ex-inmates return to their communities, they often get back into difficulty not during their job or work time but rather during their free time. Further, he felt, this unfortunate condition will remain until we find ways of assisting these people to acquire and refine avocational and social skills and attitudes which are both socially acceptable and of personal value for the individual. To assume that this can be accomplished solely in the institution with no involved commitment by the community is absurd. A similar observation was made by Julius Cohen in

his study of the post-rehabilitation failure of the mentally retarded, where he noted that two-thirds of those who had difficulty in their adjustment had problems because they were
unprepared to cope with their free time and social relationships.[15]

Recreation agencies should become and, in a few instances,
are becoming a focal point for providing meaningful and satisfying experiences to meet these needs. Although the Roman
idea of "bread and circuses" to keep the masses in hand is no
longer acceptable and organized recreation cannot be the panacea for all social ills, some recreation professionals are coming
to the realization that they do have a unique and vital role to
play in helping to minimize social disorder, deprivation, and poor
health. What is perhaps of equal significance is that society,
through its leaders, is beginning to expect community and
institutional recreation leaders to play this role.

A PHILOSOPHICAL BASE

The idea for this book has been germinated and nurtured on the
premise that special populations do in fact exist within our
societal structure. And, in spite of efforts to erase the lines of
demarcation, it is suspected that a sense of specialness will
continue to exist for many during the foreseeable future. As
long as they remain special, which for our purpose means disadvantaged, they are entitled to leisure opportunities that can
help give a feeling of worth and a measure of fulfillment to
their lives. Further, for the very reason that we believe recreation leadership should be directly involved in helping to remove
the barriers that now exist between people, we must realize
that such services cannot merely be relegated to sheltering
institutions or to highly segregated situations.

The overwhelming majority of people within the groups
discussed in most of the following chapters are not institutionalized, but are living within our communities. Unfortunately, either their presence has usually been ignored or they
have been offered a segregated program that has had the effect
of continuing their separation and isolation. This book is devoted to the task of building a relationship—a bridge, if you
will—between recreation programming and leadership in the
highly sheltered setting and those programs and leaders that

are available, or should be available, in integrated general community locales. Once this bridge has been erected, the ultimate objective is to encourage its use as a means of moving people toward regular community recreation involvement.

Earlier, rehabilitative efforts were focused upon the care, treatment, and restoration of the individual. Only recently has attention been given to the notion that total effectiveness in returning or moving the disadvantaged person into integrated community life also requires, in many instances, improving environmental conditions. It seems clear that all relevant community resources need to be brought together into a coordinated and concerted effort. Agencies and community institutions, beyond being apprised of the problems and the need for solutions, must develop some concept of the roles they can assume in aiding the physical, psychological, and social recovery and growth of the individual. Of equal importance, once such knowledge has been gained, is the need for agency commitment to provide the appropriate services which can result in opportunities for effective and meaningful community life.

The resolution of problems and the provision of self-fulfilling experiences can, and surely will, be instrumental in promoting a more satisfying life for the disadvantaged. Recreation should be, and in some cases has come to be, considered an important adjunct to the rehabilitation process. Recreation can serve as one vehicle for the societal integration of those persons who exist on the fringes of community living. One of the more important and desirable benefits that can be derived from a recreation experience is the social development that results from interaction with other people in a play setting. If this contention is accepted, it then seems logical to also assume that such experiences have intrinsic value as socialization agents for disadvantaged people, whether in the community or institution.

Just as it is true of society as a whole, individual differences within each special group are extensive. Obviously we cannot take a population of blind, elderly, or economically disadvantaged and assume that each person within a given group exhibits the same characteristics as everyone else in that group. Yet, conversely, it should also be recognized that in all cases individuals with whom we are concerned exhibit characteristics that are more similar to, rather than different from, the remainder of society. This alikeness leads to the contention that perpetual segregation of recreation experiences based solely on the criteria of age, physical or mental disability, race, or socioeconomic level is both unfortunate and extremely limiting to any person. A more useful approach, it seems, would be to base such entry into recreation program opportunities on the criteria of interest, experience, functional capacity, and skill level. This implies a degree of physical, mental, social and emotional maturation. Granted, in some special populations there are a few people who may always require a sheltered program. But too often this determination is based on the stereotyped notion that all people in a given special population are able to function at the same level of competency. If one would take the time to even casually investigate, it would undoubtedly be found that nobody fits a given stereotype.

At any rate, as conditions now stand, many persons with appropriate interests, experience, functional potential, and skill development are not being allowed into general community recreational activity; the "crippled" must play with the "crippled," the retarded with the retarded, the elderly with the elderly, the blacks with the blacks, and so on. Too often the bridge from institution to community, from sheltered to non-sheltered, or from segregated to integrated programs is non-existent. Fortunately this lack of relationship is not universal and we are seeing some stirring on the part of some professional recreators to alleviate the problem.

Recreation leaders, particularly in public or government-sponsored programs, have indicated a concern for some disadvantaged groups and have translated this concern into a process of facility and activity program development to allow for their involvement. Such action is partly a result of the impetus from private, philanthropic organizations and voluntary health agencies. This is exemplified by the "seed money" programs of the Joseph P. Kennedy, Jr. Foundation with regard to the mentally retarded and the National Easter Seal Society and its concern for persons with physical disabilities. Perhaps the greatest encouragement, as might be expected, has been provided by government at all levels. Many institutional recreation services and, to a lesser extent, community programs owe their existence and much of their growth to such official interest. However, if such concern is to be converted into new and expanded community service, it must be accompanied by a growing cadre of professional recreation leaders who have gained some awareness and understanding of the leisure problems of these disadvantaged people and who are oriented to the possibilities of providing leisure opportunities aimed at resolving their needs. Here, it is important to understand, our focus is on present and future recreators who are trained for general community service rather than on those leaders who might be considered specialists in working with a specific population.

Another essential facet in improving the lot of special groups is for recreators who function in an institutional setting to understand the program's existence and potential within the community and vice versa. There seems to be a critical need for establishing channels of communication between these two sectors of the recreation profession through which institutionalized clients, patients, inmates, or other participants can gain the experiences and competencies that will be readily transferable into ongoing community programs. The same dialogue should also be most helpful in breaking down unwarranted beliefs, on the part of community recreation personnel, that special populations require recreation leadership that has had extensive special education and training in working with such groups.

Experience has demonstrated that a professional recreator who is effective in working with people in general can be equally effective in working with people from a special population. The only provisions beyond his professional skills and understanding are 1) that he be properly oriented to any unique psychological, social, or physical difficulties and possible limitations that may sometimes be faced by persons within a given population; and 2) that he be endowed with the attitudinal capacity to work with such people. Remember, we are discussing an ability to work with *people*—nothing more! Therefore, we should recognize that such orientation and attitudinal capacity are essential in working with *any* segment of a general population, whether considered special or not.

OBJECTIVES OF THIS BOOK

The aims of this book are as follows:

1. To create sensitivity and concern for the existence of various populations which, for the present, must be considered special or disadvantaged;

2. To emphasize their need for leisure experiences;
3. To aid present and future professional recreators, as well as leaders in other social service fields, in gaining a realistic orientation to the social, psychological, and/or physical characteristics of various groups;
4. To offer demonstrated recommendations for recreation programming which can be translated into meaningful services.

Recommendations within many of the following chapters reflect previously tested techniques and ideas for integrating people, now considered disadvantaged, into regular recreation activities.

It might be of value to offer the reader some cautions and suggestions as various topic areas are discussed. First, it may be found that the philosophies expressed by some authors are not in total agreement with those presented by others. Such differences indicate that unanimity, or even consensus, has yet to be reached on some facets of procedure. Since authors have been selected because of their expertise with special groups, and since much of this expertise has been achieved in institutional settings, one can expect to find a certain amount of "institutional bias" in some chapters. However, the reader can be assured that as far as objectives are concerned, all authors are in full agreement. It is suggested that where variation is found, the reader should develop his own philosophy, preferably through testing.

Another reaction that is anticipated is the argument that dividing the book into special groups is of itself helping to perpetuate differences among people. This would certainly be a valid criticism and is accepted as such. Our only defense is based on the rationale that these groups are truly disadvantaged at the present time and that, although similar to the general population in most ways, they do have unique problems which can best be handled through concerted and specific discussions of each group. Devoting a full section to each population under consideration seemed the most effective way of providing this emphasis.

One additional comment is germane to this discussion. The reader is strongly encouraged to visualize the possibilities of transferring the approaches to programming presented for one population to those of another. Ideas which have proved successful with one group could, in many instances, be worthy of consideration with another. In this way it is hoped that the value received can be enhanced immeasurably. Further, one idea or demonstration of a program presented may, with a little ingenuity and creative thinking, result in spin-offs or adaptations which the various authors had not considered. Perhaps this could prove to be the greatest benefit to both readers and special populations alike.

PLANNING THE DISCUSSION

The procedure used in organizing the content of this work involved a selection of populations that the editors believe require special consideration and emphasis—populations which are not now being adequately served. These include the elderly, those persons who have been addicted to alcohol or drugs, the visually impaired, those who have been legally deemed offenders against society (both youths and adults), the mentally or emotionally ill, the mentally retarded, the physically disabled, the economically disadvantaged, racial minorities, and certain segments of our youth population.

In addition it was considered desirable to devote some general sections of the text to: 1) suggesting a problem-solving approach to community concerns including leadership concepts; 2) providing an understanding of ways of evaluating members of all special population groups in terms of motor development pattern; and 3) suggesting community and agency resources that could be useful in identifying potential clientle and in program development.

THE AUTHORS

All contributors are persons who are professionally trained or have had extensive experience in recreation. Some are currently serving as educators while others are practicing recreators. Each brings to this effort a knowledge and experience which we trust will provide an enriching learning experience. In order to allow each reader to have a closer identification with each author, brief résumés are presented in the following paragraphs.

Eric Errickson

With an academic background in psychology and recreation, Eric Errickson has gained a knowledge of behavior modification which was reinforced during his work as an adjunctive therapist at Topeka State Hospital and the Menninger Foundation in Topeka, Kansas. His work in psychiatric settings and with mentally retarded patients continued at state hospitals in Minnesota, where he served as Rehabilitation Therapies Director and Program Coordinator. At Fairbault State Hospital he was responsible for the development of treatment and training programs for 1700 mentally retarded patients. In addition to his efforts to develop operant conditioning activities and evaluations, Errickson conducted training classes in behavior modification and programming for the supervisory staff.

Currently, he is a doctoral candidate at the University of North Carolina, where he is continuing his studies in recreation, education, and psychology. He has served as a member of the Board of Directors of the National Therapeutic Recreation Society and has published professional articles in recreation and rehabilitation areas of concern.

Gene A. Hayes

Gene Hayes, although considered an outstanding specialist in recreation with the retarded, is also knowledgeable in the field of community recreation, having spent the early years of his professional life in that setting. In addition to his generalist experience, he was employed as a recreation therapist in state hospitals in California, North Carolina, and Kansas. Furthermore, he spent one year as a research assistant for the National Recreation and Park Association. His doctoral work was done at North Texas State University in the field of education. At present he is Assistant Professor in the Recreation Curriculum at the University of Iowa.

Among his publications relating to mental retardation is one of particular significance to the purposes of this book: an article dealing with the integration of retarded and nonretarded youngsters in a day-camp program which was based on a demonstration project. The reader should find his discussion meaningful as an orientation to serving this special population.

Marion N. and Carroll R. Hormachea

Marion and Carroll Hormachea, as they have done in a number of other publications, provide a team approach to this special population. Marion Hormachea has served as Chairman of the Department of Recreation at Virginia Commonwealth University, following many years of service with the Richmond Recreation Department. She continues to devote a portion of her time to serving as a faculty member of the Richmond Police Academy and as a consultant to the Virginia Law Enforcement Planning Council.

Carroll Hormachea is Chairman of the Department of Law Enforcement at Virginia Commonwealth University and also serves as Director of the university's Criminal Justice Institute. He has co-authored with his wife such books as *Confrontation, Crime, Demonstration and People* and *Recreation in Modern Society*.

The combined and individual backgrounds of the Hormacheas are especially valuable to the purposes of this book, particularly the areas that focus on persons convicted of crimes against society and their need for socially acceptable leisure outlets, both in the institution and upon their return to the community.

Ira J. Hutchison, Jr.

Ira Hutchison is currently Chief of the Recreation Branch of the National Capital Parks, Department of the Interior. He served in the National Recreation and Park Association first as Executive Secretary of the National Therapeutic Recreation Society and later as Special Assistant for Urban Affairs. He was employed as Recreation Director at Topeka State Hospital in Kansas and served that institution from 1950 to 1963. During the years 1963 to 1967, he did graduate work at Teachers College, Columbia University, where he received a Master of Science degree in therapeutic recreation services, and then served as Director of Therapeutic Recreation Services at St. Vincent's Hospital in Harrison, New York.

His training and experiences in promoting viable programming in the inner cities of America and his deep commitment to meeting the needs of minority groups were essential considerations in selecting Hutchison to prepare the chapter on racial minorities.

Lee E. Meyer

Lee Meyer is an instructor in the Curriculum in Recreation Administration at the University of North Carolina and is concurrently completing work towards a doctoral degree in education. After receiving a Masters degree in recreation and special education at the University of Illinois, Meyer held positions as Recreation Therapist at Manteno State Hospital and as Director of Activity Therapy at the H. Douglas Singer Zone Center in Rockford, Illinois.

His academic work, experience in working with the emotionally ill, and a profound commitment to the needs of special populations in community settings are reflected in his consultative work with state mental health agencies in Illinois and North Carolina as well as in his contribution to this book. He has also served as a member of the Board of Directors of the National Therapeutic Recreation Society.

James F. Murphy

James Murphy is an Assistant Professor in the Department of Recreation and Leisure Studies at San Jose State College. He received his doctorate at Oregon State University. He has served as a professional staff member with public recreation agencies.

Murphy's publications include articles on racial concerns in recreation education and on servicing the disadvantaged in the inner cities of our urban areas. He is co-author with John Nesbitt and Paul Brown of a recently published book dealing with recreation services to the disadvantaged in which primary emphasis is given to the economically deprived in urban society. His research into the origins of the organized recreation movement in the United States has been incorporated into this chapter.

Donald A. Pelegrino

Donald Pelegrino has spent the past ten years in the field of recreation and social services to youth, both in Chicago and in Los Angeles. From 1966 to 1970 he served as staff advisor for the Recreation and Youth Services Planning Council of Los Angeles, California. His numerous articles relating to the problems of young people and his recommendations for minimizing these concerns are indicative of his commitment to this segment of our population as well as his insight into their needs.

At the present time Pelegrino is enrolled at the University of Southern California, where he is working toward a doctorate with a major emphasis in recreation.

Peter J. Verhoven, Jr.

Peter Verhoven is head of the Curriculum in Recreation and Parks at the University of Kentucky. He received his doctorate from the University of Indiana. Prior to joining the faculty at Kentucky, he served as Research Associate with the National Recreation and Park Association, at which time he assisted in the preparation of a variety of articles and publications based on his research efforts. In addition to numerous other publications, he is co-author of three articles relating to the leisure needs of older Americans and to preparing professional personnel for recreation service with the elderly.

Although Verhoven is a generalist in the fullest meaning of the term, his many consultation and advisory assignments are indicative of his capabilities in a number of specialized areas, including the leisure concerns of the aging.

Elliott G. Young

Through practical leadership experience, Elliott Young has gained a profound understanding of persons with sight difficulties. For the past four years he has held the position of Director of Recreation and Camping Services with the New York Association of the Blind. Prior to this he served as District Supervisor of Playgrounds for the Cleveland Parks and Recreation Department and as a race relations consultant for the state of

Ohio and the Federal government. He developed the first therapeutic recreation programs at Bellevue Psychiatric Hospital and at Metropolitan Hospital in New York and was a member of the staff of Comeback, Inc. (considered the first agency concerned solely with the recreation needs of special populations). He completed his graduate work at New York University, where he majored in therapeutic recreation.

In addition to his membership in state and national professional recreation associations, he is a member of the American Association of Workers for the Blind. His chapter on recreation with the visually impaired, although offering a strong theoretical base, provides practical considerations which are obviously influenced by his firsthand experiences.

H. Douglas Sessoms

Douglas Sessoms, one of the first to major in recreation at the baccalaureate, masters and doctoral degree levels, has served as Chairman of the Curriculum in Recreation Administration at the University of North Carolina since 1963. He is recognized as an outstanding educator, as well as a leader in the recreation profession, as evidenced by extensive contributions to the literature, consultive assignments, and leadership roles at state and national levels. His published articles and textbook contributions cover a wide range of organized recreation areas, including concern for professional training, research, community leadership, and nearly the total spectrum of special populations. He has served as President of the Society of Park and Recreation Educators.

Pertinent to his contributions to this book, Sessoms has authored and co-authored a number of articles on recreation and the excessive drinker. His contribution to this book deals with leadership concepts and a problem-solving approach to community recreation concerns.

Thomas A. Stein

Although a self-avowed generalist in recreation, Thomas Stein developed a profound commitment to the needs of disadvantaged members of society during his doctoral research at the University of Wisconsin, where he studied the possible benefits of recreation experiences to physically disabled adults. He served as project director of a national program to eliminate or prevent architectural barriers to the handicapped—an effort sponsored by the National Easter Seal Society and a number of Federal agencies. At present he is Associate Professor at the University of North Carolina in the Curriculum in Recreation Administration.

Stein's growing concern for the dearth of organized leisure services for disadvantaged citizens living in the community and the necessity to sensitize all present and future recreators to the needs of such people resulted in the creation of a course titled "Community Programs for Deprived Groups." Recognition that no resource material, in convenient form and aimed at the leisure needs of a broad range of special populations, was available has been a driving motivation for this volume.

FOOTNOTES

[1] Robert Straus, "Social Change and the Rehabilitation Concept," *Sociology and Rehabilitation,* ed. Marvin B. Sussman (American Sociological Association in cooperation with the Vocational Rehabilitation Administration, U.S. Department of Health, Education and Welfare, under VRA Grant No. RD-1684-G, 1965), p. 3.

[2] *Ibid.,* p. 11.

[3] *Ibid.,* p. 12.

[4] *Ibid.,* p. 12.

[5] *Ibid.,* p. 13.

[6] Martin H. Neumeyer and Esther S. Neumeyer, *Leisure and Recreation: A Study of Leisure and Recreation in Their Social Aspects* (New York: The Ronald Press Company, 1958), p. 64.

[7] George D. Butler, *Introduction to Community Recreation,* 4th ed. (New York: McGraw-Hill Book Company, 1967), p. 86.

[8] Neumeyer and Neumeyer, *Leisure and Recreation,* p. 74.

[9] Jane Addams, *Twenty Years at Hull-House* (New York: The New American Library, Inc., 1960), pp. 97–98.

[10] Foster Rhea Dulles, *A History of Recreation: America Learns to Play,* 2d ed. (New York: Appleton-Century-Crofts, 1965), p. 212.

[11] George D. Butler, *Introduction to Community Recreation* (New York: McGraw-Hill Book Company, 1940), pp. 60–61.

[12] David E. Gray, "The Case for Compensatory Recreation," *Parks and Recreation*, April, 1969, p. 23.

[13] Butler, *Community Recreation*, p. 63.

[14] Gray, "Compensatory Recreation," p. 23.

[15] Julius S. Cohen, "An Analysis of Vocational Failures of Mental Retardates Placed in the Community After a Period of Institutionalization," *American Journal of Mental Deficiency*, Nov., 1960, 65: 371.

2   Problem Solving
and
Leadership Techniques

Courtesy Romney Staff, Photo by Douglas G. Ashley

H. DOUGLAS SESSOMS

Everyone working with special populations in the recreation setting assumes a leadership responsibility. The very nature of the service requires the execution of programs and activities. This is true for the volunteer, the paraprofessional, and professional. To a large extent, the degree to which the program succeeds is directly related to the leadership given by its personnel.

The basic concepts of leadership are the same in recreation as they are in all fields of activity. The uniqueness of this field is the mission of the recreation agency: its commitment to provide opportunities for the free time behavior of its participants. In fulfilling its responsibilities, the recreation department or service becomes one of the many organizations created by man to help him meet his social and psychic needs. And, like all social systems, it is composed of many subsystems.

The professional recreator is usually concerned with only one of those subsystems. Generally, it is the public recreation element which includes those community and institutional services supported by tax monies. However, he may be concerned with a private association where recreation is only one of the many services offered by the agency. The YMCA is an example of this. The subsystems are interdependent and join with the commercial agencies to provide a wide range of recreation opportunities, facilities, and/or programs to the public.

With the exception of those institutions created exclusively to serve the disadvantaged, most recreation programs are for the general population. They draw their support from the public and provide those services they feel the community wishes. Frequently, they minimize programs designed for special populations, stating they have neither an understanding of the problems of these groups nor the resources to provide these services. Only recently have recreation departments employed therapeutic recreation specialists on their staffs.

The recreation agencies serving special groups, then, may have two client groups and, if so, must seek to meet the needs of both: the community and the participants. By the community, we mean the larger body which gives the agency support and authority. In the case of the local recreation service, this may be the municipality or the county. For institutions, it is generally a larger jurisdictional body such as the state which creates it. The participants are those special populations who depend upon the agency for services. Each requires or may require a different set of leadership responses and techniques.

Leadership is the process of moving groups toward their goal fulfillment. In the case of recreation, it is the creation of opportunities for leisure expression. The goal of the community may be to provide and maintain a variety of selected programs and activities. Organizational concepts and methods are employed to obtain these goals. For the participant, the techniques used to achieve these ends generally relate to small group theory. The recreator seeks to identify the participant's specific recreation interest and aid him by providing programs or opportunities for involvement.

The recognition of recreation as a system is the first of three steps in effective service delivery. The second is the development of a harmonious balance between the goals and demands of each element of the recreation system. The third is the effective use of problem-solving and leadership techniques toward program fulfillment. Together, they make for success.

Every program specialist or administrator working in the recreation setting should be aware of the cross currents which spark the leadership dynamic of his agency. They stem from the needs and goals of each element of the system. They may be channeled and moved in a positive and united direction or they may become the blocks which impede progress and stifle services. In every leadership situation, there are at least four groups or interests which have goals or objectives to be met. They are the community that provides the service, the agency, the participants, and the leader. Each is moving in his own way to meet his needs and the potential for conflict is ever present.

As illustrative of this point, consider the following situation. The community creates a recreation program. It expects the agency to provide and maintain facilities and offer activities, especially for its young. The agency must live within the general mandates of the community, but, as a functioning organism, it creates its own objectives; it may seek to improve its position in the recreation hierarchy and in the hierarchy of local government. It establishes its procedures and bylaws which "guarantee" its efficiency. It decides to create a service for handicapped persons and employs a specialist. The specialist has his philosophy of activities and services and implements this philosophy through program ideas. The program attracts participants who in turn have their own reasons for taking part in the opportunities afforded. They may or may not differ from those of the agency and leader. As long as all four elements are having their needs met, the system functions smoothly.

The potentials for crisis and conflict occur when one or more of the elements becomes insensitive to the needs of the other elements. If the agency decides it needs to reduce cost, it may reschedule the hours the buildings are available. This could result in a hardship on the participants who have their own systems of time and time use. It might also infringe upon the leader, who may envision programs as being operated on a different schedule than that now enforced by the agency. As a result of these changes, the leader or participants may become apathetic and the program may be discontinued because of lack of interest. On the other hand, the participants might demonstrate their concerns, which could affect the agency's support or cost some of its leaders their jobs. The artful balancing of the objectives of the various elements is a prerequisite for a successful program and begins with the recognition of the role each element plays.

PROBLEM-SOLVING APPROACH
TO LEADERSHIP

Many professionals in the social service field have found the problem-solving approach to be an effective method of providing leadership. The approach stresses the importance of systems or comprehensive planning, services to the client, and flexibility in methods and techniques. It differs from an organizational approach to services, for in it, the bureaucracy remains secondary to meeting the needs of the participants. It takes both horizontal and vertical relationships into account, whereas the organizational approach tends primarily to stress the latter. The problem-solving approach is recommended for recreators working with special populations.

Essentially, problem solving requires the asking of certain questions and the collecting of basic data prior to decision making and program implementation. Those questions relate to: 1) the goals and objectives of the community, agency, professional, and client; 2) the issues and problems involved, both real and imaginary; 3) the forces or dynamics affecting any action, whether they be factors of movement or restraint; 4) the resources available for program implementation; 5) the selection of alternative courses of action, with the proper reading of the consequences of each action; 6) the selection and implementation of a program of action; and 7) an evaluation of both the effects of the program and the means by which it was achieved.

ASSESSING GOALS

The first step has already been discussed to some degree. It was stated earlier that a careful reading of the agency's objectives and goals, as well as those of the individual and client, is necessary if conflicts are to be avoided. The recreator working with special groups and individuals should begin with the following question: What are the community and my agency attempting to do through this program? Then he should ask, "Why am I being singled out for this assignment, what are my biases, and how can I use my skills to aid those who seek my services?" Finally, there is a question of the needs and goals of the participants.

In a sense, the problem-solving approach is deductive. It begins with the raising of general questions and comes to the specific objectives of the program. For example, the agency or community may be interested in meeting the recreational needs of the community, which include the so-called special populations. It wishes to do this in the most efficient and effective manner possible and with a minimum of problems. In addition to its general objectives, the agency may have some specific objectives of therapy or rehabilitation, or it may merely wish to offer a variety of services for use at the clients' own discretions. Within the framework of the agency's objectives, the recreator will need to establish specific goals and guidelines for his programs. Is he to offer activities and experiences which reinforce the therapy or treatment given the patient? Is he to offer diversionary experiences as a break from the educational and therapeutic experiences provided by other units of the organization? Are the objectives the same as for any other person seeking the services of the recreation agency or are they different?

Finally, there are the objectives of the participants. Frequently these are not verbalized, yet they are there and are rather specific in the minds of the clients. Is he there to meet people? To pass away time? To get away from his family, employer, or head nurse? Was he brought to the recreation service or did he come on his own volition? The question of mission and objectives of the program is a real one and all activities should be evaluated against these statements of purpose and direction.

Recreation programs, like individuals, take on personalities. They reflect the leadership style of the director and the leadership methods and techniques chosen by the staff. Sometimes they come into being as a result of crises or problems. At other times they exist because of the recognized need for recreation experiences in the lives of all peoples—the able-bodied and the handicapped. Regardless of the reason for the program, individual perceptions of its purposes vary and, in effect, so do the responses of the staff and participants. For example, the leader may believe strongly in involving all people in the social activities he has planned. He takes nonparticipation as a problem. He may get upset when he sees people talking or seated on the side rather than dancing or playing his game. He may attempt to bring them into the activity, perceiving their lack of participation as fright or activity illiteracy. In reality, the nonparticipants may be thoroughly enjoying themselves and should be encouraged to continue their activity and to join with the larger group only if they want to. Of course, the nonparticipant may be a problem, but the recreator needs to carefully read the situation before he goes to the next step in his leadership process.

What are the forces that affect his decisions? Every situation, whether it be the question of program development or the moving of a participant into a group, is affected by a variety of dynamic factors. Some years ago Kurt Lewin, a social psychologist, described this phenomenon. He said that decisions or actions were affected by a variety of forces, some of them working toward action and others working against it.[1] He likened social decisions to a magnetic field in which the polar forces pull against any object within the field. Most decisions involve a choice between at least two directions. His field theory has much relevance for recreation programming.

There are no inherently negative or positive forces. Each factor affecting the recreation program decision may be viewed as a restraining or moving dynamic. For example, agency traditions, a dynamic, may shape and encourage the development of such programs as afternoon teas or sports events, while deterring efforts to establish a dramatic or literary activity. The same may be true for the traditions of the community. The attitudes people have 'toward recreation experiences and the value system of their social class set the perimeters of their involvement in organized recreation programs. Program successes or failures often depend not on planning or the degree of financial support but on the proper reading or misreading of the dynamics at work. If the time and attitude are supportive of a particular undertaking, the battle is largely won. If the program is theoretically sound and properly conceived, but contrary to the values of the participants, the struggle is enormous and success is in doubt.

Among the major factors affecting the program development are time, sequence of events, organizational structure, traditions of the community or agency, values of the community and the participants, attitudes toward organized recreation, availability of financial and physical resources, the degree and support of the power structure, and the relationship of the recreation service to other systems and subsystems. As an illustration of this point, consider the growth of the programs for the mentally retarded. The interest of the late John F. Kennedy and his family in mental retardation served as a moving dynamic. The Congress did not restrain the efforts but supported his interest by enacting favorable legislation. The social welfare and medical traditions of the country shaped the nature and scope of the programs. Money was made available, with health education systems receiving a major share. Local power structures and traditions channeled the efforts of the interested parties and set the priorities of services. The role of the recreation department and the kind of programs it was expected to provide were affected by these actions. The same has been true in other areas where specific powerful groups were involved.

For local community recreation departments, there is little tradition or expectation by the public for them to serve special populations. Consequently, the "in" programs have been of a general nature with the able-bodied and highly motivated participating in their offerings. As a result of some recent social

crises, such as riots and drug abuse, community recreation
programs have begun modifying their objectives and directions. Many communities are beginning to ask their recreation
agencies to provide services to the ghetto, to aid in keeping
the "cool," to prevent narcotic use among teenagers, and the
like. Some departments have moved aggressively into these
programs while others have been more hesitant to act. The decision to program for special populations is largely affected by
the agency's perception of its mandate, the skills and training of
its staff and its traditions.

Each recreation program has a set of unique resources
which it may call upon to meet its objectives. The therapeutic
recreation specialist is not alone in his work. He needs only
to involve his allies to assure a quality program for those he
serves. The task is one of identifying and nurturing these resources.

Paramount among the resources are the participants
themselves. Each individual brings a wealth of experience and
skill to the program. The involvement of participants in service to themselves and other groups enhances the probability
of meaningful experiences in the recreation setting. Every effort
should be made to include the participants in each phase—
planning, conducting, and evaluation—of the program. When
this is done, a variety of experiences is assured and the program
is less likely to slip into a set of stereotyped activities.

Next to the participants, the community is the best source
of aid. It contains a wealth of volunteers, with all of their skills,
and it is also a key source for physical and financial support.
This is true whether the community is an institution or a geo-
political unit. A critical reading of the power structure and the
systematic inventorying of facilities and personal skills available
will aid the recreator in his job. His choices of alternative
courses of action will reflect his understanding of these resources.

Finally, there is the agency and its potentials. These resources, like those of the community, extend beyond the boundaries of the immediate organization. For example, each agency
has its professional relationships and professional groups with
which it deals. The recreator may draw upon these relationships to supplement his knowledge and skills. Likewise, each
community has ties with other bodies and political organiza-

tions. Federal aid and state aid are available to local communities for certain types of programming. These sources of assistance should be cultivated, utilized, and strengthened. Then, too, within the agency there are frequently professionals who do not come in contact with the handicapped but who do have certain expertise in program areas. They may be involved directly as skilled personnel or may aid the recreation specialist's work with the handicapped as consultants.

PLANNING A COURSE OF ACTION

Having identified the goals of all those involved and having carefully read the dynamics affecting the decisions and resources available in programming development, the recreator's next step in the problem-solving process is to plan the course of action. It requires the identifying of available alternatives and the selection of the most feasible one. What approach should the recreator take in working with special populations? What style of leadership should he employ? What is the relationship between his special program and the general program of the agency? What are the priorities and what sequence of events should he plan? These are among the few questions required when selecting alternative courses of action.

Basic to the success of the program is the selection of an appropriate leadership style. Leadership is the key component in the action phase; the ability to select the proper techniques and approaches for the group to be served is essential. How the recreator chooses to use his power will affect both the productivity of the group and the satisfaction of its members. The more authority he assumes, the less freedom will be experienced by the group. If, on the other hand, he chooses to involve the members in the planning and implementation of the program, he must be willing to give some of the power of his position to the group.

According to Warren Schmidt and Robert Tannenbaum,[2] there is a leadership pattern which ranges from a leader-centered style to a group-centered one. Depending upon the dynamics at work, the personality of the leader, and the maturity of the group, the leader within accepts or delegates authority to the group. The five dominant patterns of leadership behavior are described below.

Telling. Telling is the most autocratic leadership form; the leader makes the decision and announces the course of action to be followed. Although the interests of the members may be considered, they do not participate directly in the decision-making process. The power is vested in the leader and coercion may or may not be used or implied.

Selling. The leader who employs the selling style of leadership makes a decision and attempts to persuade the group to accept it. He describes the benefits of the alternative he has chosen and how it relates to their needs and the needs of the organization. It is a sugar-coated form of *telling.*

Testing. When the leader begins to involve the group in the decision-making process by asking for their ideas and questions, he is using the testing technique. Although he may ultimately disregard the opinions of the group (he makes the final decision), he is honest in his attempts to seek their reactions to his plan and to modify his approach if their reactions and comments indicate his thinking is faulty.

Consulting. The consulting pattern is a group-centered form of leadership in which the group members have a chance to influence the decision from the outset. The leader presents the problem and the pertinent information to the group, but allows the group to develop the plan, to consider the various alternatives, and to recommend a course of action. Inasmuch as the group members are involved in the planning process, the leadership generally involves them in the implementation phase.

Joining. The ultimate in group-centered leadership is the joining style, in which the leader participates as a member of the group and agrees, in advance, to carry out the decisions the group makes. The power is vested in the group; it contains the authority and it must accept the responsibility for its actions. The leader is simply the executor of the group's decision.

As indicated earlier, the choice of leadership styles will depend upon the situation, the personality and skills of the leader, and the experiences, expectations, and abilities of the group. A good recreator must modify his leadership approach depending upon these dynamics. No single style is recommended for every situation. To illustrate the point, consider the differences in people. All recreators do not share the same value system or philosophical approaches. Even a particular individual's confidence in the group will vary according to his experiences with its members; his own degree of certainty or uncertainty will affect his willingness to share responsibility. Then, too, there is the ever-present factor of his personality. Some leaders are inclined to be democratic, while others prefer the authoritarian style.

Likewise, the factors at work in the group have tremendous impact upon the appropriateness of a leadership style. If the members have come to expect an autocratic leader and tend to be uncertain and unready to accept responsibility, the group pattern (consulting and joining) would probably be unproductive. The decision to involve the members in the program planning should be based upon their knowledge and understanding of the goals of the organization and their willingness to accept responsibility. If they are uninterested in the problem, they are likely to be unwilling to share in its resolution; consequently, the leader will need to assume a leader-centered position.

Finally, the situation must be considered, along with the pressures of time and the complexities of the problem. Do these forces allow for discussion and debate of the alternatives, or must the leader act alone and fully accept the consequences of his action? Continuing reliance on the more leader-centered pattern will produce dependent members, whereas the utilization of group-centered styles may result in an occasionally frustrated leader. The group may not always wish to do the things he would prefer them to do. Generally speaking, the leader's choice of leadership styles is limited as he deals with day-to-day problems, but he does have some flexibility as he moves toward the achievements of his long-range objectives.

If one of the objectives of the recreator is to develop morale and involve participants in the decision-making process so that they may grow through recreation experiences, then he must move toward the leader-centered style for many program undertakings. The successful recreator will be characterized as neither a strong nor a permissive leader but rather one who can assess the situation and choose those techniques which allow all to benefit from his wisdom and professional skills.

EVALUATION

The test of the problem-solving approach to program development is in the program itself. The fruition of planning is the action of program implementation. The alternatives cease the moment the program is put into effect. All that remains is the evaluation process. Evaluation is a continuous activity. It begins with the establishment of the objectives. The success of the program must be measured against the objectives stated by the agency, the participants, the leader—all those involved in the process. Not only should the program be measured against those objectives, but it should also be analyzed according to the techniques used. Evaluation involves looking at both the process and the accomplishments. The means, as well as the ends, are under scrutiny.

All those participating in the program should contribute to the evaluation process. The views of the participants, the director, and the leader should be solicited and reviewed. They become the basis for planning for the next program and for determining the agency's progress in reaching its long-range goals. All programs, regardless of the degree of success enjoyed, should be evaluated to determine why they achieved that level of acceptance.

As a quick review the following outline may be used as a guide for action.

PROBLEM SOLVING AND
PROGRAM DEVELOPMENT:
A GUIDE FOR ACTION

A. First, determine whether the program is actually needed and/or desired.

B. Concurrent with this determination, evaluate your reasons for being involved:

1. Need for the program

2. Overall agency and community objectives

C. Determine your role in program development:
  1. To initiate action
  2. To call attention to the alternatives
  3. To act until the program is developed, regardless of the length of time required

Once the foregoing actions have occurred, you are ready for the problem-analysis phase.

D. Develop data about the following factors: (1) program; (2) resources available; (3) dynamics affecting the program; (4) interrelatedness of the program; (5) power structure and its willingness to implement the program.
  1. The program—its dimensions and history
    a. immediate and long-range needs
    b. desired or needed
    c. previous action taken; residues of experience
      (1) apathy or bad planning
      (2) poor preparation
      (3) faulty sponsorship
      (4) poor timing
      (5) poor leadership
      (6) wrong approach
  2. The resources
    a. within the agency
    b. within the community
    c. outside the community
  3. Dynamics affecting the program (negative–positive)
    a. traditions
    b. power structure
    c. social factors
    d. national events
    e. economics
    f. awareness and communications
    g. tensions
    h. values, etc.

4. Interrelatedness of the program
   a. systems approach
   b. consequences of its development
5. Power structure
   a. Who? (diverse or singular)
   b. How obtained?
      (1) ascribed
      (2) social
      (3) political
   c. When to use?
   d. How is it used?
      (1) authority
      (2) influence
      (3) capacity to influence

E. Now, for action:
   1. The plan
      a. objectives of action
      b. organizational needs
      c. decisions about factors affecting the decision
      d. increasing the driving forces
      e. decreasing the restraining forces
      f. combination of both
      g. delegation of tasks
      h. timing
      i. choosing the appropriate leadership role
      j. choosing the appropriate procedures
      k. utilization of resources

F. Finally, the overall evaluation:
   1. Procedure
   2. Accomplishments

The problem-solving approach to program development is adaptable to every level of activity. It can be implemented when considering the agency's overall program or it may be the basis for planning a single activity or event. It requires the leader to be systematic in his understanding of self, his responsibilities, and the people with whom he works. It encourages the professional to involve the participants in the program process, since, without them, there is no need for the recreation service.

FOOTNOTES

[1] Kurt Lewin, *Field Theory in Social Science,* ed. Dorwin Cartwright (New York: Harper & Brothers, 1951).

[2] Robert Tannenbaum and Warren H. Schmidt, "How to Choose a Leadership Pattern," *Harvard Business Review,* Vol. 36, No. 2, March–April, 1958, pp. 95–101.

BIBLIOGRAPHY

Bass, Bernard M., *Leadership, Psychology anl Organizational Behavior.* New York: Harper & Brothers, 1960.

Beal, George M., Joe M. Bohlen, and J. Neil Raudabaugh, *Leadership and Dynamic Action.* Ames, Iowa: The Iowa State University Press, 1962.

Blake, Robert R., and Jane S. Mouton, *Training for Decision-Making Groups.* Austin: University of Texas, 1958.

Knowles, Malcolm, and Hulda Knowles, *Introduction to Group Dynamics.* New York: Association Press, 1966.

Shivers, Jay S., *Leadership in Recreational Service.* New York: The Macmillan Company, 1963.

Tannenbaum, Robert, Irving R. Weschler, and Fred Massarik, *Leadership and Organization: A Behavioral Science Approach.* New York: McGraw-Hill Book Company, 1961.

3 Meeting the Recreational Needs of Special Populations in the Community

Photo by Tania D'Avignon

ERIC ERRICKSON

One of the primary self-deceits imposed upon the general public and ourselves as recreators is the homily "Recreation for all." This concept is far from being practiced. Organized recreation has not serviced the needs of the total population. The recipients of the service have in fact excluded those who need it most: the ill, disabled, retarded, poor, blind, and aged. How this deception came into being and, more important, what can be done about it are essential areas of concern which precede a discussion of recreation service delivery.

Murphy indicates that part of the deception has resulted from "the assumption that in meeting the needs and problems of predominantly white, middle-class Americans, blacks and other minorities were included."[1] This is one part of the fallacy; it is not the total. Meeting the needs of middle class America is becoming less and less the goal of community recreators as middle class America becomes more affluent. The recreation needs of middle class America, by and large, are being met privately. However, the less affluent are not being adequately dealt with by the public recreator. Indeed the special group members are being turned off and away at an extremely high rate. Elliott Avedon indicates the recreation field has "tunnel vision"—a restricted outlook based upon limits or handicaps of individuals rather than their abilities. He points out that tunnel vision results in either 1) provision of no service or 2) provision of service that results in increased dependency.[2] A review of current practice verifies these assumptions.

In a study of community recreators by Stracke, he found that:

1. Only 16% of respondents who were community recreators felt the services offered by their agencies for the handicapped were adequate.
2. Only 37% of the respondents had a person working *full or part time* with the handicapped groups.[3]

Andres reports on services to mentally retarded. Questionnaires were sent to 166 cities in the United States, those with populations of 100,000 or more or those being one of the two largest in each of the 50 states. There were 121 replies with the following results: 55% indicated they had some type of municipal program for the mentally retarded. Andres states, "This represents an improvement over earlier surveys, however . . . there are still far too many departments which are not providing services for the mentally retarded, especially retarded adults."[4] Silson and co-workers report on recreation resources for chronically ill and disabled children and youth, giving the following findings. There is a need for:

1. The identification of a variety of recreational resources which are providing services to the handicapped children and youth.
2. The identification of a large variety of potential resources for handicapped children and youth.
3. Concentrated . effort to eliminate architectural barriers for handicapped children and youth.
4. More recreation programs integrating disabled and non-disabled children and youth.[5]

These studies give some scope to the idea of lack of service and clearly support the first assumption of tunnel vision—lack of service. Avedon's second assumption, that of continued dependency, is a more difficult one with which to deal. Perhaps turning to some examples of dependency-creating situations would be helpful. Avedon reports:

A middle aged woman used to do a great deal of swimming before her leg was amputated. When she was back at her job as secretary she thought she would like to take up swimming again. She went to the local Y but was told that the cerebral palsy group conducted "swimming for the Handicapped" on Wednesdays from 1 to 3 and she would have to see them. She explained she didn't need swimming lessons. She was told the only time she could use the pool was Wednesday from 1 to 3 p.m. because of insurance and all that.[6]

One of the problems causing resistance to the community placement of long-term mental patients has been the inability of the patient to use his leisure time. This inability is enhanced and perhaps created by the institutional recreator. The long-term mental patient has received a long history of assistance in meeting his leisure needs—weekly dances, movies, bus rides, ball games, etc. He has been given so much that he lacks the ability to find recreational opportunities on his own. But is it his fault? No! He is responding as the institution wants him to respond—in a dependent fashion.

The first lady, because she had an amputation, was restricted to swimming with the cerebral palsy group. The recreator still doesn't know if she can swim.

Many community programs only borrow the tricks of the institutional recreator when dealing with the handicapped client and thereby continue his dependency. The custodial approach has been adopted by the community as a way of dealing with the handicapped, complete with bingo, bus rides, the weekly dance, and the movie for all people.

What is needed, then, are programs that allow the client to learn skills of interaction and of leisure behavior and that provide opportunities to practice those skills. But more than that, what is needed is a realization of the causes for segregation of special populations. Society's attitude toward the handicapped gives us a clue.

While working at a state mental hospital I found myself coach of the hospital basketball team. Our team suffered a great many problems. Psychiatrists discharged our best players; that was called rehabilitation. Many of our team members were tranquilized, some with drugs and others with fatigue after jogging up and down the floor twice. However, we rallied together and played several games. Following one of these games we were lying breathless in front of the gymnasium, when who should appear but the Grey Ladies bearing gifts of cigarettes and candy. (Grey Ladies is one of a number of volunteer groups who provide good will services to people in hospitals.) I am usually giving up something. This time it was food (dieting) and smoking (because of the Surgeon General's report). I explained my restrictions to one kind lady who was offering me her wares (cigarettes and candy). She didn't want to take no for an answer. I talked with her for about five minutes politely, thanking her but refusing her goodies. She was adamant. Finally with an exasperated gasp I got my keys, shook them in her face, and said, "I don't have to take them. I work here."

Perhaps my erratic behavior would have convinced her. However, I doubt it. I think it was necessary for me to show my keys, indicating a peer association (that of the non-mental patient), before she would terminate her giving behavior. My assumption is that she and society feel that mental patients cannot make choices by themselves. Let's look at that conclusion and see if it can be validated.

Beatrice Wright indicates that society's devaluation of handicapped groups is expressed in many ways, for example, giving "money to help poor little crippled children." Humor gives another example. Jokes about handicapped individuals tend to ridicule the handicapped more than the jokes about professional classes. The devaluation extends vocationally as most job requirements ask specific questions about physical and emotional problems and eliminate potentially successful workers even though they would be able to do the job. Wright further states that "many members of the favored majority wish and frequently insist that the minority group member not only know his place but keep it." Wright cites a study by Cowen, Unterberg, and Verrillo, conducted in 1956, which analyzed correlates of attitudes toward blindness. The investigators found that negative attitudes toward blindness correlated significantly with anti-minority feelings, anti-black feelings, and pro-authoritarian attitudes.[7]

Wolfensberger discusses attitudes toward retarded persons. He suggests that we may view the retardate as a "sick person."[8] This view is strongly supported by many physicians. Another attitude toward the retardate is that he is a sub-human organism; retardates are often referred to as vegetables. Vail uses the term dehumanization to indicate the occurrence of less-than-human status for handicapped groups. He suggests that all handicapped groups may be dehumanized to a certain extent.[9] This, then, is the public status of the handicapped. This perception is hopefully changing but ever so slowly.

The recreator who adopts the "charitable" attitude toward the handicapped, who applies a group stereotype to the ex-mental patient, or who desires to keep people in their place, tends to a program for the handicapped which is doomed from the beginning. Only when the community recreator accepts the members of the special populations as human beings, with dignity, worth, and potential, can he begin to assist them in meeting their recreational needs. Realistically, then, a prerequisite to any program offering delivery of service to special populations is the recognition of their right to that service. Individual recreators must carefully work through their feelings

toward special group members if they are to assist the handicapped in obtaining recreation services.

GUIDELINES FOR PROVISION OF
RECREATION SERVICES TO
SPECIAL POPULATIONS

The prerequisite for provision of recreation services to special
populations rests upon one fundamental base. Community recreators must recognize their responsibility to provide service to
special populations and the concomitant right of the handicapped individuals to receive the service. As our economy moves
toward automation it is recognized that growing amounts of
nonvocational time are becoming available to the handicapped
group members. Public recreation organizations can have a
significant role in helping special group members to constructively utilize this time. In order to provide this assistance, fundamental elements of service delivery are necessary. The
following outline is suggested to assist community recreators in
provision of services to the handicapped population.

1. Establish a philosophical commitment to expand or establish
   the program of recreation services to special populations.
2. Sell this commitment to the public, the recreation board, and
   the consumer.
3. Establish a coordinating council made of professionals working with the handicapped, clients and recreators who are interested in provision of services to special populations.
4. Identify the population to be served.
5. Begin the program.

Each of these elements will be discussed and expanded in this
section.

Philosophical Commitment

Behavior therapist Dr. Leonard Fielding says, "I listen very
carefully to what you do."[10] If one listens carefully to community recreators, one hears: "Yes, we should provide programs
for the handicapped—but." The "but" often includes lack of

staff, money, or facilities. This and other similar statements can be expanded in order to provide a rationalization for no service. Observable behavior in terms of programs for the handicapped is perhaps the best evidence of a philosophical commitment. Members of special populations and their friends and relatives can assist the recreator in obtaining a commitment to serve by strategically applying pressure on the general public, then the recreation board, and finally the recreator.

Selling the Special Program

In his attempt to sell the special program to the public, recreation board, and consumer, the recreation professional may attempt to oversell the value of his services. Recreation participation will not cure mental illness, stop riots in cities, end addiction, or halt the aging process. Recreation participation can allow people to successfully utilize their time in a more constructive fashion. Recreators must be careful not to promise the world in program development. Sessoms indicates that recreators can no longer be Don Quixotes in pursuit of windmills. He suggests attacking the real windmills: i.e., the problems of people in using leisure time.[11] Recreators must sell, but not oversell, service to the handicapped. A logical, well-publicized campaign, using other professionals serving the handicapped as well as the recipients of recreation services, their family, and friends, is most important and can be effective in developing public support for programs to serve the handicapped.

In many cases the client poses massive problems. The client may also need to be sold on the value of recreation services. Recreators need to find out from the client what his desires, needs, and wants are, and then assist him in obtaining appropriate recreational experiences. This mutual process is basically an educational one and gives cause for specification of educational techniques useful in selling our services to clients. Utilizing the concept of operant conditioning, we will consider some factors useful in reinforcing participation of the client.

Operant conditioning refers to the increase in frequency of a behavior resulting from previous presentation of a reinforcer. A practical example can be offered. Let us assume that you are asked to predict the leisure behavior of an individual with only the following evidence: He shoots golf in the seventies and bowls in the eighties. Almost all of us would guess that the most frequent leisure behavior would be golf. The behaviorists' rationale is obvious: golf in the seventies is more reinforcing than bowling in the eighties.

Behavior, then, is controlled by past experiences, current circumstances, and genetic and physiological predispositions. The recreator should consider what reinforcers or rewards are available to offer the client for participation in a recreation program. The recreator's problem is to structure the activity so that the experience is reinforcing. What rewards can be offered? Among the many reinforcers or rewards available, several immediately come to mind: food, attention, and pleasurable activities. If it is insured that activity participation brings the client into contact with these reinforcers, we can hopefully assume that the participation of the client will continue.

The client's mode of participation can be modified in small steps. The use of small steps reduces the possibility of failure. Contrary to general belief, failure impedes rather than assists in the learning process. Rubin has outlined the program at the Rehabilitation Institute of Chicago; aspects of his program are presented here for consideration.

To cite an example: Recently, clients from the Institute (clients in the Homebound Program in the Chicago Chapter of the National Multiple Sclerosis Society), participated in a fishing derby held for the general public at a harbor in Lake Michigan. The beginning process was simple but effective. Fishing skills were taught to the handicapped group by professional municipal recreators. This assured that the handicapped client had the skills necessary to participate in the activity. The client did not feel failure. Then, after the skills were developed, the clients were able to compete with the general public. Successful participation in the program might be hypothesized as the reward. Nothing special was done, but client achievement was assured before entry into the program. Rubin does not report whether his clients caught any fish. However, the likelihood of future participation in other programs offered by the Chicago Recreational Department was increased because of the initial successful experience.

Rubin has used other activities such as swimming, ceramics, and other crafts available at community recreation centers, emphasizing first the preparation for the activity, gaining the skills necessary for successful participation, and, finally, joining a mixed community group.[12]

Rubin, in essence, was teaching the skills in small steps. After the client gained needed beginning skills, these skills were transferred to a community program. The recreator finally faded out of the picture as his client returned to the community, reinforced by his participation in community programs. This kind of effort on the part of the community recreator can assure successful participation on the part of the handicapped client and his return to other community based programs.

Establishing a Coordinating Council

Where practical, all people who have an interest in the development of recreational services to special populations should be gathered together by the community recreator in order to outline the needs and coordinate service delivery. This group should include public recreators, professionals working with the disabled groups, and clients. The total group can then coordinate, plan, and assist in the service delivery to clients. The development of the coordinating group may also help ease the burden of finances as in the example cited by Trommer. The coordinating agencies included the Arthritis Foundation, the Eastern Pennsylvania Chapter of the United States Public Health Service, the Philadelphia Recreation Department, and the National Recreation and Park Association.

Trommer describes the technique by which, through a coordination of agencies' services, a community recreation referral program was established. These essential attitudes were considered important:

1. There was a concern for an excess of client leisure time by all parties, including the community, physicians, health agencies, and clients.
2. The community recreation agency recognized its role in providing the service.
3. An interdisciplinary effort was established.[13]

Their procedure is a simple one which could be followed by all. It involves placement of chronically handicapped in Philadelphia's existing recreation programs. A typical client is Rose-marie, a 20-year-old girl who has rheumatoid arthritis. She has no clearly visible handicap; however, she does have severe and persistent pain and progressive hand deformity and afflic-tion of lower extremities which limit the amount of time she can place weight on certain joints. She dropped out of high school and was afflicted with arthritis after a short period of employ-ment. Her contacts and activities were largely limited to her home and periodic visits to the arthritis clinic. Her physician felt that she was becoming a recluse and, with her consent, referred her for the community recreation experience. The referral procedure had the following characteristics:

1. Referral by physician with client consent
2. Inclusion of material which outlined the client's functional capacities
3. Selection of appropriate activities
4. Integration into established and routine community programs
5. Operating costs shared by the client and the health agency

As a result of this approach, Rosemarie was able to partic-ipate successfully in the community recreation program, thus breaking the lack of activity cycle previously established. Trommer concludes that "the basic approach in voicing, explor-ing and solving the practical problems relating to community leisure experiences can be achieved through the united ef-forts of the local health and welfare council and the public recreation department. . . . In this manner, not only will years be added to life but . . . life to years."[14]

It is suggested that coordinating councils should include recipients of service wherever possible, for they can vocalize needs and wishes of the handicapped which others can only as-sume. Too much of service delivery has resulted from others imposing their ideas on the handicapped. Consequently, pro-grams that are established which do not include recipients of service at all stages of development may be doomed to failure.

Identifying the Population to Be Served

A clear function of the coordinating council is the identifica-tion of the population to be served. At this point Kraus wisely suggests that the time for emotionalism is over. "Pity for the handicapped is destructive. . . ." Instead, those in charge of organizing recreation services for the handicapped must be professionally competent. They must approach the task with a knowledge of sound recreational principles, a full awareness of the needs, capabilities, and limitations of those they serve.[15]

After deciding to serve the handicapped, the most important factor would seem to be placement of the handicapped in appropriate recreational groups. Among the variables that need to be considered for this placement are motivation of the individual; physical requirements of the activity; social and verbal requirements of the activity; and activity skills possessed by the individual. Each one of the variables may determine the placement in a specific activity for any handicapped person.

Motivation of the individual needs to be the first factor discussed. Motivation is a psychological term which represents what others call needs or interests. It becomes, for the most part, a reaction expression of what the individual will work to achieve. We are all familiar with examples of people who display an extraordinary amount of tenacity, endurance, and skill necessary to achieve an objective. Glen Cunningham, a famous miler at the University of Kansas, overcame severe burns in early childhood to achieve a world class rank. In working with a handicapped individual the recreator must assess realistically the motivational level of the client. If you will recall, we offered the earlier example of the amputee who wanted to swim.

Physical requirements of the activity also need to be considered. Despite the high motivation and the presence of a great many skills, it seems improbable that aging athletes can compete with younger athletes—George Blanda, Gordie Howe, and Hoyt Wilhelm not withstanding. It seems improbable that folks who are in wheel chairs can compete in regular baseball. The wise recreator should consider, then, placement for the handicapped individual in recreation activities in which he has adequate physical competence. Degree of mobility seems to be the primary consideration for activity selection for many physically disabled persons.

Just as the lack of physical competence restricts many of us from participation in activities, so does the lack of verbal and social skills. Of handicapped groups, perhaps the severely and profoundly retarded offer the best examples. Separate recreation programs often must be developed for this group of the severely retarded. They simply don't have the verbal and social skills necessary to reinforce others, nor to gain appropriate kinds of reinforcers for themselves.

Similar to the concern for physical requirements is the need to consider skill requirements of the activity. An individual may be motivated, have the physical requirements and necessary verbal and social skills, and yet still be restricted in his participation because of the lack of specific skills.

The prime function of the recreator working with handicapped clients is to assess the client and the potential activity within the framework of the client's existing living situation. The client's present stage of development and his function level are important variables which require consideration. The first additional variable becomes the program offerings of the community recreation program.

A simple assessment scheme can be offered which may have some utility. For each activity the client can be assessed on the following scale:

Client's Motivation

1	2	3
Low	Medium	High

Physical Requirements of the Activity

1	2	3
Low	Medium	High

Client's Verbal and Social Skills

1	2	3
Low	Medium	High

Client's Activity Skills

1	2	3
Low	Medium	High

Different activities can therefore have different prerequisite capabilities for successful participation. The value of this scheme would seem to be the recognition of different kinds of competencies for specific activities. Spectator events could allow participation by all. Other activities have more specific requirements which the majority of the population might be unable to meet.

The use of such a scheme, additionally, allows for client

advancement. All of the variables, i.e., motivation, physical limitations, social and communication skills, and activity skills, can be modified. We know that client motivation can be increased by successful participation in activities. Physical limitations can be modified by increasing physical skill and successful adaptions. Verbal and social skills can be gained by practice. Sometimes activity skills are improved by practice. All of these variables are externally controlled and can assist the client in gaining higher levels of recreation participation.

Beginning the Program

In a practical way, the beginning program should probably start with the most competent handicapped, i.e., the client who receives a preponderance of 3's in his evaluation. The majority of participants from special populations probably fall in this category. This approach also allows for the use of existing programs which can successfully accommodate handicapped clients.

The primary service offered here may be one of recreation counseling. The client needs to know what kinds of facilities and services are available to him and how he can use them. The counselor, in turn, should have some knowledge of the abilities of his clients, any limiting circumstances, and knowledge of available public and private recreation resources. In the development of services to handicapped clients the counseling service is primary.

The counselor also functions with the client who has specific disability, motivation, social, and activity problems. This client will have an activity profile which consists mainly of 2's. The counselor will be able to give the client suggestions as to sources of recreational activity and also provide necessary information to recreation personnel who will be providing the leadership. Program delivery for the included person also involves teaching those skills necessary to successful community experiences. It may be a structured exposure to services preceding discharge from a rehabilitation facility, or it may involve teaching the client skills (for example, fishing) prior to entry into community programs. In this area it is important that the recreator structure the experience so that the client succeeds.

The person who has significant disabilities, i.e., mostly 1's, may require special programs. Retardation offers a good example. Severely and profoundly retarded children and adults may not be able to participate in all typical programs. Involvement with normal age groups may bring failure, which can be very damaging to them. Obviously the handicapped youngster in a wheel chair cannot participate with his peers in playing regular baseball. Some special programs may need to be developed in order to provide recreational outlets for these individuals. The special programs will necessarily involve, for the most part, people with special orientation. The community recreator may function very effectively as a facilitator with these special groups. Program delivery may rest with personnel from day activity centers, the Association for Retarded Children, or other volunteers. The recreator serves as a facilitator in assisting these individuals in total use of existing recreational facilities. The community recreator may provide materials, training to volunteers, and some special programs to particular groups to allow them to meet their own recreational needs. In some situations recreators, oriented and prepared to work with specific handicapped groups, may be hired by community recreation departments.

Steps necessary in programmed planning for special populations have been outlined and discussed. These include the initial problem of developing a commitment to providing recreation services to handicapped groups, gaining support for these programs, coordinating service planning and delivery and using appropriate educational techniques in structuring the program. There are, however, specific resources which will be of value in developing recreation programs for special populations as well as specific problems which must be recognized.

PROBLEMS AND RESOURCES IN DELIVERY OF RECREATION SERVICE TO SPECIAL POPULATIONS

The philosopher must come to grips with reality on, at least, some issues from time to time. Linn Rockwood suggests we are in a "patent medicine" stage. He suggests that the picture of the recreation and parks administrator working in a "happy, humanistic organization moving toward well-accepted goals" is unrealistic[16]—and it is. A major problem, and at the same time one of the greatest potential resources in program development for the handicapped, is money. In this time of inflation and rising costs, all governmentally supported services require finances; yet all too soon the buck stops. Our first problem, then, is money; what resources does the community recreator have?

Money

The community recreator's first resource is his budget. A simplistic assumption would be that funding for special programs might well come from that. But budgets are already being spent. Resources are needed from other areas. In order to deal with finances and possible resources completely, let us examine in depth sources of additional money in one area—retardation—and imply that additional resources are available for other special population groups.

The following programs indicating federal support of recreation services are outlined by Hillman:

> The Division of Educational Services of the Bureau of Education for the Handicapped, U.S. Office of Education gives money to state related schools to enhance their services to handicapped children. In 121 of these projects . . . there were identifiable activities or components of recreation services. . . . Thirty of these projects were totally aimed at leisure related services.[17]

It would seem possible that the community recreator could associate himself very effectively with such programs.

In a program formerly administered by the Division of Mental Retardation, a number of projects incorporating recreation services are supported. These include daytime activity centers for retarded children and adults as well as recreation services for discharged mentally retarded adults at the San Francisco Recreation Center for the Handicapped, Inc. Research and demonstration monies are also available from the Bureau of Education for Handicapped Children, Children's Bureau and from the Resource and Demonstration Program of the Social and Rehabilitation Services.[18]

On a local level, participation with community day activity centers and local public education programs for the retarded may facilitate obtaining additional funds for recreation programs for the handicapped. A significant resource available for the retarded is the influential National Association of Retarded Children and Adults. With national, state, and local chapters, local support is almost assured in provision of services for the retarded. Local community chests, service organizations, church groups, private foundations, and interested private individuals provide additional resources in obtaining money for programs with special groups. Investigation of other resources may reveal additional national, state, and local groups who are able to assist in funding program support.

Staff

It appears that if adequate monies were available for the community recreator, he could buy additional staff. Realistically, however, shortages of trained personnel make staffing a problem. How is it to be handled? Peters and Verhoven in a study of Kentucky nursing homes suggest, in a word, "volunteers." They suggest that with appropriate orientation, including short courses, in-service training, workshops, and other training services, volunteers could effectively provide recreational services for the nursing home aged in Kentucky. They conclude that college training programs have the responsibility to train professionals to serve as consultants and to serve as catalysts for the initiation and implementation of short-term or in-service training programs.[19]

A program in Cincinnati, reported by Mary Bradshaw Miller, suggests similar success in training recreation aides to serve 1050 elderly residents in 18 sheltered care institutions in the Cincinnati area. The average age of the 76 recreation aides was over 60. This program points out other difficulties, however, as federal funding for this program was terminated. Miller concludes, "while the phase out of our project affected several low income people, the success of the project has opened the doors to the future . . . recreation service will continue to meet the needs and interests of all ill and handicapped people . . . not just the elderly."[20]

Miller's use of older training staff to work with institutionalized home-bound elderly has other advantages which should be considered when working with special populations.

Students in training in graduate and undergraduate programs in recreation, like many other programs, are underrepresented in numbers of handicapped, lower socioeconomic and ethnic groups. The Alcoholics Anonymous model of using alcoholics to work with alcoholics may be effectively applied to other special groups. Staff shortages can then be alleviated by judicious use of volunteers (and paraprofessionals) under the supervision of trained recreators.

Inappropriate Facilities

Stein has discussed the continuing need for removal of architectural barriers. Of major importance is the need to stop constructing facilities which cannot be used by all.[21] Rubin points out another area demanding attention, the commercial recreator, and indicates a source of power for the handicapped:

> We take the patients to bowling alleys where they pay their way. When we visit stores and emporiums and restaurants on shopping sprees these "special populations" spend the same brand of money as the able-bodied spend. . . . When the commercial recreator discovers that the group is willing to pay their way . . . more and more doors are thrown open to them.[22]

For the majority of special populations, additional facilities are not needed. What they need is acceptance and assistance in using existing facilities.

Knowledge of the Disability

Many community recreators express great concern over their lack of knowledge about special populations. This concern may have been aided and abetted by the activity therapist, adjunctive therapist, or therapeutic recreator. Since there are limited data in this area the author is forced to return to his sample of one—himself. During my years of experience in the field, I found it necessary, in order to function in a treatment setting, to identify myself with those people who were important, i.e., the people who were treating rather than those who were simply caring for the individual. In order to be important in the medical structure, the recreator was required to put on the cloak of the healer. The recreator learned to speak as glibly as the next "pseudotherapist," and in that way managed to confuse all other recreators with whom he had contact.

The fact that hospital recreators did the same things as community recreators, with the same kind of clients—some in and some out of institutions—made little difference. We were therapists first and recreators second. Now is a good time to clear the fog. Recreators engage in the same activities and have the same goals in both institution and community settings.

Unless the community agency has unlimited resources, the services of one recreational therapist may be of little value. Many therapeutic recreators do not feel comfortable in working with a variety of handicapped groups. Unless we can begin mass producing these individuals trained to work with specific groups, our solution would seem to lie in the area of knowledge of recreation skills first and reliance on other professionals for specific information about the handicapped second.

Psychiatrists, physiatrists, gerontologists, psychologists, and other specialists can give the recreator all the needed information about working with handicapped groups. Call them and ask. The client also is able to tell the recreator of his abilities. To work with special populations does not require complete medical, psychological, or sociological knowledge of the handicapped. What is required is that the recreator know where to get information necessary to assist the client in meeting his recreational needs.

Research and Evaluation Techniques

Programs should not be started unless they are accompanied by explicit evaluation techniques. By the same token, we have little research to support the provision of recreation services for any population. Little is known about why people play, why they choose a specific leisure behavior, or how patterns of leisure behavior are modified. The effects of recreation experiences on normal and special populations are the immediate concern of recreation researchers.

Statements are made about recreation and mental health, recreation and crime, recreation and mental retardation. One wonders what kind of relationship exists. To date, research has not been done to provide the answers. Developing techniques that are effective begins with measurement of different techniques. If recreation is to grow as a profession, we need to develop a body of knowledge about recreation for others. Recreation does not have that body of knowledge today—and it is unlikely to obtain it if research programs are not begun.

Work with special populations gives us a magnificent opportunity for research since recreators will not work with all members of a special population. Therefore, the effects of recreation service to the group receiving it could be measured and compared with the group not receiving service. However, it takes maturity to question the profession's actions. Recreators may not be ready to risk such insightful, critical, and introspective evaluation.

In this section money, staffing, facilities, lack of knowledge and research, and evaluation techniques have been discussed as possible problem areas in delivery of recreation service to special populations. Possible methods of overcoming these areas of difficulty have been discussed. The practical and fundamental problems seem logically to lead us to the next section.

TOWARD LEISURE PARTICIPATION FOR ALL

A primary challenge of the community recreator during the latter part of the twentieth century will be dealing with the leisure behavior of special populations. The key to successfully meeting this challenge lies in refuting the "puritan ethic." Self-fulfillment must come increasingly through avocation pursuits. It would seem that the schools offer a place to begin this educational process. However, in addition to didactic training, dynamic demonstrations of successful programs are needed.

Special populations offer the recreator the sample on which to develop recreational programs for the remainder of society. The need for research has already been mentioned. Research must begin now giving the answers to how people learn recreational skills, how people utilize leisure time, and, finally, the best methods of service delivery. Special populations offer the subject matter for this research. If we can assist them, we can assist the total population.

The recreator of the future will have a multiplicity of roles. He will be a teacher of skills and activities. He will be a counselor at directing people into appropriate leisure pursuits. He will be a planner and developer of recreational resources. Finally, he will supervise the maintenance of these facilities. If recreation professionals are not willing to meet these objectives, some other professional group will.

A cautious evaluation currently grants the recreator professional expertise in supervision and maintenance of facilities. Proficiencies in the other areas have to be developed if the recreator is to take his appropriate role in helping to mold behavior during leisure time, which is becoming available to all members of our society.

FOOTNOTES

[1] James F. Murphy, "Recreation Education . . . for White or Black America," *Parks and Recreation*, August, 1969, p. 29.

[2] Elliott M. Avedon, "Enable the Disabled," *Recreation*, February, 1965, pp. 70–71.

[3] Dick Stracke, "The Role of the Therapeutic Recreator in Relation to the Community Recreator," *Therapeutic Recreation Journal*, Vol. III, No. 1, First Quarter, 1969, pp. 26–29.

[4] Catherine Andreas, "The Status of Municipal Recreation for the Mentally Retarded," *Therapeutic Recreation Journal*, Vol. IV, No. 1, First Quarter, 1970, pp. 1, 30.

[5] John E. Stilson et al., "Availability and Utilization of Recreation Resources for the Chronically Ill and Disabled Children and Youth in the United States," *Therapeutic Recreation Journal*, Vol. IV, No. 4, Fourth Quarter, 1970, pp. 36–37.

[6] Avedon, "Enable the Disabled," pp. 70–71.

[7] Beatrice A. Wright, *Physical Disability: A Psychological Approach* (New York: Harper & Row, 1960), pp. 13–15.

[8] Wolf Wolfensberger, "The Origin and Nature of Our Institution Models," *Changing Patterns of Residential Services for Mentally Retarded* (Washington, D.C.: President's Committee on Mental Retarded, 1969), pp. 63–171.

[9] David Vail, *Dehumanization and the Institutional Career* (Springfield, Ill.: Charles C Thomas, 1967).

[10] Leonard Fielding, personal communication.

[11] H. Douglas Sessoms, personal communication.

[12] Arthur Rubin, "The Recreation Revolution," from an unpublished paper given at the National Recreation and Park Association Congress, Chicago, Ill., 1969.

[13] Phillip R. Trommer, "A Community Recreation Referral Project," *Parks and Recreation*, August, 1967, p. 19.

[14] *Ibid.*, pp. 19, 37, 40.

[15] Richard Kraus, *Recreation Today* (New York: Appleton-Century-Crofts, 1966), p. 342.

[16] Lynn R. Rockwood, "The Credibility Gap in Recreation Administration Literature," *Parks and Recreation*, February, 1970, p. 50.

[17] William A. Hillman, "Federal Support of Recreation Services Related to Mental Retardation," *Therapeutic Recreation Journal*, Vol. III, No. 3, Third Quarter, 1969, pp. 6–11.

[18] *Ibid.*, pp. 6–11.

[19] Martha Peters and Peter J. Verhoven, Jr., "A Study of Therapeutic Recreation Services in Kentucky Nursing Homes," *Therapeutic Recreation Journal*, Vol. IV., No. 4, Fourth Quarter, 1970, pp. 19–22.

[20] Mary E. Bradshaw, "Cincinnati's Community Action Therapeutic Recreation Project for the Aged," *Therapeutic Recreation Journal*, Vol. II, No. 3, Third Quarter, 1968, pp. 16–19.

[21] Thomas A. Stein, "Environmental Barriers to Persons with Physical Disabilities," *Therapeutic Recreation Journal*, Vol. IV, No. 1, First Quarter, 1971, pp. 11–12, 45.

[22] Rubin, "The Recreation Revolution."

4 Recreation and the Mentally Retarded

GENE A. HAYES

Each child is equipped at birth with basic biological drives and will manifest certain psychological, physical, and emotional needs and desires. Some infants, because of one or many reasons, will not be able to realize the full potential of the learning process so vital to becoming an adult. Many of these children will be mentally retarded, a result of some developmental abnormality. This limits the child's ability to benefit from the learning process, both formally and socially. Many of these children will additionally suffer from some personality or behavioral disorder and become emotionally disturbed. This further interferes with the individual's ability to participate fully in the learning process. These children may also be physically handicapped and, very likely, may experience some strong emotional feelings because of their condition, as well as because of the way other people react to the condition.

The mentally retarded have been labeled as being different from other members of society. This fact is heightened by the very existence of institutions where individuals are taken from the mainstream of society and placed in a situation with individuals who have similar conditions. This isolation reinforces their feelings of being different from the people outside of the institution. This will most assuredly affect their self-confidence, self-concept, and their ability, or willingness, to interact with their social environment.

HISTORY

Mental retardation is a very complex medical, social, and economic problem, the ramifications of which are difficult to fully comprehend. The concept of retardation involves a varying combination of factors including a lack of uniformity in definition, terminology, classification, treatment, and training. Its challenges are considered of equal importance with any known to man.

It is estimated that approximately 3 per cent of the total population of the United States is mentally retarded and that approximately 126,000 children born each year are retarded at birth. This means that there are at least 5 million retarded persons in the United States. Of all rejections from military service during World War II, 700,000 were because of mental retardation. Twice as many individuals are afflicted by mental retardation as by blindness, polio, cerebral palsy, and rheumatic heart disease combined. At the present time slightly more than 200,000 individuals are confined to residential institutions. In addition to the billions of dollars lost in productivity, local, state, and Federal agencies annually spend close to $3.5 billion for services to the mentally retarded.[1]

There is little recorded history of mental retardation. It is known that prior to the nineteenth century society's record of dealing with the mentally retarded was one of the "most pathetic chapters in the history of man."[2] Survival of the fittest was one of the first rules. In ancient Sparta parents exposed their handicapped offspring to the natural elements to perish. In the Middle Ages the retarded were often exploited as fools or jesters for the pleasures of the royalty and the well-to-do. During the Protestant Reformation it was thought that the handicapped or deformed were persons "possessed with the devil," and a common form of treatment was to literally beat the devil out of them. During the time of Luther and Calvin the church provided perhaps the only salvation for the weak, disabled, retarded, or otherwise afflicted. Asylums were established primarily as sanctuaries for those unable to survive in a cruel and competitive society. No attempt was made to provide treatment or education for the retarded or the other inmates of the asylums.[3]

The prevailing philosophy concerning retardation prior to the eighteenth century was that retardation was due to heredity. The consistent belief was that once a person was retarded he was always retarded and nothing could be done. Followers of this theory were known as hereditarians or naturalists.

At the close of the eighteenth century some physicians started rejecting the naturalists' theories and the new slogan of these sensationists or environmentalist followers was "practice makes perfect." They believed that learning came only through the senses and that all persons could develop the ability to learn if given adequate stimulation. This controversy of heredity-environmental philosophy that has existed for so many years is still debated. However, a great many professional people now believe that the cause of retardation does not have to be either heredity or environment but can be both heredity and environment.

The nineteenth century brought a sudden flare-up of interest in the education and welfare of the mentally retarded. In a sense, the nineteenth century became the renaissance for the care of the retarded. Most of the treatment of the retarded was carried on by young men in their early twenties who were unafraid of going against the established principles of the time. Itard proceeded against Pinel's judgment and Seguin had in Esquirnol a benevolent, though highly skeptical, friend and mentor. Itard leaped into prominence as one of the originators of the education of the feebleminded because of his efforts on behalf of the Wild Boy of Aveyron, whom Pinel thought was faking his wildness and was nothing but an incurable idiot. Seguin became known as the apostle of idiots and devoted his life to the study of idiocy and its treatment. He laid down many basic principles for teaching the mentally retarded that are still followed. Guggenbuhl, Howe, Kerlin, Fernald, and Montessori are other prominent names associated with the care, treatment, and education of the retarded during the nineteenth and early twentieth centuries.

DEFINITION OF MENTAL RETARDATION

Several traditional definitions of mental retardation exist. Among the definitions receiving the most attention in the recent past have been those of Tredgold, Benda, Doll, and Kanner. Each author emphasizes, in perhaps slightly different ways, the fact that retarded mental development, because of limitations in intellectual capacities, deters the individual from adequately adapting to his environment. According to Robinson and Robinson,[4] "the older definitions stressed standards appropriate to adult behavior but were quite inapplicable to children. . . ." The older definitions seem to leave too many unanswered questions or to foster erroneous assumptions.

In 1959 the American Association on Mental Deficiency published a valuable manual on terminology and classification in mental retardation.[5] A very thoughtfully worded definition of mental retardation was included; it is anticipated that this definition will find greater acceptance than any definition thus far published. The AAMD has defined mental retardation as "the subaverage general intellectual functioning which originates during the developmental period and is associated with impairment in adaptive behavior."[6] This brief definition leaves much unsaid; thus, it is important to clarify each salient term in the statement. Therefore, the following quote from the AAMD manual is included:

> Subaverage refers to performance which is greater than one standard deviation below the population mean of the age group involved on measures of general intellectual functioning. Level of general intellectual functioning may be assessed by performance on one or more of the various objective tests which have been developed for that purpose. Though the upper age limit of the developmental period cannot be precisely specified it may be regarded, for the practical purpose, as being at approximately sixteen years. This criterion is in accord with the traditional concept of mental retardation with respect to age and serves to distinguish mental retardation from other disorders of mental behavior.
>
> The definition specifies that the subaverage intellectual functioning must be reflected by *impairment in adaptive behavior*. Adaptive behavior refers primarily to the effectiveness of the individual in adapting to the natural and social demands of his environment. Impaired adaptive behavior may be reflected in: (1) maturation, (2) learning, and/ or (3) social adjustment. These three aspects of adaptation are of different importance as qualifying conditions of mental retardation for different ages.
>
> Rate of *maturation* refers to the rate of sequential development of self-help skills of infancy and early childhood such as, sitting, crawling, standing, walking, talking, habit training, and interaction with age peers. In the first few years of life adaptive behavior is assessed almost completely in terms of these and other manifestations of sensory-motor development. Consequently, delay in acquisition of early developmental skills is of prime importance as a criterion of mental retardation during the pre-school years.
>
> *Learning* ability refers to the facility with which knowledge is acquired as a function of experience. Learning difficulties are usually most manifest in the academic situation and if

mild in degree may not even become apparent until the child enters school. Impaired learning ability is, therefore, particularly important as a qualifying condition of mental retardation during the school years.

Social adjustment is particularly important as a qualifying condition of mental retardation at the adult level where it is assessed in terms of the degree to which the individual is able to maintain himself independently in the community and in gainful employment as well as by his ability to meet and conform to other personal and social responsibilities and standards set by the community. During the pre-school and school age years social adjustment is reflected, in large measure, in the level and manner in which the child relates to parents, other adults, and age peers.

It is this accompanying deficiency in one or more of these aspects of adaptation which determines the need of the individual for professional services and/or legal action as a mentally retarded person.

Because of the different roles of maturation, learning, and social adjustment for the pre-school, school, and post-school aged groups, the definition specifies that it is necessary for the subaverage intellectual functioning to be reflected by impairment in only one of these three aspects of adaptive behavior in order to confirm a diagnosis of mental retardation. In actual practice, however, it will be found that a great percentage of individuals diagnosed as mentally retarded will be impaired, or have a history of impairment, in all three areas of adaptation.[7]

Therapeutic recreation service may make its greatest contribution in the area of *social adjustment*. This is not to imply that recreation does not contribute to the maturational process or to the individual's learning ability, for it most assuredly does. Play is the child's world and it is through play that the child perfects his skills of infancy and early childhood such as crawling, walking, running, eating, and talking. Learning is also enhanced through many of the games and forms of play in which the child participates with other children and with his parents. Growth in maturation and learning should be concomitant results of involvement in play and social adjustment activities and groups structured for socialization purposes.

CLASSIFICATION

There remains some divergence in the use of terms to define the various levels of mental retardation. Educators seem to rely quite heavily on the use of levels of measured intelligence, assigning to the determined levels such names as slow learner, mentally defective, dull-normal, educable, trainable, and custodial. The current education vogue appears to be to label those persons with an intelligence quotient of from 75 to 89 as either dull-normal or borderline; the retarded person with a measured intelligence quotient of from 50 to 75 is classified as being educable. This category represents approximately 85 to 90 per cent of all retarded persons. The trainable mentally retarded category includes those individuals with a measured intelligence quotient of from 25 to 49 and would encompass from 7 to 8 per cent of the total number of retarded. The third, and smallest, group is classified as custodial—individuals whose intelligence quotient is below 25. This group represents only 2 to 3 per cent of the total retarded population.[8]

Of the more than 5 million individuals who are considered to have some form of retarded mental development, only 4 to 5 per cent (approximately 201,000) are residing in institutions. These statistics would seem to support the expenditure of funds and the establishment of programs in the community so that the vast majority of the retarded persons could derive some benefit from professional services in their local communities.

There are, of course, different objectives and expectations established for the retarded in each classification. For instance, it is expected that the educable retarded child can achieve at least the third grade level academically, with some reaching the sixth grade level by the time they are old enough to finish school.[9] In most instances the educable retarded person achieves suitable social skills to maintain himself in some unskilled or semiskilled occupation; however, it is not likely that the trainable retarded person will be able to achieve any functional academic skill to the extent of the educable. Appropriate social and self-help skills to aid in adjustment within a controlled environment are the major goals of their learning experiences.

A word of caution is appropriate here. Some people are

too concerned with what the book says a retarded person can or cannot do. Each retarded person should be considered on an individual basis and steps should be taken to determine and utilize the procedures that will enable that retarded individual to achieve his maximum potential. Different methods and techniques should not be avoided just because they have not been tried before. New and innovative programs should not be avoided just because someone says the retarded are not capable of doing a certain thing. This impedes progress.

The American Association on Mental Deficiency has developed a system of classifying the retarded in five different groups or categories.[10] This system does not reflect the same intelligence quotient guidelines as those utilized or advocated by Ingram[11] and other educators. The five classes and the IQ range of each, as compared with the levels advocated by Ingram and others, are listed below:

AAMD

Level	IQ Range
Borderline	68–83
Mild	52–67
Moderate	36–51
Severe	20–35
Profound	0–20

From R. Heber, *Manual on Terminology and Classifications in Mental Retardation* (Washington, D.C.: The American Association on Mental Deficiency, 1961), p. 59.

INGRAM ET AL.

Level	IQ Range
Dull-Normal	75–89
Educable Retarded	50–75
Trainable Retarded	25–49
Custodial	0–24

From Christine P. Ingram, *Education for the Slow-Learning Child* (New York: The Ronald Press, Inc., 1960), p. 7.

There is considerable agreement that a relationship exists between the intelligence quotient score and academic success. However, this does not mean that the ability to achieve in an academic situation and general intellectual ability are synonymous. It has been noted that, "An IQ taken in isolation, as a matter of fact, appears to be a somewhat poorer predictor of academic achievement among retarded than among normal children."[12] For this reason it is important to consider more than just an IQ score when attempting to determine the future potential, or aptitude, for educational placement and achievement for the mentally retarded. Consideration should be given to such factors as the social and cultural history, the etiology of the retardation, special disabilities, family relationships, behavioral disturbances, and skills and abilities that have been developed or neglected.

ETIOLOGY

Through research efforts a great deal of light has been cast upon many causes of mental retardation and new understandings have been achieved. At present there appear to be more than one hundred causes of mental retardation; but, with the remaining number of unknown etiologies, science has just begun to scratch the surface. There have been many attempts to classify the various types of etiologies. Authorities have, in the past, separated the different causes of mental retardation according to: organic or functional causes; prenatal, paranatal, and postnatal causes; and hereditary and environmental or cultural causes. In an attempt to achieve as much consistency as possible with people working in all phases of mental retardation, the *Standard Nomenclature of Disease and Operations Manual* of the American Medical Association, with minor revisions, has become the basic reference for retardation etiologies advocated by the American Association on Mental Deficiency. These revisions were made in an effort to avoid some inconsistencies of some of the newer developments in the mental retardation field with the manual as originally published. The American Association on Mental Deficiency developed both a simplified and an expanded version of the classification system because of the variation in diagnostic services available to the retarded in the many different types of mental retardation facilities around the nation. The two classification systems are the same with the exception that the expanded version is more detailed and comprehensive within each of the eight categories. The AAMD's eight classification categories are presented below with a brief description of each category, including examples to illustrate each category.

The etiological classification system described in Table 1 is essentially consistent with medical practice since medical authorities are more concerned with mental retardation as a manifestation of a disease process or medical condition. However,

TABLE 1

THE AMERICAN ASSOCIATION ON MENTAL DEFICIENCY'S MEDICAL
CLASSIFICATION OF MENTAL RETARDATION ETIOLOGIES

Category	Description	Examples
I. Mental retardation associated with diseases and conditions due to infection	This grouping is to be used for the classification of those cases in which mental retardation is the result of residual damage from an intracranial inflammation due to an infection. Within this division diseases are subgrouped in terms of whether the infection occurred prenatally or postnatally.	Rubella contracted by the mother during the first three months of pregnancy, and syphilis as prenatal causes.
II. Mental retardation associated with diseases and conditions due to intoxication	All cases of mental retardation associated with cerebral damage due to serums, drugs, or other toxic agents are classified in this division.	Lead has been the most significant. Lead may be absorbed from paint, lead toys, lead acetate ointment, and cosmetics. Other toxic agents may be carbon monoxide, arsenic, quinine, ergot, etc.
III. Mental retardation associated with diseases and conditions due to trauma or physical agent	Cases of mental retardation associated with injury of the brain due to trauma, or mechanical or physical agent are classified in this division.	Prenatal injury may result in mental retardation. Also maternal asphyxia is a factor. Complications during labor may also result in brain damage at birth.
IV. Mental retardation associated with diseases and conditions due to disorder of metabolism, growth, or nutrition	All conditions associated with retardation directly due to metabolic, nutritional, or growth dysfunction are to be classified in this category. This includes the cerebral lipoidoses, disorders of carbohydrate and protein metabolism, and nutritional deficiencies.	Tay-Sachs disease is the most common form of cerebral lipoidosis. Phenylketonuria, galactosemia, Wilson's disease, and Hurler's disease are examples of Category IV.
V. Mental retardation associated with diseases and conditions due to new growths	This group includes all diseases and conditions associated with cerebral new growths. This does not include those cases of growth which are secondary to trauma or infection or cases in-	Examples are neurofibromatosis, tuberous sclerosis, and other intracranial neoplastic conditions.

From R. Herber, *Manual on Terminology and Classifications in Mental Retardation* (Washington, D.C.: The American Association on Mental Deficiency, 1961), pp. 20–41.

TABLE 1   (*Continued*)

Category	Description	Examples
	volving overgrowth of fibrous tissue resulting from atrophy or degeneration.	
VI. Mental retardation associated with diseases and conditions due to (unknown) prenatal influences	This division is intended only for the classification of those conditions for which no definite etiology can be established but where it can be established that the condition existed at or prior to birth. These are conditions which, otherwise, would be classified as due to unknown or uncertain causes with the structural reaction manifest.	Macrocephaly, hydrocephaly, and acrocephaly are the most common types of this category.
VII. Mental retardation associated with diseases and conditions due to unknown or uncertain cause with the structural reaction manifest	This category is intended for the classification of postnatal diseases and conditions where the structural reaction is manifest but where the etiology is unknown or uncertain. Those conditions which are presumed to be of an hereditary or familial nature, where no other etiology can be assigned, are included in this category.	Sclerosis of the brain, spinal sclerosis, and Schilder's disease are examples of Category VII.
VIII. Mental retardation due to uncertain (or presumed psychologic) cause with the functional reaction alone manifest	This category is used for the classification of those numerous instances of mental retardation occurring in absence of any clinical or historical indication of organic disease or pathology which could reasonably account for the retarded intellectual functioning. No case is to be classified in this division except after exhaustive medical evaluation. Cases in this group are specified in terms of psychogenic and psychosocial factors which appear to bear some etiological relationship with the retardation in functioning.	Cultural-familial retardation, psychogenic mental retardation associated with environmental deprivation and associated with emotional disturbance.

the social or environmental conditions that may be inherent causative factors in mental retardation should not be over- looked. To consider mental retardation in a strictly medical classification system would be somewhat short-sighted. For this reason, and because of recent developments in research, the American Association on Mental Deficiency incorporated some minor modifications in the classification to include genetic and environmental factors. For a thorough discussion of the medical and behavioral etiological classification of mental retardation, the AAMD's *Manual on Terminology and Classification in Mental Retardation* should be consulted.[13]

It is well recognized that there is rarely one cause or sim- ple explanation for any type of mental retardation. In some instances, the deficit seemingly is a result of the hereditary en- dowment; in other instances, the environmental factors are primarily connected with the retardation. Finally, the condition may result from a combination of both factors. An individual may be affected at any time during his life—before, during, or after birth. Likewise, retardation may be attributable to one incident at one time, or it may occur as a result of a series of related events over a period of time. Mental retardation has no respect for age, sex, race, or socioeconomic status. There is, however, research which indicates that certain groups may be more susceptible to specific etiologically produced retardation. For instance, poor lower class families who live in culturally de- prived environments may have more mentally retarded children as a result of cultural-familial causes, poor nutrition, inadequate medical care, and lack of treatment during pregnancy.

MONGOLISM

Mongolism (Down's syndrome) is important and should be given special consideration. Solving the mystery of the etiology of mon- golism is an excellent example of progress in scientific investi- gation. All the questions are not answered, but the discovery of the cause of mongolism represents a classic scientific break- through in the study of mental retardation. Lejeune, Gautier, and Turpin are credited with first publishing the discovery of extra chromosomal material in the cells of mongoloid individuals in 1959.[14] Until that time mongolism was categorized as being associated with diseases and conditions due to (unknown) prenatal influences. It is now known that all mongoloid children carry extra chromosomal material and by far the majority of mongoloid children have a total chromosome count of forty-seven instead of the normal forty-six. In the numerous research efforts directed toward the study of mongolism, it was discovered that many systems of the body are involved, which would indicate many different kinds of symptoms. The most common and reliable finding associated with mongolism is that children with this syndrome are generally born to older women.[15] For instance, the risk of a mother from 45 to 49 years of age having a mongoloid child is 55 times greater than that of a mother who is between the ages of 20 and 24.

Mongolism is of particular interest because it is the single syndrome most frequently accompanied by severe retardation and its symptoms are generally very clearly defined. This does not mean that all mongoloid children are severely retarded. Some mongoloid individuals are mildly or moderately retarded and a very few may be borderline, but very few. There are many symptoms utilized in identifying the mongoloid, and most children with mongolism resemble one another in facial and bodily structure. The slanting Oriental shape of the eyes is the most noticeable symptom. Other symptoms include a small skull; eye abnormalities; a large, fissured tongue which is usually protruding from a small mouth; a short, broad neck; square and flat hands; and sparse, fine hair. Another very common and important symptom is that the mongoloid child may have a congenital heart condition. This fact should always be checked before involving a mongoloid child in a rigorous recreational program.

Generally, the mongoloid individual is more personable and more easily managed than other retarded persons. Quite frequently the mongoloid child becomes a favorite of the recreation specialists. They are often the bright spot in the recreation program, many times taking the initiative in involving other children in a recreation game or activity. The mongoloid is generally of a less aggressive-hostile nature and is less involved in attention-seeking kinds of behavior than other retarded children.

PSYCHOLOGICAL FACTORS
IN MENTAL RETARDATION

When we consider the psychological problems faced by people during their lifetime, we realize that the mentally retarded are not unique. They encounter many of the same obstacles and problems faced by most other members of our society. Their inability to meet, understand, and deal effectively with these problems is the factor which creates some of the psychological or emotional trauma for the retarded.

There are some problems that arise specifically because an individual is mentally retarded. The stigma that is still associated with mental retardation causes a great deal of consternation among families in which there is a retarded individual. A retarded child may become emotionally disturbed as a result of repeated rejection on the part of his parents, other adults, and/or his peer group. What happens to the child who is always chosen last, never chosen, or verbally excluded from peer group play? The child who does not have the opportunity to experience love, acceptance, belonging, success, and friendship is destined to develop some form of psychopathology.

Recent concepts of intelligence view it not as a constant, but as one part of the total personality. Anxiety, emotional conflict, and rejection have all been shown to affect mental alertness and school performance adversely. Fear of failure and rejection may contribute to the performance of the mental retardate. As Dexter has noted:

> Even severely retarded persons appear to be responsive to variations to incentive conditions; social reinforcement in the form of social praise, verbal praise and encouragement, or just simple attention appears to be at least as effective as with normal persons. There is a strong suggestion that the performance of retardates may be depressed as a function of generalized expectations of failure and that proportionately more retarded than normals may respond to the threat of failure with decreased rather than increased effort.[16]

When the higher-level retarded are young, they are able to keep up with their age peers in performing many simple games and in individual play. As they approach adolescence, they are faced with the psychological problem of accepting the limitations in their abilities. According to Carlson and Ginglend:

> As bodies develop, all young people realize that they are no longer children but not quite adults, only "in-betweeners." The trauma of being an in-betweener can be especially hard on the emotional development of the retarded teenager, because it is during this period of adjustment that he realizes, more than ever before, that he is not like other people. The problem becomes crucial. He wants to identify himself with his peers, .but he cannot do the things that other people his own age do, and there is no promise that he can do them next year, or the next.[17]

Retardates are also faced with problems relating to self-confidence, which is derived from, and enhanced by, the successful experiences the individuals have encountered. They generally have difficulty in establishing realistic goals for themselves. The most common problem is that they set their goals too high, making them unattainable, thus fostering failure and a greater loss of self-confidence. If this process is repeated many times, the retardate may soon have little, if any, ego strength in reserve and he will withdraw from his social environment.

The mentally retarded must be taught to establish realistic limits just as they must be taught how to effectively utilize their leisure time. Those retardates who are employed in the community are occupied during the working hours; but when left to their own devices and ingenuity after working hours, many problems may be experienced.

Fine and Dawson, in a study of mentally retarded adolescent girls, have indicated:

> Failure to adjust to the community was found to be largely the result of the patient's inability to utilize her own free time. She would have no difficulty on the job, but the long weekends would "hang heavy" on the girl and result in her becoming depressed, restless, or getting into trouble, necessitating her return to the institution. In essence then, each girl had to learn how to play as well as to work in order

to assure her optimal chances for success in community living.[18]

Not only is it important that the mentally retarded learn to properly utilize leisure time to function in the community, but also they must learn to accept or tolerate rejection, scorn, and ridicule because of their handicap. It is imperative that the retarded develop the ability to overlook the people who may scorn and reject them and, instead, work through their own feelings about being different from other members of society. Basically, the greatest psychological problem facing the mentally retarded is discovering how to control and express emotions appropriately. They have to understand the feelings within themselves and then learn how to communicate these feelings to others. It is also necessary to acquaint them with methods by which they can alleviate pent-up emotions, such as anger. If the retarded child can adequately handle his emotions and establish some self-control, he will encounter fewer problems.

SOCIAL FACTORS IN MENTAL RETARDATION

Mental retardation is a social problem of considerable proportions. It affects at least 3 percent of the nation's population directly. When we include the families, relatives, friends, and professional people who are affected by, and come in contact with, the mentally retarded, that percentage could increase to at least 10 percent of our total population. Mental retardation is an undesirable condition. However, through care, treatment, training, and education, this condition can be ameliorated, and through expanded research efforts, some types of retardation could be eliminated.

The specific handicaps affecting the retarded child—the slowness of his development, the necessity for special arrangements for his physical care, training, companionship, and the familial adjustments which must be made concerning the expectations for the individual—unite to multiply the inordinate pressures affecting the present and future home situation. Added to this pressure may be tensions created by the child's difficulties in interpersonal relationships, his immature self-control, and his handicap in communications. At the same time the parent-child relationship is intensified by the child's prolonged dependency and isolation from a peer group.[19]

The parent-child interaction is likely to be more intense with a retarded child. Thus, from the standpoint of the child's emotional stability, it is important that parental conflicts and anxieties do not disrupt this relationship. However, studies show a high incidence of marital problems and divorce among parents of retarded children.[20] The instability in the home environment may produce instability within the child.

The socially inappropriate or unacceptable behavior of the retarded is often propagated by the lack of adequate recreational opportunities to function as potential outlets for physical and emotional energies and tensions. The fact that there are not sufficient numbers of clubs, social activities, and athletic events provided in the community for the retarded lessens the opportunities for increased social awareness, with the concomitant results of prolonged immaturity.

Opportunities often must be structured to provide social experiences for the retarded which the nonretarded take for granted. For instance, the teenage retardate may be exposed, through field trips, to: buying stamps, using the public telephones and laundry facilities, riding elevators, dressing as a teenager on specific occasions, addressing a policeman or a minister on the street, utilizing public transportation, and seeking out and joining the appropriate recreation agency. These are but a few of the very simple abilities that must be mastered before a retarded individual will be able to make a satisfactory adjustment in the community. If, indeed, the retarded are to become assimilated into the community, their social development program must be enhanced with the opportunities to put into practice, not within the confines of the institution but in the real world, the skills they have been taught as part of their training and education programs. One of the most effective places to do this is in the recreation and leisure time program.

The rationale for a recreation program for the mentally retarded is well documented. However, the plans for such programs are not so well defined. There are numerous research studies which offer isolated implications for physical development of the mentally retarded. These ideas, in addition to knowledge of how the retarded learn most effectively, can be integrated into guidelines for recreation programs for mentally retarded persons. It is also important to be cognizant of the physical, mental, and social characteristics of the retarded when attempting to structure a program in which the retarded may benefit and experience success. Ingram presents an extensive discussion of the physical, mental, and social characteristics of the educable mentally retarded. Part of that information is reproduced here to provide a basis for understanding the kind of knowledge that is essential in working with the educable retarded.

Physical, Social, and Mental Traits
of the Mentally Retarded

FIVE, SIX, AND SEVEN YEARS

"*Physical Traits:* Control and coordination of the fine muscles and the wrists, hands, and fingers are slow to develop. Chalk, pencil, crayon, and brush are used with big strokes and scribble. Children like scissors, hammers, and saws for sheer manipulation. By seven years, the majority can color to line and cut with scissors to line.

"Walking, running, and jumping are carried on readily by the majority; ability to skip is acquired slowly.

"*Mental Traits:* Mental development approximates that of average children three to five years of age, but slower perception and association affects the quality and quantity of concepts and ideas. Children in this group generally are not curious or persistent in their questions about things and people in their environment. Their sense of time is developing, but they are still more interested in the 'now' than in the future. Counting and grouping objects to 4 or 5, a common task for the average five- and six-year-old child, is rarely achieved by these children until the age of seven years or later.

"Language and vocabulary are developing, but are still 25 to 50 per cent or more below the standards for average children.

"*Social Traits:* The five-, six-, and seven-year-old child may still tend to play as an individual if opportunity for and specific guidance in play with others has not been given. As opportunity for supervised play with others is extended, he will share equipment and toys for longer periods of time, although his interests are still likely to be self-centered. He tends to be a follower in a group, with little, if any, initiative or imagination.

"By seven and eight, his imitative play of family roles, the milkman, the postman, the fireman, and so on, is increasing. He tends to follow others in these roles.

"He enjoys listening to records and stories and likes to hear favorite ones again and again. He learns to enjoy group situations for stories, finger plays, and demonstrated rhythms. He takes pleasure in singing and can beat time to even rhythms. Since he is slow to develop auto-criticism, he looks for approval and is pleased with any comment of praise. The majority are sensitive to censure or adverse comments made about them or to them."

EIGHT, NINE, AND TEN YEARS

"*Physical Traits:* Muscular control of limbs is well developed. Walking, skipping, running, and jumping are done with ease, except in occasional cases of especially inferior coordination. Muscular control of hands tested in baseball throw and catch at distance, bean-bag toss for accuracy, and standing broad jump are slightly inferior to the norm for children of average ability.

"Muscular control of fine muscles of hands and arms is fairly well developed. Chalk, pencil, crayon, and brush are used with neatness and considerable precision. Paper cutting, hammering, and sawing are carried on, but construction in woodwork is likely to be crude.

"*Mental Traits:* Mental development approximates that of average children five to seven years of age. Situations such as playing games, making toys, and listening to stories are of interest to the more retarded.

"At eight years of age weakness of power of association, fundamental to language development, is noticeable. At ten years more ability to associate is evident, but development continues to be consistently slow. More activity and manipulation may continue to satisfy at these ages, but there is greater stimulation to think and to talk about pursuits. Expression in play or conversation is less than that of the average child.

Estimated vocabulary is 25 to 35 per cent below the eight-year-old standard.

"*Social Traits:* Period of individualization is past and transition to social group has been made to the extent that the child has more or less learned to expect certain reactions from persons and things around him, and realizes that certain things are in turn expected of him. The majority want to have a place in the family group and enjoy sharing in the housework and the care of younger children.

"Suggestion and imitation dominate in conduct and play. Running games with 'choices' element such as tag, singing games like 'The Farmer in the Dell,' seasonal games like marbles, jackstones, and spinning tops, and ball playing are enjoyed. The ego is too dominant to allow for being a 'good sport' in play. Make-believe play must involve elements that have become very familiar through actual experience or pictures, such as playing school, house, policeman, aviator, Indian, and the like.

"Stories to be successful dramatizations must be familiar. Satisfaction is obtained from repetition of stories, plays, and games. Rhythm, music, folk dances, and mimetics set to music are enjoyed, as well as picture books, fairy stories, animal stories, and descriptions of child life. The distinction between true and imaginative stories is appreciated."

ELEVEN AND TWELVE YEARS

"*Physical Traits:* General motor control is good, except in extreme cases of mental defect or physical disability. Eye and hand coordination tends to increase—manual skills are carried out with less inaccuracy and bungling. Greater attention to and interest in ways of doing things and the finished product are shown. Creditable results can be obtained from manipulation of tools and materials.

"*Mental Traits:* Range of mental development approximates that of average children seven to nine years of age. Ability to counteract distinction and to give voluntary attention to a task is increasing. Greater effort is used to overcome difficulties. Rote memory is good but memory of images and logical memory continue to be poor.

"*Social Traits:* Children of similar mental ability and of

the same sex are preferred as companions. Individual interests and personal concern dominate activity, although sensitivity to group approval as well as to adult approval is developing, with obedience a fairly well-formed habit. The fact that others must be considered is recognized in more and more situations.

"Power to sacrifice immediate for remote ends is increasing. Sense of individual and cooperative ownership is growing.

"Growing interest is shown in constructing and in using things—doll clothes, doll furniture, autos, boats, and airplanes are enjoyed. Play is usually with others in some form of game. Many of the play materials noted at earlier years continue. Element of competition is especially strong in boys—'starring' in contests, running the fastest, jumping the farthest, and so on. Games of chance, such as card games and table games, guessing games, games of memory, and ball games of all kinds are enjoyed. Interest in make-believe drops off. Variety is not self-initiated but has to be developed through an outside stimulus. Radio and television are popular."

THIRTEEN, FOURTEEN, FIFTEEN, AND SIXTEEN YEARS, AND OLDER

"*Physical Traits:*   Many individual variations occur as in average children. Taller boys and girls reach periods of rapid growth and subsequent periods of slower growth at earlier ages than shorter boys and girls.

"Breathing capacity and physical strength and endurance generally increase as in the normal. Work can be carried on for longer periods. Voice changes occur during these ages.

"Motor ability and eye-hand coordination improve with a resulting increase in kind and number of hand skills and in ability for sustained effort and interest to do work well.

"*Mental Traits:*   Mental development approximates that of average children eight to ten or eleven years of age. The power of voluntary attention and concentration on a given task has increased. Rote memory is good; memory of images and logical memory are improving.

"Simple interpretations of situations in pictures may be made, but lack of creative imagination is striking. Responses may even be the description of action alone.

"Language expression is still far below expectations for the average child. Learning ability in practical situations is increasing. More adequate adaptations are made in new situations.

"Greater general interests and a tendency toward participation are noticeable in the majority.

"*Social Traits:*   The company of the opposite sex is sought earlier by girls than by boys, with average boys of the same age or older dull boys as the selected companions.

"Remunerative jobs attract, the girls helping with home duties and service jobs, and the boys doing odd jobs—running paper routes, working in stores and factories. Both sexes may become involved in pre-vocation or vocational training programs. After-school employment is frequent.

"With increased sensitiveness to situations in the environment—the home, financial status, clothes, foreign background —limitations are more keenly felt. There is also a strong urge toward independence with some resentment at being told repeatedly what to do and what is expected. Active play interests, such as skating, hiking, swimming, baseball, football, basketball, card games (such as poker and rummy), and others predominate in the boys and also to a lesser extent in the girls. Relay and team games are also popular with boys.

"Less interest is shown in group organizations, clubs, and leagues than by other children because of inferior ability to fulfill requirements. 'Gangs,' or group chumming (cliques), develop among the boys and girls."[21]

SOCIAL DYNAMICS OF RECREATION
FOR THE MENTALLY RETARDED

Every person belongs to a variety of groups, formal and informal, i.e., family, work groups, clubs, informal friendship groups. This is also true of the mentally retarded, especially the institutionalized retarded. They are members of a cottage (dormitory) group, may belong to a work group, group therapy, friendship groups (or cliques), and will occasionally attend or join a recreational group.

Persons who participate in such groups can be viewed as having different positions, or tasks, within these groups. When considering the allocation of individuals to positions, McGrath identifies two main avenues through which this occurs:

Ascribed positions or roles are those the individual comes to occupy (or be excluded from) because of some inherent or immutable characteristics such as age, sex, race, type of illness, level of retardation, etc.

Achieved positions are those the individual acquires on the basis of his performance and his choice.[22]

Too often the roles and positions the retarded obtain are ascribed rather than achieved. This has been the nature of the large institutions; the residents are told what to do, when to do it, and how to do it. This is an area where recreation can help the retarded. In a recreation group the individuals have an opportunity to achieve their own roles and positions.

There are two kinds of groups that are a very important part of every person's life and which contribute greatly to the social learning process. According to Krech, Crutchfield, and Ballacher, these are:

Membership Group: A group in which an individual is a member and in which he has face-to-face relations with other members of the group. The membership group generally functions as a primary group for the individual. The primary group consists of two or more persons in intimate face-to-face associations. The most important primary groups are the family, friendship, and work groups. They are primary in the sense of their enduring influence upon the individual. The membership groups of the individual shape the formation of his attitudes only insofar as the individual identifies with them, that is, uses them as reference groups.

Reference Group: Any group with which an individual identifies himself, in that he tends to use the group as a standard for self-evaluation and as a source of his personal values and goals. The reference group of the individual may include both membership groups and groups to which he aspires to belong. Non-membership groups may function as reference groups for the individual and significantly influence his attitude development.[23]

Membership and reference group forces are at work in any hospital or training center facility for the mentally retarded. As the boys and girls grow older and mature, they are moved from one cottage to a more advanced one. For instance, Donald is a 15-year-old, mildly retarded boy who lives in Oak Cottage (his membership group). At the age of 16 he will be moved, if his behavior, attitude, and development warrant it, to Elm Cottage with boys of 16 years of age and over who function at the mild and borderline level (his reference group). Donald's desire to become a member of this reference group is reflected in his behavior in all instances of interaction within his social environment.

As previously stated, a primary group is most commonly illustrated by the family situation where members are in face-to-face interactions. In the hypothetical case of Donald, the residents generally do not have a family as a primary group to serve as a builder of attitudes and behavior. Many of the residents may have families but they are not living with them. Therefore, it is the cottage nursing personnel, other residents, and, often times, the recreation leader with whom the residents readily identify and, thus, who become their primary group. Because there are so many different people involved in the primary group situation, there are many instances where a resident, in seeking out the group in which the attitudes are most congenial with his, will play one staff member against another. Many times a new member in the group (new resident in the cottage; new member in a recreational group) will attempt to "buy" the friendship or acceptance of other members with money, gifts, or favors.

It is hoped that recreational groups could serve the function of both the membership and the reference groups. This would probably not be true for the same individual at the same time. But, the recreational group could, and should, serve at least one of these functions for each individual. A recreation group might be a primary group for the resident in that it should allow opportunities for friendship to develop. There should be a degree of rapport between the residents and the recreation leader so that the leader's influence might have a positive and lasting effect in the attitude development of the resident.

Each retardate should have a recreation membership group—a group that he is a member of simply because he wants to be. This allows him to identify with the group members, the leader, and, more importantly, with the ideals, attitudes, and behaviors which the members and leader have set. By strongly identifying with the membership group and by utilizing the group standards as a source of his own personal values, attitudes, and behaviors, the retarded person may also use his membership group as his reference group.

In many instances the retarded are not given a choice as to whether or not they want to join a group. This is particularly true in the "therapy" programs where the primary objectives and purposes are therapeutic in nature. There must be some opportunity for the retarded individual to exercise his freedom of choice and his decision-making abilities. These opportunities are most often present in the leisure time program; e.g., the resident could be given the choice of joining a social group, a photography club, a choir, or a square dance group. This freedom of choice (and the ability to exercise that freedom of choice) is a necessity as a precursor, or pre-discharge requisite, to extending the leisure time program into the community.

Individuals who become members of groups will certainly be affected in that their identity, attitudes, and other personal qualities will be shaped by the group according to the significance placed on the group by the individuals. Through a knowledge and understanding of groups and group dynamics, the therapeutic recreation specialist may structure them so as to achieve desired results. In understanding groups, it should be remembered that the group can produce either good or bad consequences and that groups are not inherently good.

Accepting the above proposition, it would appear that a very effective method of working with the retarded in attempting to shape their behavior and enhance their adaptability would be through the group process.

The early forms of therapeutic recreation primarily included programming activities for as many patients, or residents, as possible. The more people involved, the better the program. Needless to say, this resulted in providing mass activities which, in itself, was not bad as long as the mass activities were not the total program. In mass activities the emphasis is on the activity, not on the individual; however, if the activity is to be therapeutic, the emphasis should be on the individual. This can be accomplished in small groups and in individual activities.

Social group work was one of the earliest disciplines to recognize that groups could be managed to bring about desired changes in group members. Being responsible for the operation of clubs, recreation groups, and athletic teams, group workers came to realize that their techniques of dealing with people had important effects on group processes and on the behavior, attitudes, and personalities of those participating in these groups. Through attempts at building character, providing constructive recreation, keeping kids off the streets, and, later, psychotherapy, it gradually became evident that whatever the objective, some techniques of group management were more successful than others.[24]

In therapeutic recreation, as in group work, the ongoing group meeting is a basic experience; the group is a means and context for treatment. The treatment, or helping process, takes place in and through the group. It is the group leader's skill in guiding this process toward defined goals that permits him to help the members.

Some of the objectives of working with groups in recreation might be listed as follows:

1. To provide opportunities that will enhance the retarded individual's propensity for functioning in a socially acceptable manner; providing everyday social experiences and contacts including those with the opposite sex.

2. To develop social, recreational, and leisure time skills (solitary and group) that are appropriate for community adjustment and that can be carried on in any setting in the community.

3. To increase the range of social interaction from that of none, or a small group of peers, to other peer groups, adults, and individuals outside of the institution.

4. To provide the opportunities that will aid the retarded person in accepting himself and help him develop the ability to utilize those capacities that will increase his feelings of self-esteem.

5. To help the retarded learn how to play and have fun in socially acceptable and appropriate ways.

6. To provide a "laboratory of learning" for the retarded to practice and experience those skills of daily living and social interaction that they have learned, and must be able to utilize after

discharge from the institution, in their educational and training programs.

7. To provide the opportunities that will help the retarded person learn to make decisions and then require him to make decisions on his own volition.

8. To provide opportunities that will develop and enhance the ability to share materials and experiences with others.

9. To develop the individual's perceptual and motor abilities to their maximum potential.

There will, however, be different goals and objectives established for individuals who are of various ages and classified in different levels as well as those who are physically handicapped. For example, the objectives for a retarded person who is 40 years of age and considered to be severely retarded will be different from the objectives established when working with an adolescent who is only mildly retarded. For the severely retarded, some of the basic objectives would be to focus on the routine tasks of daily living such as eating, dressing oneself, and toilet training, as well as the ability to socialize within a small group of peers. Because the more severely retarded usually have more physical handicaps and neurological impairments than do the mildly retarded, another objective would be to increase their sensory-motor and perceptual-motor abilities. As for the younger, mildly retardate, a more realistic goal would be to focus on those activities important in maintaining oneself in society, i.e., appropriate personal hygiene and social skills.

The social learning process, as McGrath points out, occurs in an interactive context. It takes place initially within the framework of the family. The "significant others" who represent society in the individual's environment, not society as a whole, participate most directly in the socialization and learning process.[25]

RECREATION AND LEISURE TIME NEEDS OF THE MENTALLY RETARDED

The purpose of recreation is not to make champions or even talented athletes or performers of the mentally retarded. The purpose is to use the full impact and potential of recreation to enable each individual to become better prepared physically, mentally, emotionally, and socially, to make his place in society as a self-sustaining adult who is capable of living the fullest, most satisfying, and most worthwhile life possible. To achieve this purpose, greater emphasis needs to be placed on the use of physical education, recreation, and leisure time activities for the retarded.

Leisure time needs of the mentally retarded are especially crucial because so many are incapable of adequately filling their free time with profitable activities. For these retarded persons, leisure time is often a curse rather than a blessing. Through appropriate exposure to recreational activities, the retarded can be taught to utilize their leisure time more meaningfully. Too often in the lives of the retarded, leisure time is filled with passive amusements such as watching television and listening to the radio. More stress should be placed on the importance of socio-recreative programming to prevent social isolation of the retarded, especially during the formative years.

As indicated in the research, motor and physical development progresses at a slower rate in the retarded than in the normal individual. According to Lillywhite and Bradley, "almost all clinical experience with the mentally retarded and research data reveal the fact that motor development does not follow a normal pattern, but generally is delayed in proportion to the amount of retardation."[26] The higher the level of functioning of the retardate, the less neurological impairment, motor deficit, and gross physical disability the individual will suffer.[27] In other words, the mildly retarded individual will have suffered less neurological impairment, or be less physically handicapped, than will be the severely or profoundly retarded. For this reason it is more important to emphasize physical education and motor development activities with the lower functioning mentally retarded.

Intensive programs in physical education and motor development can result in increased intellectual and academic performance for the retarded. However, there must be more than mere involvement. For instance, in a summary of a recent study by Rarick and Broadhead, Cratty emphasized that:

> Using a physical education program in which retarded children were required to solve various movement problems, either alone or with another child ("With your partner see

how many ways you can cross a line"), it was found that significant changes in scores on the Peabody Picture Test of Intelligence were obtained. It would thus seem that the physical activities will improve intelligence to the extent to which the program requires that the children think about the activities they were engaging in. Exercise without thought makes small muscles larger. Thinking improves thinking.[28]

On the basis of the results obtained by Rarick and Broadhead and the philosophy expounded by Cratty and others, it appears that merely offering a physical education or recreation program of physical activities without taxing the thought processes of the participants will produce only physiological results. To enrich the learning ability of the retarded, activities must be provided in which the participants must consciously think about the processes in which they are engaged.

Appropriate forms of recreation experiences at crucial points in an individual's physical emotional, intellectual, and social development can provide a great deal of impetus in helping reduce some of the retardates' limitations. For instance, a retarded person may experience greater social and peer acceptance as a result of improved motor proficiency.

ACTIVITIES FOR THE MENTALLY RETARDED

It is neither possible, nor desirable, to list the recreation activities appropriate for the mentally retarded. Basically, the retarded can participate in any activity in which the nonretarded can participate. In some instances, however, there may need to be some adaptations made to allow for specific handicaps or problems that the retarded may have. The activity in which the retarded participates is immaterial. Whether volleyball, four-square, walking a balance beam, red-light–green-light, arts and crafts, or a square dance is programmed for the retarded is inconsequential. The important factors in programming are knowing the participants, understanding their individual needs, setting goals for and procedures to satisfy these needs, and selecting the most appropriate activities that possess the greatest potential for the fulfillment of the participants' needs.

In order to accomplish the foregoing purpose in program-

ming for the retarded, it is necessary that the recreation specialist be cognizant of all the inherent qualities of the activities
which he plans to use as well as the extrinsic values that
depend on the skill of the recreator. It is unlikely that each
participant will need activities that provide for all of the factors
listed below. However, it is very important that the therapeutic
recreation specialist be aware of the specific needs of the retarded and, based on his professional expertise, select those
activities which will most effectively meet these needs. When
selecting activities, the recreator should consider the following factors and questions:

Social Interaction—To what extent will the participant be required to interact within the context of the activity? Does
the activity require isolated or parallel play, or will the individual have to interact with one or more persons in the
activity in either a cooperative or competitive manner?

Cognitive Processes—What kind, or what level, of knowledge is
required before one can participate in the activity? What
kinds of learning will take place and to what extent will
knowledge and intellect be developed as a result of participation in the activity? Understanding, problem-solving
ability, concept formation, and imagination should also be
considered in selecting activities.

Perceptual Awareness—To what extent will the individual be required to be aware of his relationship to his environment
and to others in his environment? To what extent will the
participant be expected to have developed or refined his
motor skills? What demands will the activity place on the
individual's eye-hand, eye-foot, hand-foot, and eye-hand-
foot coordination?

Emotional Responsiveness—Will participation in the activity
require the individual to express specific affective feelings?
Will the participant be able to express anger in an appropriate manner toward a person or object without experiencing
any dire consequences? Will the individual in the activity
be able to laugh, cry, smile, display friendliness, or express
himself nonverbally in a way that is appropriate to the situation while engaged in the activity?

Physical Fitness—Will participation in the activity enhance the
physical condition of the individual? Which of the physical
factors are developed as a result of participation in the ac-

tivity? To what degree will strength, flexibility, balance, speed, and coordination be used and developed?

In listing and discussing the preceding factors, no attempt is made to attach any judgment to the relative value of any aspect of the factors. If the therapeutic recreation specialist is knowledgeable of all values of the activities, he can then structure activity groups designed to enhance whatever needs the retarded might have. For instance, there may be one or more retarded persons who need to begin their socialization training with isolated play experiences, whereas others may need to concentrate on widening their range of socialization skills. In another situation there may be several individuals who, because of a specific disability, need to have intensive programming in flexibility and agility or balance and coordination, whereas another individual may need to concentrate specifically on strength. The determination of what activity will be best for the retarded is the responsibility of the recreation specialist, based on the known needs of the individuals with whom he is working.

One factor that contributes to the difficulty in selecting activities for the retarded is the wide range of abilities represented in any group. If possible, for ease in programming, it is best to maintain as much homogeneity, with respect to abilities, as possible in recreation groups. This, however, is not always feasible.

The following program guides will be of assistance in helping the recreation specialist work with the mentally retarded.

1. Repetition is important. The mentally retarded learn more slowly than the nonretarded.

2. Demonstrate as much as possible. The retarded can learn by imitation; it is therefore important to use fewer explanations and more examples or demonstrations. Speak clearly and use vivid gestures.

3. Progression is important. The retarded, like others, learn best when starting with simple routines and activities and progressing to the more difficult tasks. However, progression is usually slower for the retarded and it involves more repetition.

4. The retarded seem to perform best in activities of a solitary nature or with a few other people. However, group activities

in which team work and cooperation are stressed are important. The retarded strive more for individual rather than team success.

5. Don't overburden the retarded with rules and regulations all at one time. Simplify the rules and regulations and introduce new ones gradually. However, rules, regulations, and restrictions are important and necessary.

6. Self-satisfaction is important for the retarded. Use help sparingly because it is important that the individual experience the satisfaction of accomplishing a task by himself. Allow a suitable amount of time for task completion.

7. Success and praise are necessary. It is very important to praise the retarded person when he has performed well according to his ability. The retardate needs encouragement, praise, and success.

8. Transition from one activity to another should be carefully planned. Don't confuse the retarded when moving from one activity to another. Plan the activities so that there is a smooth transition from one activity to another.

9. Use discipline when appropriate. It is necessary to use discipline in an appropriate manner when there is danger to the participants (when an individual endangers himself or others), when there is extreme destruction of equipment, or when the entire program is in danger of being totally disrupted.

Some of the purposes of play and recreation for the mentally retarded are the releasing of energy and tension in a constructive way, providing opportunity for creative expression, providing opportunities for the development of skills which bring about a sense of accomplishment, creating interest in new hobbies, and providing opportunities for strengthening and developing the body. It should be remembered that the leader's approach is very important to the retarded individual. In general, the leader should present a friendly and understanding, yet firm and convincing, attitude toward the retarded. The role of the leader, or the therapeutic recreation specialist, is to create the opportunities in which the participants will have a recreative experience and, where indicated, this experience will be therapeutic in nature.

Through the efforts of the therapeutic recreation specialist, appropriate opportunities for sublimation may be provided in recreation activities which may help the retarded relate to others in a variety of social patterns. Each activity in which the child with retarded mental development participates is a step in encouraging him to explore the possibilities for enjoying satisfaction from a variety of recreative experiences.

It should be remembered that programmed recreational activities can assist in the education of the retarded. Through a coordination of efforts, recreation can complement the training and education programs of speech and hearing therapy, special education, and vocational training, to mention just a few. Recreation experiences may lead to exciting new interests, help to develop new skills, and stimulate the individual to attain his maximum growth in a social, emotional, creative, physical, and intellectual context.[29]

COMMUNITY AND INSTITUTIONAL RELATIONSHIP IN PROGRAMMING FOR THE MENTALLY RETARDED

The recreation and leisure time program must be extended into the community if the retarded are to be expected to make a smooth and successful transition from institutional to community living. Cooperative efforts must exist between recreators in treatment facilities for the retarded and recreators in community and municipal recreation agencies. The therapeutic recreation specialist in the treatment facility should not wait for the community recreator to approach him to begin a community-based program for the retarded. The retarded are just one of many groups with which the community recreator is concerned. It therefore behooves the therapeutic recreation specialist to take the initiative in establishing a liaison with all appropriate community resource persons. All community recreation facilities (parks, zoos, museums, playgrounds, etc.) and programs offered by the public recreation department, YMCA, YWCA, Boy and Girl Scouts, churches, schools, fire and police departments, and private businesses and agencies should be used. After the retardate has been exposed to, and included in, the various community resources, he may beneficially occupy some of his leisure time there before being released from the treatment facility. An ultimate goal of the institution's recreation program should be to prepare the retarded person so that he may leave the institution and immediately begin to function in the community in his avocational as well as his vocational activities. This is very difficult to do unless there is communication, cooperation, and consistency between the institutional and community programs and endeavors.

There are few municipal recreation departments that have employed therapeutic recreation specialists for purposes of coordinating and conducting programs for "special" groups such as the mentally retarded and physically handicapped. This has been verified by surveys conducted by Marson,[30] Andres,[31] Peters,[32] and Hayes.[33] In those programs reported, it appeared that the greatest emphasis was on the physical dimensions of the recreative experience.

The impact of mental retardation on the individual and his family, plus the concomitant lack of community understanding, has frequently resulted in the mentally retarded not taking advantage of community recreation resources, even when available to him. The organizational structures of agencies such as municipal recreation departments, the YMCA and YWCA, Boy Scouts and Girl Scouts, 4-H, and the like, which are oriented to community and neighborhood needs, potentially offer the same recreation advantages to the retarded as they do to the so-called normal individual. The majority of the retarded could benefit from participation in the activities of these kinds of organizations. More and more municipal agencies are following this lead. There is a critical need for more recreation and leisure time programs for the mentally retarded and other handicapped in the community. The private and voluntary agencies cannot, by themselves, fill the void. Cooperation and coordination of efforts are essential.

FOOTNOTES

[1] Irving Phillips, "Common Misconceptions Concerning Mental Retardation," *Psychosomatic Disorders and Mental Retardation in Children,* ed. S. A. Szurek and I. N. Berlin (Palo Alto: Science and Behavior Books, Inc., 1968), p. 144.

[2] Alfred Deutsch, *The Mentally Ill in America,* 2d ed. (New York: Columbia Press, 1952), pp. 1–38.

[3] Deutsch, *The Mentally Ill in America,* p. 333.

[4] Halbert B. Robinson and Nancy M. Robinson, *The Mentally Retarded Child* (New York: McGraw-Hill, Inc., 1965), p. 29.

[5] Rick Heber, *Manual on Terminology and Classifications in Mental Retardation* (Washington, D.C.: The American Association on Mental Deficiency, 1961).

[6] Heber, *Manual on Terminology,* p. 3.

[7] Heber, *Manual on Terminology,* pp. 3–4.

[8] Christine P. Ingram, *Education for the Slow-Learning Child* (New York: The Ronald Press, Inc., 1960), p. 7.

[9] Robinson and Robinson, *The Mentally Retarded Child,* p. 461.

[10] Heber, *Manual on Terminology,* p. 59.

[11] Ingram, *Education for the Slow-Learning Child,* p. 7.

[12] Robinson and Robinson, *The Mentally Retarded Child,* p. 462.

[13] Heber, *Manual on Terminology,* pp. 20–41.

[14] Robinson and Robinson, *The Mentally Retarded Child,* p. 104.

[15] C. E. Benda, "Prenatal Maternal Factors in Mongolism," *Journal of the American Medical Association,* April, 1949, 139:975–985.

[16] L. A. Dexter, "A Social Theory of Mental Deficiency," *American Journal of Mental Deficiency,* March, 1958, 62:920–928.

[17] Bernice W. Carlson and David R. Ginglend, *Recreation for the Retarded Teenager and Young Adult* (Nashville: Abingdon Press, 1968), p. 32.

[18] Roswell H. Fine and Jales C. Dawson, "A Therapy Program for the Mildly Retarded Adolescent," *American Journal of Mental Deficiency,* July, 1964, 69:23–30.

[19] Robinson and Robinson, *The Mentally Retarded Child,* p. 506.

[20] Alan C. Ross, *The Exceptional Child in the Family* (New York: Grune and Stratton, 1964), p. 59.

[21] Ingram, *Education for the Slow-Learning Child,* pp. 48–55.

[22] Joseph McGrath, *Social Psychology, A Basic Introduction* (New York: Holt, Rinehart and Wilson, 1964), p. 68.

[23] David Krech, Richard Crutchfield, and Egeston Ballacher, *Individual in Society* (New York: McGraw-Hill, Inc., 1962), p. 214.

[24] Darwin Cartwright and Alvin Zander, *Group Dynamics, 1960 Research and Theory* (New York: Row, Peterson Co., 1960), p. 12.

[25] McGrath, *Social Psychology,* p. 67.

[26] Harold Lillywhite and Doris P. Bindley, *Communication*

Problems in Mental Retardation (New York: Harper & Row, 1969), p. 35.

[27] Bryant J. Cratty, *Movement, Perception and Thought* (Palo Alto: A Peek Publication, 1969), pp. 9–10.

[28] Cratty, *Movement, Perception, and Thought*, p. 11.

[29] Jay S. Shivers, "The Need for Public Recreational Programs for the Mentally Retarded," *Recreation for the Ill and Handicapped,* June, 1966, 10:6–8.

[30] Ruth Marson, "National Survey of Community Recreation Services to the Mentally Retarded and Physically Handicapped," Unpublished Master's Thesis, New York University, 1965.

[31] Catherine Andres, "The Status of Recreation for the Mentally Retarded," Unpublished Master's Project, University of Minnesota, 1967.

[32] Martha Peters, *A Study of Recreation Services for the Ill and Disabled in the State of Illinois* (Champaign: Field Service, Department of Recreation and Park Administration, University of Illinois, November, 1967).

[33] Gene A. Hayes, "Recreation Services for the Mentally Retarded in the State of Kansas," *Therapeutic Recreation Journal,* (Washington, D.C.: National Therapeutic Recreation Society of the National Recreation and Park Association, May, 1969), Vol. 3, No. 3, p. 13.

5 Recreation and Youthful and Adult Offenders

RFK Youth Center, Courtesy U.S. Bureau of Prisons

MARION AND CARROLL HORMACHEA

Through neglect, both deliberate and thoughtless, society has attempted to place the field of corrections on a dark and dank back shelf. Society wants to "put away" the person who violates the mores; while at the same time demanding that he be returned after serving his sentence, a contrite and rehabilitated soul who promises, "it won't happen again."

Such attitudes hang like a specter over the various institutions that make up the system of corrections. Broadly defined in the system of criminal justice, corrections is the means whereby society, as a collective entity, punishes those who violate its laws. In addition, the system of corrections has as its charge the preparation of the offender to return to society as a productive member.

Corrections, as one of the main members of the system of criminal justice, is made up of many elements. In order to better understand the relevance of corrections to the entire system, it must be understood that the administration of justice begins with the arrest of the offender. The offender goes through three distinct phases: arrest, trial, and corrections and/or release.

The offender usually enters the system of corrections when he is placed in a local jail or the police lock-up following his arrest. He will be held there pending bail and possibly until his trial. Following the trial, if the offender has been adjudged guilty, he may be sentenced to a number of different types of correctional institutions, or he might have his sentence suspended and thus be placed on probation.

The type of correctional institution to which the prisoner is sent for rehabilitative treatment and incarceration is governed by a number of factors, including the crime of which he was adjudged guilty. Other considerations will include age, sex, his prior offense, if any, and his psychological outlook. If his crime was particularly grave or if he is considered dangerous, he may well be sentenced to a maximum security institution. Here he will serve his sentence working within the confines of the prison itself. On the other hand, if he has been convicted of a lesser offense or if he is a first offender, he may be sentenced to serve in a correctional camp or prison farm.

Juvenile offenders are generally held in detention homes

pending trial or juvenile court hearing. These facilities usually are intended as holding areas and are not designed for long-term incarceration. The use of such facilities for long-term incarceration is, and should be, discouraged.

When it becomes necessary to commit the juvenile to a correctional institution, he is usually sent to a training school. Such a concept has replaced the reform school which was prevalent some years ago.

As mentioned earlier, the first introduction of the adult offender, and in some cases even the juvenile offender, to the system of retributive justice is the local jail. Although the jail is usually considered as a holding facility, persons may be sentenced to serve short terms, usually up to a year, at such institutions rather than being sent to the penitentiary or other correctional facilities.

In recent years, with the development of the rehabilitative approach to corrections, pre-release centers and halfway houses have been introduced to assist the offender in his return to the "outside." Under this system, the prisoner will spend the last few months of his sentence in a special area of the prison or outside the institution where he will undergo orientation for his return to society. Here he will receive assistance in seeking employment and a place to live. He also will be helped to make constructive use of his leisure time and leisure contacts.

According to the President's Commission on Law Enforcement and the Administration of Justice of 1967, more popularly known as the Crime Commission, there are approximately 1.3 million persons being held within the correctional system on any given day. The annual cost of these programs to federal, state, and local governments is over one billion dollars annually. Even in light of such staggering statistics, this element of the system of the administration of justice is probably the most neglected and the most antiquated. Some states still use facilities which are well over 150 years old. Provisions for basic human needs, such as heat in the winter, have not always been available in some institutions and some few isolated prisons are still using on the inmates correctional methods that are just as old and repressive as some of the antiquated facilities.

DEVELOPMENT OF PUNISHMENT
AND CORRECTIONAL PHILOSOPHY

Punishment for the violation of existing laws probably has been around since the days when men were cave dwellers. Even then there was a problem of how to punish the offender who had wronged an individual or the community as a whole.

As man became more civilized and urbanized, the problem grew. In the quest for a means of maintaining order through laws, there developed the law of retaliation, later to be known as Mosaic Law: "an eye for an eye and a tooth for a tooth." Though it was believed that Moses originated this philosophy, the law actually was developed some six or eight hundred years earlier, in the writings of Hammurabi, the King of Babylon. Hammurabi developed his system of law sometime between 2200 B.C. to 1800 B.C. The code was based on the concept of retaliation, which provided for the offended to extract an equal payment from the offender, but no more.

Many other codes and practices developed. Some were more barbaric than their predecessors. The development of punishment and corrections was void of logical progression and grew with little conscious direction. Consequently a new attitude gained prominence. The new idea was simply one of "let the punishment fit the crime." This attitude served to keep alive the inhuman punishments of flogging, symbolic mutilation, and other cruel forms of punishment and death. A favorite punishment during the middle ages, and even during the Age of Enlightenment, was exile. Exile was said to be an extremely cruel form of punishment since it cut the offender off from all things familiar, as well as from friends and neighbors. It must be remembered, also, that during that time most people were born, lived, and died in their local community. Strangers were not offered many opportunities for developing new lives in other communities.

Dungeons, torture chambers, and ordeals as measures of punishment and justice enjoyed popularity for many centuries. The Spanish Inquisition of the fifteenth and sixteenth centuries stands alone as an example of the cruel treatment devised by man to take revenge on his fellow man.

The English gaol, forerunner of the modern jail, appeared

sometime in the middle ages around the twelfth century. In these jails, as in later history, the offender was required to pay his own and his family's keep while he was held awaiting a trial. In later years, a spirit of humanism in prisons was encouraged by the writings of John Howard. Howard wrote of the filth and corruption of the jails and of the inhuman treatment of the prisoners. Experienced criminals and debtors were imprisoned together, as were women and children.

Shortly after the first wave of Englishmen landed on the American shores, England began to transport convicted criminals to the colonies as indentured servants. These persons had been convicted of a variety of crimes and were sentenced to serve their masters for a specified period of time as retribution for their wrongdoings.

Two systems of prisons developed in colonial America in the years that followed. The first, known as the Pennsylvania system, developed in the prison at Cherry Hill in 1829. The Pennsylvania system, devised by the Quakers, called for solitary confinement of the prisoners and forbade any communication between inmates. The prisoner was not allowed to leave his cell. Inmate meals were taken in the cell and all work by the prisoner also was done there.

The other model was developed a few years earlier in New York at Auburn. Sing-Sing Prison was developed along the lines of the Auburn philosophy. This system provided for the prisoners to work together and eat together, but communication between the inmates was forbidden.

Under the former system it was felt that the individual would have a great deal of time to contemplate the error of his ways and this would lead to his eventual reform. Throughout the development of corrections in this nation, various religious groups have played an important role in bringing about reforms.

The federal system of prisons was quite slow in developing. In 1889, the Congress established three prisons: one in the North, another in the South, and a third in the Eastern portion of the nation. Prior to 1889, offenders convicted of federal violations were sentenced to state and territorial prisons and virtually forgotten. The first of these institutions was located at Fort Leavenworth, Kansas in 1895. The others were located at Atlanta, Georgia and McNeil Island, Washington.

Originally, correctional philosophy had developed along the lines of revenge and retribution. For centuries the whole concept was to punish the offender physically as well as mentally, make him sorry for his sins, cause him to repent and, in many cases, forget him. Through the years, persons with humanistic motivation deplored the conditions they found in the prisons here and abroad. They found prisoners having to pay for their food, prostitutes and young boys jailed together, debtors being held in prison until they paid their bills, and the use of cruel and inhuman corporal punishment.

Corporal punishment is not a thing of the past, but rather still exists in some states. It has long been considered an unacceptable practice by progressive penologists. However, until quite recently one or two states still maintained the philosophy that prison was to punish rather than to rehabilitate the offender.

As the prison system developed in America, penologists began to realize the value of returning the "whole" man to society. This was partially brought about by the hue and cry of the public after seeing the movie exposes of prison life which were produced in the early thirties. Great strides have been made in developing the rehabilitation concept in modern penology. While those in the field are furthering this concept, it must be admitted that society is neglecting more than a portion of its role. Most states strip the convicted offender of most of his civil rights upon conviction. These rights are generally not restored upon release. In some states the offender may petition the governor for restoration of his rights as a citizen. Such situations make it difficult for the offender to accept the rehabilitation doctrine. He finds that his debt to society will never be marked "paid in full" regardless of the time he serves or the extent of his repentance.

REHABILITATION AND CORRECTIONS

In order to help the inmate adjust within the prison, as well as to prepare him for his eventual release, the prisons maintain staff chaplains, psychologists, teachers, counselors, and other professionals. In addition to these professionals, the institutions employ a staff to help the inmate develop a trade. In more recent years, forward thinkers in corrections have advocated the work-release programs whereby the inmate goes into the community to work by day and returns to the institutions at night. A similar program of study-release is under way, allowing the younger offender to attend school in the community and thus earn a high school diploma or college degree. Progressive thinking of this nature has done much to aid in the rehabilitation of the offender. Further, the use of halfway houses and pre-release centers better prepare the inmate for what he will face upon his return to society. It is here that he receives instruction on how to cope with his new freedom and the problems that his former life might present.

The old adage concerning "all work and no play" probably is more true in a prison environment than in almost any other setting. Convicted persons upon entering prison undergo a traumatic experience, being drawn from the normal world of society into the highly regulated and often insensitive world of corrections. As the offenders begin their sentences, they are stripped of all "outside" reminders including their identity and dignity. It is made clear to them that they must undergo such treatment because they violated the rules of the "outside" world.

In his new and highly ordered life, the offender finds that he is no longer responsible for himself. All decisions are made for him. He is told when to eat, to sleep, to work, and even when to play. It is because of this extreme orderliness that considerable thought should be given to developing a meaningful program of recreation that will enable the person to maintain a grasp of reality and at the same time offer an avenue for frustration-letting.

Prison movies have given the public a seamy look into prison complexes. They depict the exercise period as one where the convicts walk aimlessly around the prison yard and plot escapes and mayhem. Occasionally, prisoners are seen playing catch with an old baseball. To say that the Hollywood version of the "big house" was false would be an untruth in itself. Rather it should be said that conditions were, and even today in many cases continue to be, almost that bad.

THE ROLE OF RECREATION
IN CORRECTIONS

There is no doubt of the value of recreation as a rehabilitative tool. By giving the convict a more balanced life, combining work and play, the prison workers are able to work more effectively with the man and his problems.

While sports do tend to be one of the major forms of recreation found in correctional institutions, it is by no means the only one that will offer benefit to the inmates. A comprehensive program should be developed to offer the inmate the choice of leisure time activities. This program should offer a potpourri to serve the needs and interests of the inmates. Consideration should be given to those who are not physically or psychologically able to participate in the more active games. Another part of the program should concern itself with the over all physical fitness of the individual.

Leisure in the institution comprises a larger block of time than is realized by those on the "outside." According to Clemmer, 44 percent of the inmates' waking hours are devoted to leisure-time activities.[1] Such time is divided into what is termed as collective recreation and private recreation.

The importance of occupying the many leisure hours with a constructive program cannot be over emphasized. Dr. Karl Menninger writes, "the proper direction of recreation and play is both corrective and preventive as far as mental health is concerned. We do not understand play scientifically, but know that it is very important and must be taken seriously. A balance of work and play is what men live by. It makes it possible for us to live, love, and control our aggressive tendencies, and thus enables us to have good mental health."[2]

While the foregoing applies specifically to prisons and long-term institutions, it is imperative that the short-term institution not be neglected. Jails and juvenile detention homes often are overlooked in planning because of the very nature of their primary function as holding facilities.

Persons confined to these facilities are also in need of an organized program to keep their equilibrium while undergoing confinement. This program should be extensive enough to keep the inmate alert and prevent physical and mental deterioration.

Leisure activities are often neglected in these facilities since they lack trained personnel and are usually short-staffed. Additionally, space is not usually available for such a program. This lack of activity can serve as an albatross to the inmate by subjecting him to long hours of inactivity with nothing to do but to consider his plight.

As mentioned earlier, a meaningful program must be one that offers something for everyone. Studies have shown that many inmates do not enjoy sports and thus other outlets are necessary. At this point a more concise approach is indicated. Leisure activities refer to the use of time off the job, other than taking meals.

Meyer, Brightbill, and Sessoms, in their discussion of the delinquent, liken recreation programs in youth correctional settings to that of usual community recreation. However, they also point out that the program must be geared to sustain morale and to assist in the rehabilitative process. Such recreation programs are not the main function of the institution, but rather are of a secondary or supportive nature and should be beneficial in helping prepare the individual to return to society.[3] Although the preceding authors state their premise in relation to juvenile offender training schools, there is no reason why this philosophy should not be applied to adult corrections.

In order that recreation might be more meaningful, it is necessary that during the classification period of the offender's entry into the corrections system, his interests in leisure activities be well established. Classification is that period which every inmate undergoes when he is tested by prison officials and indoctrinated into the system. During this period a definite program is mapped out for the individual which is intended to develop an attitude conducive to the rehabilitative process.

Without trained personnel to implement and administer it, the recreation program will be ineffective in meeting the inmates' needs and the institution's goals of inmate adjustment and rehabilitation.

Leadership in recreation programs is necessary to establish order and to assure continuity and program progression. Leadership should come from a person within the central administration of the institution who has an understanding of the role of recreation. It should be his or her duty to develop the overall program, in consultation with various staff members. Ideally this person should carry professional credentials in the field of recreation.

Consideration must be given to the funding of such programs and to furnishing the necessary physical facilities. The importance of the foregoing cannot be overemphasized. The recreation administrator should handle such items as funds and physical facilities, in addition to planning. Ideally the staff should have various recreation leaders who will actually conduct the program.

Among these leaders should be persons trained in arts and crafts, music, and physical education. Correctional officers should be used to assist in the implementation of the program. Such is a recommendation of the American Correctional Association in order to have a more efficient and better managed program.[4]

Research has found that most recreation programs in institutions are inadequate. This inadequacy is usually the result of poor planning or a lack of knowledge of recreation and its advantages as well as its application. Too often the concern with prison and inmate security prevents the recreation program from getting off the ground.[5] However, security should be kept in mind in developing recreation programs, since many pieces of equipment could be turned into weapons for use by the inmates.

Variety should be considered in program planning. In addition to the usual team sports, which offer more opportunity for spectators than for actual participation, some emphasis should be placed on the physical fitness of the individual. In some cases a program of physical therapy might be necessary. Other activities should include music, crafts, movies, television, literary, and other group activities. The individual should not be neglected, but rather should be allowed to develop his own *thing* whenever possible.

Equipment, facilities, supplies, and personnel for recreation activities should be budgeted in the allocation of funds for the institution. The budget for these activities should be carefully planned to meet the needs of the inmates. Care should be taken not to overemphasize one area of the program at the expense of other areas or the inmates' choices.

Physical facilities are a necessary element of a successful recreation program. It is necessary that planning be coordinated with the prison administration in order to develop the area allocated to recreation. Both indoor and outdoor recreation activities must be considered in the development of such a plan. Recreation consultants are available to outline such needs. The multipurpose concept is suggested in designing any building for use in the recreation program. This concept tends to make greater use of the facility as well as stretching the budget appropriated for the program.[6]

The multipurpose facility should provide space for a gymnasium with a bleacher or spectator section. In addition, it is necessary that a locker room be built to accommodate the players. The gymnasium might also double as an auditorium with a stage for dramatic productions as well as serving as a movie theater. This multipurpose facility should provide space for an arts and crafts shop where the inmate can use various handcrafting tools. It is desirable also to have a music room where the inmate can not only listen to records, but also be furnished with musical instruments and a practice room. Inmates should be encouraged to form musical groups as a means of working together. All recreation facilities should be kept to standard sizes for the utmost benefit to the inmate. The alert prison administrator will readily realize that money spent on recreational activities is a good investment.

Thought must be given to the safety and security of the equipment and the facility itself. Faulty or inferior equipment must never be used, especially in contact sports. Often in an attempt to save a few dollars, inferior equipment will be purchased which may result in inmate injuries.[7] Further, it is necessary that this equipment be inspected on a regular basis by the officer in charge or by the recreation supervisor. Such inspection provides a preventive maintenance program for the equipment, as well as providing an additional safety factor for the inmates.

The second factor is that of security. Security is a major item in any correctional institution. Its breach numbers among the seven deadly sins of corrections. Studies have shown that many items of sports and recreation equipment can be converted to use as weapons by a clever inmate. It is generally recommended that the recreation supervisor review his equipment purchases with the security officer to determine if any of the desired items could prove dangerous. Additionally, it is recommended that the equipment undergo periodic inspection by the security officer.[8]

Generally the same criteria for recreation as outlined above will apply to those institutions for juvenile offenders. Exceptions would be basically stated in the program. Certain institutions might have a broader or narrower program, depending upon available facilities and equipment.

Programming in the correctional institution must be geared to the needs of that individual institution. It is imperative that the recreation supervisor consider this point in his ongoing evaluation of the program. Due to varying needs, the program should be adaptable to suit different situations. The supervisor should keep in mind at all times that the mission of his program is to develop desirable traits of discipline and self-control in the inmates, as well as to occupy leisure time constructively.

SPECIALIZED RECREATION PROGRAMS

Specialized programming is a necessity in the development of any plan for a correctional institution. Institutions vary and with these variations come differences in the needs of the inmates and differences in the means of satisfying these divergent needs. It is important that the recreation supervisor consider all elements in formulating his ideas. He must consider not only his population, but also the available facilities and even the weather. For instance, the cold snowy climate of certain areas of the country would greatly curtail outdoor activity at times.

In the development of specialized programming, the supervisor must also consider the overall mission of his program. With this thought in mind, he should attempt to evaluate his program and the effect it will have on the inmates. Some state institutions have carried on excellent programs of a specialized nature that have attracted nationwide attention. For instance, the Texas State Penitentiary at Huntsville offers an annual prison rodeo. This rodeo features inmate cowboys and has been an outstanding success in the southwest. Another such program is in a Nevada prison where the inmates have a gambling casino for their own use.

While such programs tend to raise the eyebrows of the more conservative in the field, the therapeutic value to the inmates of such activities is immeasurable. The inmates, through such activities, can recapture their lost identity. The search for identity in the correctional setting is very real.

Other innovative programs have allowed inmates to attend sporting events on the outside. This is often limited to trustees and to special situations. Such practice is more prevalent in youth correctional institutions where inmates are taken to outside events more frequently. In some states, the Youth Training School for Boys will hold dances for the Training Schools for Girls and vice versa. Other coed recreational activities that are undertaken in some areas include picnics, movies, and stunt nights.

Sometimes the inmate devises his own recreation. Such a situation was recalled by a former inmate who told of building an automobile out of snow and ice. A great deal of interest was generated among his fellow inmates who offered cat-calls at first but later turned to offering help in building the life-size model car. The car became a total project for a number of inmates and served to create a pattern of team work among the men.[9]

The recreation specialist in the institution should be aware at all times of the possibilities offered by the natural environment. The foregoing is an example of how the men themselves made good use of their "off-time." "Off-time" in the late afternoon hours is most important; it is at this time that many inmates experience a psychological letdown after the day's activities.

Many institutions are seemingly content to offer competitive sports, an occasional checkerboard, and a very inadequate library, with an occasional movie thrown in, as their recreation program. By the very nature of the desired results, recreation is most important and must be considered so by the administration of the institution.

At best, prison is a highly artificial life. The unnatural regimen, the loss of identity, and the feeling of punishment contribute to insecurities and anxieties of the inmate. Recreation is a part of the "normal" life outside, and if the inmate is to be rehabilitated, it is important that he maintain a link with the outside, such as recreation. Professional recreators have found that often the knowledge and skills learned in the institution are carried over upon release and aid in the post-release adjustment.[10]

Programming should include a variety of athletic events. Care should be taken, however, to make the program broader than just football or baseball since, as was mentioned earlier, these are played by relatively few and tend to create a corps of spectators. Many of these spectators, according to a variety of sources, often attend for no reason other than to leave their cells.

It is suggested that the athletic program be divided into the areas of individual sports, team sports, and combative sports. Such categories offer something for almost everyone.[11]

Individual sports are those that allow the inmate to play by himself, such as bowling, swimming, weightlifting, and gymnastics. These also afford him the opportunity to develop his technique. Often the individual sports offer the avenue by which inmates come into the recreation program. While individual sports provide the inmate much of the release he seeks, the recreation supervisor should bear in mind the value of co-operation that develops in team sports, and encourage these men to participate. Likewise, the "loner" should be encouraged to enter a diversity of activities where he is in contact with other inmates.

Dual sports offer possibilities for skills which can be used over a lifetime as well as making a good use of "off-time." These sports usually are attractive since they offer a chance for competition through leagues and tournaments.

Team sports offer a different kind of challenge since the individual must not only display skill in the game, but also must have gained the acceptance and cooperation of his teammates. Organization of such a program should be on a skill basis since the lack of skill and prowess can serve, in many cases, to reinforce feelings of insecurity and inadequacy in the inmate. This is especially true with the youthful offender.

With team sports, it is possible for games to be scheduled with other institutions and outside teams. While the scheduling of outside teams can create some security problems, the end result can be one that will have a good effect on the inmates. College teams are often willing to come to the institution to play varsity sports with the inmate teams.

In addition to the opportunities of outside competition, team sports offer possibilities for intramural play. Actually such a program is the grassroots of the recreation program since it offers a chance for the men to compete against one another.

This can be done by cell-blocks, by building, or by any other design.

Intramural sports offer a chance for inmates to participate in numerous sports activities. These teams are comprised of inmates who did not make the varsity team. Thus, this program allows a greater number of men to participate in the activities who, otherwise, would be relegated to sitting on the sidelines.

Combative sports, such as boxing and wrestling, offer an opportunity for the more aggressive inmates to work off steam. Great care should be taken, however, to see that such programs are properly conducted and supervised. Through the proper conduct of such programs, it is possible for the inmates to develop courage and control over emotional stress.

Fair play and good sportsmanship are essential in all recreation activities. The recreation supervisor must see that the rules are observed and the game carried on in such a way that fair play becomes a meaningful experience.

Another major category of activities is cultural activities. These activities can include arts and crafts, music, drama, literary events, discussion groups, radio, television, and movies. Such activities can offer as much in the way of character building as does the athletic program. Persons who cannot or should not participate in the athletic program should be encouraged to participate in these programs. However, the programs should not be limited to these men and women, but should be open to all who wish to participate.

Arts and crafts offer an outlet for the inmate and give him the opportunity to satisfy his creative urge. This program media offers him the opportunity to fill his leisure hours meaningfully and to gain satisfaction from his handwork. Such programs are fairly new to prison communities. Prior to World War II, some inmates satisfied this creative urge by carving out figurines from any available material, including fruit pits. While such makeshift recreation seems unthinkable, it must be remembered that changes in correctional philosophy have been slow in evolving. This partially explains why recreation does not enjoy a high priority in prison systems. However, one major reason, apparently, is the lack of funds.

The arts and crafts program should be supervised by a trained instructor. Overseeing the craft shop, including the distribution and use of tools and materials, is an important part of his responsibility. It is recommended that each inmate purchase his own supplies and that a strict inventory be kept of these items. The instructor must be sure that all regulations regarding the program are observed. Often this program allows the inmate to make Christmas presents for his relatives and friends. Some prisons offer an opportunity for the inmate to sell his wares in a prison store or bazaar, i.e., persons from the outside are allowed to buy hobby articles and paintings.

Music offers still another opportunity for the expression of talents, abilities, and interests. The music program should be under the direct supervision of the recreation supervisor or a music instructor. Should a qualified individual not be available, this program offers the opportunity to use inmates, especially those with professional experience, in such a capacity. Such a procedure would enable the inmate to make use of his talent and at the same time develop leadership qualities which could aid his personal rehabilitation.

Inmate orchestras and combos can be formed. These groups can perform at inmate functions including athletic events, variety shows, plays, and special events programs. In some cases, groups of a professional nature might even appear in concert for the general public, outside of the prison. Musical instruments sometimes are difficult to obtain because of budget limitations. The recreation supervisor should consider going into the community and soliciting contributions of instruments from civic organizations and women's clubs. Usually these groups are actively seeking good causes which they can support.

Additional outside participation should be encouraged by the recreation supervisor by extending invitations to outside musical groups to come to the institution and perform for the edification of the inmates. Professional musicians could also be solicited to work with the inmates in the development of the music program. These professionals can be especially helpful in working with the inmate whose musical talents tend to be of a more creative nature, e.g., in composing and arranging.

Drama is most important in a well-rounded recreation program. There is little, if any, difficulty in getting the interested inmates to present plays, variety shows, and the like. Such a program offers a therapeutic value to the inmate by enabling him to act out his inner feelings.

In addition to acting, the inmates interested in drama can

become involved in the building of sets and props and in the designing of costumes. Inmates also should handle the important production roles such as producer, director, stage manager, and others.

It has been suggested that this portion of the program provide dramatic presentations rather frequently in order to give a larger number of inmates the opportunity to participate and to sustain their interest. Dramatic presentations should be carefully considered. Plays requiring an all-male or all-female cast, as the case may be, are usually the easiest for inmates to perform. However, this should not be a limiting factor on dramatic productions on the "inside."

Special events and holidays should be celebrated within the institution to keep the inmates aware of life on the outside. The drama department can provide programs for special events and the music groups can also participate by providing music for such events. In addition, interest in activities can be developed by having special days or weeks set aside for sports, music, dramatics, and movies. For instance, on one weekend it might be possible to have a comedy film festival. Such a program would provide wholesome and varied entertainment which would appeal to most inmates.

Movies, like plays, should be carefully selected. Many sources suggest that a screening committee of inmates and prison personnel choose films to be shown at the institution. Such action makes the inmate feel that he has a definite stake in the program. Attendance at movies, and for that matter other similar events, should be voluntary. To force someone to participate in recreation for his own good and against his will is futile. The total effect is lost for the inmate concerned, and it may also damage the attitudes of others playing with him.

Television and radio offer a diversity all their own. Most institutions have few television sets, so it is necessary to work out a definite pattern of programming. As with movies, a degree of censorship must be imposed to achieve satisfactory results. Since the budget often does not allow for more than a few television sets, the recreation supervisor might try to raise funds through inmate activities, the arts and crafts sales, etc., to purchase and maintain additional sets.

Radio is easier and less expensive to maintain and control. Experience has shown that inmates should be offered some choice of radio presentations. Rather than having a central loudspeaker in the cell or nearby, it is suggested that the inmate desiring to listen to the radio be furnished with earphones for listening. Private listening allows the nearby inmates to listen to the programs of their choice.

Reading and writing help to pass away the leisure hours in the institution. Libraries usually have something for everyone, as well as providing private entertainment. Regretfully, many institutions do not have adequate libraries for their respective populations. Here again, it behooves the recreation supervisor to request aid and assistance from civic and service organizations, as well as churches and other groups in the community, to collect discarded books which would be of value to the inmates.

Writing can be of a personal as well as a creative nature. For the purpose of this discussion, it will be stipulated that the writing of letters home and to friends provides a very necessary outlet for the inmate. However, creative writing also should be considered as an outlet for the inmate. Some institutions have their own magazines and newspapers which encourage such contributions. Like drama and music, writing provides the individual with a chance to express himself.

Some institutions have provided some photographic equipment for inmates with an interest in this area. Here the inmate can learn the principles of photography and possibly better equip himself for a job after release. When possible, he should be taught darkroom technique as well as picture composition. The result of his photographic handiwork can be printed in the prison publications. Photographic competition among the inmates should also be considered as a worthwhile program. However, great care should be taken not to violate any prison regulations concerning the recognizable photographing of inmates or the institution.

Another concern in recreation programming should be social games. These may include chess, checkers, cards, ping-pong, and other games which do not require an organized group or team. Special equipment and clothing are usually not necessary for such programs. Most of these games can be played indoors in recreation halls, and some can even be played in the individual cells.

Certain forms of group activities also can be beneficial to

the inmate. Special interest groups such as stamp collectors, poetry readers, literary groups, and others offer an outlet for the inmate and give him the opportunity to continue hobby interests and to develop new ones. Model airplanes, cars, and railroads all offer the inmate the possibility of developing his leisure-time interests. These activities recall the incident, which was recounted earlier, of the inmates who built the snow car.

In programming recreation in a correctional institution, one should be aware of and sensitive to as many of the inmates' needs as possible. It is not enough to offer leisure-time activities; some concern also should be given to the physical fitness of the individual. While basically seen as recreation in a correctional institution, physical fitness programs serve a variety of goals, not the least of which is developing the total person. This program will serve to put men in shape. It can help individuals to develop a pride in their own well being. During World War II, many inmates who planned and hoped to be released often undertook a military drill, marching in formation around the yard while carrying broomsticks for rifles. The military drill served to develop a military bearing in the inmate and he took pride in the results.

Physical fitness tests serve to tell the prison officials something about the individual and his health. Such tests can give some hint as to his assignment, whether or not he is capable of heavy work and, in general, his strength and endurance. Through the physical fitness program, the inmate gains the stamina necessary to carry out his duties while in the institution.

The recreation activities of the inmates, as well as their physical fitness reports, should be studied often to judge the progress of the individual. Methods of play and team work can be of value to the prison staff in evaluating the performance of the inmate.

RECREATION PROGRAM NEEDS

It has often been said that research is lacking in the causation and treatment of crime and criminals. Perhaps this is the reason that crime is running rampant through the cities of America. Such a lack of knowledge is stipulated. However, it also must be stated that there are few areas that have been more neglected by the researchers than corrections. There has been little written in the area of recreation in corrections. The lack of knowledge has not encouraged the development of recreation in correctional institutions, but probably has retarded it.

It is easy enough to suggest many other programs which are needed in correctional institutions for the leisure hours of the inmates. However, there are many considerations which come to mind and must be dealt with by the recreation supervisor. As mentioned earlier, many persons holding such positions are working in antiquated buildings and with less than up-to-date equipment. In addition to the age and condition of the facilities, many of the persons engaged in corrections must cope with extreme overcrowding in the institutions.

An over-capacity population makes an institutional planning difficult, since the recreation supervisor cannot provide the services as frequently or as fully as he might desire. In addition, overcrowding usually means a lack of sufficient equipment to go around. Despite the inconveniences, the recreation supervisor is powerless to control the population of the institution. Hopefully he can obtain a larger budget for the provision of recreation services.

Recreation should rank high among necessary programs in corrections. Regretfully, such a priority is difficult when the other facilities needed by the institutions are considered. Antiquity in many of the institutions creates certain priorities that must be considered for the very survival of the individual inmate. It has only been in recent years that a certain western prison installed a heating system. Comparable situations can be found in other institutions throughout the nation. These are not carry overs of "inhuman" wardens and staff, but rather the lack of recognition of the problem and the general attitude towards corrections displayed by various legislative bodies who must appropriate the money produces these conditions.

Security measures which are essential in the institution make it difficult for the recreation supervisor to bring in volunteer workers. The use of such groups could contribute to the expansion of the program by providing additional personnel to conduct the various programs. Consideration should be given to the use of such persons, especially in the recreation program.

However, the recreation supervisor should proceed with caution. Such a plan should not be confused with using individuals who are professionally trained to assist in the program.

Volunteer workers must be thoroughly screened to be sure that they are not relatives or friends of inmates, seeking to circumvent prison regulations. In addition, these persons should be warned about the severe consequences of providing contraband to the inmates whom they are attempting to serve. Further, it should be made clear that violating prison rules is not in the best interests of the inmates.

Volunteer workers could be most beneficial, particularly in performing needed services which the prison cannot afford. For instance, volunteers could be brought in to referee or umpire sports events. Professional entertainers can be of great value to the morale of the inmates and are often most anxious to perform for such groups, free of charge. Arts and crafts also offer a number of opportunities for outside assistance. Various club groups might contribute funds for arts and crafts supplies and materials.

Additional services performed by volunteers are done by such groups as Alcoholics Anonymous and similar organizations. While the primary mission of such groups is not necessarily recreation, they can assist by providing services and ideas as input into the organized program.

RECREATION IN PRE-RELEASE
AND HALFWAY-HOUSE SITUATIONS

Pre-release programs and halfway-houses offer special problems for the recreation planner and supervisor. Organized pre-release programs are generally new to the field of corrections. This is not by oversight, but often because of a lack of staff and necessary funds. The program is designed to ease the adjustment of the offender, adult and juvenile, into the new status of freedom. During the program, he attends lecture sessions on employment problems and their solutions, the return to the family and friends, as well as being brought up to date on changes in the outside world since his imprisonment. Recreation during this crucial period should be carefully planned to give the inmate more of the feeling of the outside than before. The programming should be concerned with teaching the inmate how to properly use his leisure time after release. This is particularly true since many offenders return to old neighborhoods and associates upon release, thus increasing their chances of getting into trouble and returning to the institution.

During this transitional period, the offender is sometimes transferred from the institution to a local YMCA or similar organization, where he begins to mingle with the free world again. During his stay, he will be allowed to have visitors, venture into the community to seek employment and other activities. During this time he may utilize the recreation activities available at the facility.

Since the inmate enjoys a greater degree of freedom while in the pre-release center or halfway-house, he should be encouraged to develop his own leisure activities. For instance, he may attend movies in the community rather than in the institution. He may visit the local library, go bowling, play golf or any other number of varied activities, as long as he returns to the facility by the prescribed time. The curfew in this situation is a means of control which is important, especially in these early periods of preparing for release.

It should be remembered that the inmate is now functioning as a product of the socialization that has taken place in the institution. During his imprisonment, whether the offender be adult or juvenile, all decisions have been made for him. His life has been strictly regimented. His friends and associates were all fellow inmates, all subject to the same restrictions. Now, all of a sudden, he is placed in a situation where he can make decisions and he can choose his leisure activities.

He will naturally be hesitant to move ahead and may have to be encouraged to take advantage of his new freedom. Part of this encouragement can come in the form of using leisure time. He might wish to attend a sporting event or a cultural event, which he should be encouraged to do.

CONCLUSION

All in all, recreation for the inmate in a correctional institution is not unlike that found in other specialized situations. The major difference is the regimentation of the individual. Another is the limitation of the institution. That is to say, the inmate is not free to come and go as he pleases. Certain other prohibitions relative to leisure activities are also present.

The student or new recreation worker should be cognizant of the role that recreation can play in the redevelopment of the individual. He should see that the program must be a meaningful one, if it is to be effective. This positive approach contributes to the overall success and acceptance of the program. Further, the worker should be prepared for the frustrations which will present themselves because of the lack of available funds and equipment, as well as the apparent lack of interest the inmates might demonstrate until they learn to trust him.

Professional recreators as well as allied professionals wishing to work within the correctional framework should be cognizant that an additional effort on their part is warranted. In addition to their professional skills, they will need to develop an attitude of communication between themselves and the inmates. Often such empathy calls for more understanding from the professional than from the inmate. Such communication is essential to the success of the recreation program.

As the field of corrections moves ahead in prominence and is no longer seen as a forgotten area or one that is not mentioned in polite company, recreation will be seen as a vital element in the rehabilitation process. Generally, the apparent lack of recognition of the importance of recreation in correctional institutions is due to the necessary priorities which have been set, rather than an ignoring of its very important role.

FOOTNOTES

[1] Donald Clemmer, *The Prison Community* (New York: Rinehart & Company, Inc., 1958), p. 207.

[2] *Manual of Correctional Standards*, 3rd ed. (Washington, D.C.: The American Correctional Association, 1966), p. 519.

[3] Harold D. Meyer, Charles K. Brightbill, and H. Douglas Sessoms, *Community Recreation*, 4th ed. (Englewood Cliffs, N.J.: Prentice-Hall, Inc., 1969), p. 362.

[4] *Manual of Correctional Standards*, p. 521.

[5] Larry E. Decker, "Recreation in Correctional Institutions," *Parks and Recreaton,* Vol. IV, No. 4 (April 1969), pp. 31–33.

[6] *Manual of Correctional Standards,* p. 523.

[7] *Manual of Correctional Standards,* p. 525.

[8] *Manual of Correctional Standards,* p. 525.

[9] "All the Prisoners Drove Away," *The New Yorker,* Vol. 39, No. 48, January 18, 1964.

[10] Decker, "Recreation in Correctional Institutions," pp. 32–33.

[11] The following material in this section has been developed from: *The Manual of Correctional Standards,* 3rd ed., pp. 526–537, and is presented here by permission of the American Correctional Association.

6 Recreation
and the
Mentally Ill

Photo by Tania D'Avignon

LEE E. MEYER

Since the new mental health practices of the 1960's which emphasized a community-based approach, communities have been developing services for their citizens who suffer from mental illness. Implicit in these new perspectives is the necessity to provide a community environment which is conducive to sound mental health. The purpose of this chapter is to review the development of organized recreation services for the mentally ill from its beginning in isolated institutional settings to the modern community-based programs. We will also be concerned with the development of the roles and functions of the professional recreator. The nature, purpose, and services of organized recreation programs for the mentally ill have been defined and shaped by mental health practices and public attitudes toward the mentally ill. For these reasons it is necessary to review the changing public attitudes and the resultant changes in mental health practices for the care and treatment of the mentally ill from the seventeenth century to the present. First, let us begin by attempting to gain a clearer understanding of what mental illness is and is not, along with some viewpoints regarding its nature and cause.

MENTAL ILLNESS—MENTAL HEALTH

Mental illness is considered by many to be the number one problem in society today. Mental health is a major American industry. Mental health programs are being developed by a wide range of government agencies, private volunteer groups, schools and universities, commercial and industrial enterprises, and religious organizations. According to the annual budget of the National Institute of Mental Health, expenditure for mental health care, research, and education is almost 400 million dollars. This is only one federal government program. The need for mental health efforts and programs is crucial not only for those suffering from the disabling effects that characterize mental illness, but also to insure an environment which provides the ways and means to successful living for all people.

But what is mental illness? For that matter, what is mental health? One might say that mental illness is the absence of mental health or a deviation from normalcy. But what is normality? Are "normal" people "normal" all of the time? Realizing that human feelings and behavior are extremely variable, we would admit that normality does not mean being the same at all times, but that it refers to a rather wide range of human emotions and reactions.

One is usually very happy upon receiving a gift from a friend or joyful when starting out on the yearly vacation. When news is received that a loved one has passed away, sadness and depression may often result. Anxiety, sadness, ecstacy, and giddiness are not in themselves signs of mental illness or abnormalcy unless they are inappropriate within the social or personal context. David Mechanic proposes two ways in which we usually recognize deviations from "normal" mental health. One way is when a person behaves in a manner which is noticeably inappropriate within his particular situation or circumstance. It is important, though, to emphasize that knowledge of the context in which the behavior takes place is necessary to make an assessment. Two, personal suffering not easily explained by the life circumstances of the person may also indicate such deviations from normalcy.[1]

Next we must ask—are deviations from "normal" therefore indicative of mental illness? One facet is the difficulty in determining the appropriateness or inappropriateness of someone's behavior in a given situation due to the variations in social norms and values that exist and the range of possible responses. Usually, digressions from the normal are not regarded as mental illness unless they are persistent or so extreme that no other explanation is possible. In effect, inappropriate behavior itself is not necessarily mental illness even though it may be out of the range of behaviors considered to be "normal." Mental illness then seems to refer both to the degree of inappropriate behavior and also to the duration or persistence of behaving in such a manner. The popular classification of a person as "mentally ill" usually goes beyond describing the degree or duration of inappropriate behavior but implicates the person's entire self as being affected. This is one of the many misconceptions of mental illness and one which has resulted in serious consequences for those suffering from emotional ill health. One should be cautious when attempting to define mental illness on the basis of social adjustment level. Mechanic warns that the assumption that failure to conform implies a disorder or that to regard all deviants as sick may be misleading and result in our

failure to appreciate the extent to which nonconforming behavior is the result of learning.[2]

Classifying and labeling a person as mentally ill has had
serious consequences for the person so designated. As mentioned earlier, the labeling of someone as mentally ill implicates the person's total identity and personality. The labels
"mad," "crazy," and "lunatic" result in unsolicited shame, de-
rision, and isolation for the person who is emotionally ill. As
popularly conceived, these labels evoke in others fear and hostility towards the one who is mentally ill, or so labeled.

Many misconceptions of mental illness have been brought
about through fear. These misconceptions have further reinforced and perpetuated the stigma of mental illness. Some of
these misconceptions are:

1. All psychiatric patients are "crazy" and therefore destructive
   and a threat to everyone.
2. All mental illness is the result of a person's sinfulness or per-
   versity.
3. Heredity is the main cause of mental illness.
4. People are either "sane" or "insane."
5. A nervous breakdown is a disease of the nerves.
6. Mental illness is a disgrace.
7. Mental illness is incurable.[3]

To further complicate a clearer understanding of mental
illness is the variety of conceptions of its nature and cause. The
most "interesting," if not noteworthy, include imbalance of body
fluids, bad blood, sin, and witchery. Today the popular notions
range from physical disease, intrapsychic disturbance, dynamic
interactive effects of the self with its environment, and those
who view failures in adjustment due to environmental circumstances.

The disease notion is commonly referred to as the medical
model which is characterized by the descriptive diagnostic labels
used in classifying mental illness. Psychiatric opinion, regarding
these diagnostic categories, ranges from viewing them as disease
categories to ways of grouping reaction patterns. The reader
should be aware that not all psychiatrists ascribe to the disease
notion. Also, in some contexts, "medical model" is used to refer

to the practice of viewing behavior as symptomatic of an underlying cause and that the cause is essentially within the person who is mentally ill.

The American Psychiatric Association divides psychiatric conditions into three major groupings: 1) organic impairment, 2) mental deficiency, and 3) psychogenic disorders without clearly defined causes. The third major grouping (psychogenic disorders, i.e., of psychological origin) is further divided into five subcategories: 1) psychotic disorders; 2) psychophysiologic, autonomic and visceral disorders, e.g., spastic colon, migraine headache; 3) psychoneurotic disorders, e.g., phobias, anxiety or depressive reaction; 4) personality disorders, i.e., antisocial reaction or addiction; and 5) transient situational personality disorders, e.g., combat fatigue, situational conflicts and severe stress.[4]

For our purposes the psychotic disorders subgrouping represents the most serious forms of mental illness. Further divisions of this subcategory include schizophrenia which has ten differentiated forms, as well as the divisions: paranoia, paranoid state, and involutional psychosis. Persons classified as psychotic, more commonly referred to as schizophrenic, are usually those who are sent to public or private institutions. When we speak of state mental institutions, the majority of persons receiving care have been classified as schizophrenics (that is, in those institutions where the descriptive diagnostic classifications are employed).

The *Psychiatric Glossary* defines *psychosis* as a major mental disorder of organic and/or emotional origin in which there is a departure from normal patterns of thinking, feeling, and acting. Its common characteristics include loss of contact with reality, distortion of perception, regressive behavior and attitudes, diminished control of elementary impulses and desires, abnormal mental content including delusions and hallucinations. *Neurosis,* or more properly psychoneurosis, is the second major category of emotional illness (psychiatric condition). Psychoneurosis is usually less severe than psychosis, with minimal loss of contact with reality although thinking and judgment may be impaired. Persons exhibiting such reactions are usually not in state mental hospitals.

Basically, the disease model or medical model concerns itself with maladaptive or inappropriate behavior in terms of symptom formation and categorization. This model views a person's inappropriate behavior as abnormal or diseased because of some underlying cause. Overt abnormal behavior "is considered to be indicative of the presence of a particular disease and because this disease rather than the overt behavior must be treated, categorization of the behavior becomes of crucial importance."[5]

Not all psychiatrists ascribe to the disease model. Some hold a psychodynamic view of emotional problems. They are not concerned with the disease diagnosis. Rather, they attempt to reconstruct a developmental picture of the patient's personality. The psychodynamic psychiatrist assumes that disturbed behavior is continuous with normal behavior and is explained by the same theories of personality development and social functioning. Traditionally, this approach views the problems resulting from defects in the person rather than external difficulties.[6]

A modification of the psychodynamic view is the "interactive" notion of the social-psychiatrist who sees difficulties as the complicated outcomes of the interaction between an individual's personality and the nature of his social environment. They have increasingly recognized that variations in social circumstances may have varying adjustment effects on persons who have similar personality strengths and weaknesses. Coping ability is a significant concern of these psychiatrists. Generally, a well-integrated personality will cope with most situations better than a person with personality weaknesses.[7]

The psychological or behavioral model today is becoming a popular alternative to the medical model. Essentially, the behavioral model regards maladjustment or abnormal behavior as a learned behavior rather than symptomatic of some underlying defect or disease. The development and maintenance of behavior is the same whether it is normal or abnormal. The behaviorist applies the theory of learning which holds that what we do is what we have received reinforcement for doing. The behavioral model is specifically concerned with changing particular aspects of the person rather than toward psychic reintegration.[8]

In general, it would seem most helpful to view persons with psychiatric (emotional or behavioral) problems as having difficulties in interpersonal relationships, as being inadequately trained, or as being deficient in social skills. The terms psychiatric condition and mental illness are too often associated in the public mind with the stereotype (misconceived also) of severe psychoses and the image of a person totally incompetent. This is inaccurate and succeeds only in building barriers to adjustment and meaningful living. It is also important to realize that emotional ill health is not restricted to persons in state hospitals, *nor* is it a constant condition. It is not as easily identified as are disabilities which are visible.

The more we can view mental illness as resulting from an inability to meet life demands because of a lack of necessary skills and abilities, the easier it will be to view a person with emotional problems in a more accepting and understanding manner. It is then possible to focus one's personal and professional efforts toward providing the necessary opportunities for learning those skills that will contribute to meeting personal and social living demands. This particular perspective of mental illness has not always been acceptable.

EARLY PERSPECTIVES ON MENTAL ILLNESS AND THE MENTALLY ILL

The mentally ill, for most of the history of our country, have been a rejected and feared population. Over the years the public's attitude has been influenced by religious, moral, and pseudo-scientific beliefs. In turn the public's attitude has greatly determined the fate of the person who was judged mentally ill. Over the years there have been various attempts by professionals and laymen to bring about changes in the attitudes toward mental illness and to effect changes in the care and treatment of the mentally ill.

In Colonial America, in the late seventeenth century, mental illness was regarded as a natural consequence for wickedness and for innate inferiority. Contempt characterized the attitudes toward the destitute and dependent individuals or groups. A person who needed help received attention only when his condition threatened to be a social danger or public nuisance. Then he was disposed of. The violently insane were whipped and put into dungeons. Sometimes they were burned at the stake or hanged. The pauper insane often roamed the country and were at times whipped and jailed. Frequently these people were auctioned off to work as free laborers for some farmer who in turn received a payment from the town. This practice eventually led to houses of correction, workhouses, and almshouses which assured the custody of the mentally ill.[9]

The first American hospital to admit the mentally ill was founded in 1751. This was the Pennsylvania Hospital. The intention of its founders was to provide for the sick, the poor, and the "cure of lunatics." Accounts describing the methods employed in the Pennsylvania Hospital indicate that patients' scalps were shaved and blistered. Patients were bled and alimentary canals were purged. The chaining of patients to walls was a common practice.[10]

During this period the treatment of the mentally ill was neither rational nor humanitarian. Rejection was obvious and physical brutality was seen to be the best method of cure. Superstition seems to have been the basis for the practices of purging, bleeding, induced vomiting, blistering, and various types of water cures such as ducking and near drowning.[11]

The eighteenth-century reforms in Europe, particularly in France and England, focused attention on human understanding and respect for personal freedom and paved the way for reform in the care of the mentally ill. The rise of humanitarianism and the scientific perspectives in mental health were first introduced in France by Dr. Philippe Pinel, a French physician. He advocated moral treatment as opposed to the medical and surgical treatment of the times.

His approach proceeded from the principle of setting for the patient an example of how he is expected to behave and, thus, appealing to his moral sense and arousing him to give as good as he receives. This approach contained the basis upon which the more tolerating and accepting attitudes that characterize modern psychological and social treatment techniques were formulated. Moral treatment of the mentally ill was introduced in this country by the Quakers who opened the Friends' Asylum in Philadelphia in 1817. Its objective was "to fetter strong madness in a silken thread."[12]

During the early nineteenth century the moral treatment movement spread to a number of the American mental hospitals. In these institutions patients were treated with kindness and sympathy. Their day was filled with a variety of activities, work and play. Meals were eaten with the group. Absent were the physical torments and the rejecting, dehumanizing attitudes. Pinel's program had its basis in the belief that psychological factors were important causes of mental illness. Also, Pinel saw social factors and inadequate education as equally important. Treatment then was only a form of education and intelligent understanding associated with a minimum of organizational restraints.[13]

Although the moral treatment of Pinel did have an impact on the care and treatment of the mentally ill, it was not unanimously accepted nor did it actually affect the lives of most of the poorer classes who suffered from emotional disorders. For the most part, moral treatment facilities were available only to the more affluent persons. It was through the efforts of Dorothea Dix and others, who crusaded against the inhuman treatment received by most of the destitute mentally ill, that state institutions for the mentally ill came into existence. Although not intended, this reform movement resulted in the large custodial institution system which has been the mainstay in the mentally ill for most of the twentieth century in the United States.

The period from about 1830–1900 is difficult to capsulate due to the variety of forces that existed and the variation of influences from one place to another. In general, moral treatment declined with the rise of large state hospitals. As the states began to assume responsibility for the indigent insane, the towns and county almshouses and farms transferred their burdens to the state hospitals. These institutions quickly became crowded with chronic mentally ill persons with a poor prognosis for recovery.

A contributing factor to the overcrowding of state institutions was the industrial revolution in America. It was accompanied by changing social conditions, increased urbanization, and heavily increasing immigration. The difficult process of adjustment within the new urban settings was overwhelming for many, especially the unskilled immigrants who were unfamiliar with the American culture and the rapidity of social change. The public reaction was that the mentally ill, i.e., those exhibiting peculiar or bizarre behavior, should be removed from the community. The limitation of facilities and resources demanded that patients be regimented and all that could be hoped for was providing the basic physiological needs: food, shelter, and clothing.

Another event during this period, which dealt a crucial blow to the moral treatment movement, was the position taken by Dr. John P. Gray in 1885 who acted as the spokesman of American psychiatry. He maintained that mental patients were really physically ill with a disease of the brain. He rejected the psychological and educational implications of moral treatment and the concept of mental illness. No doubt the crowded conditions in the institutions would not have been conducive to moral treatment methods. This may have contributed to some of the unfavorable opinions of moral treatment.

During this period attitudes of rejection increased and the belief that insanity was an incurable affliction prevailed. The general situation, at the turn of the century, has been aptly described in the *Action for Mental Health,* a report of the Joint Commission on Mental Illness and Health:

> . . . the profile of the state asylum for the incurably insane was stereotyped, both professionally and socially—it was an institution where hopeless cases were put away for the good of society.
>
> Mental hospital superintendents who saw patients accumulate and continue to live their lives out in locked wards became steeped in this negative outlook. Far from feeling they had failed in a social and medical responsibility, these first psychiatrists apparently were satisfied that they were fulfilling the mission that the state had assigned them. This was to take custody of any and all persons committed to their institutions by the courts and thenceforth guard the public and patients against the latter's irrational acts, if any. The superintendent's primary responsibility ended, under state laws, with keeping the mentally ill alive, the emphasis being on physical rather than mental well being. For example, if the patient would not eat, he was forcefed; but if he would not talk, it was not considered important to encourage him to do so.[14]

Basically, this was the prevalent notion toward mental illness and the method of care to cope with the problem at the time the recreation movement began to mobilize around the 1850's.

THE RECREATION MOVEMENT— A PARALLEL TO THE MENTAL HEALTH MOVEMENT

The recreation movement sprang from some of the same humanitarian and moral reform roots seen in the Pinel and Dix movements in mental health. The initial focus of the recreation movement was on the environmental crises in the newly forming industrial urban slums. The industrial revolution in America brought about hope for economic prosperity but also introduced long working hours, small wages, congested conditions, and alterations in the accepted moral and social standards and values in American society. The social consciousness during this period began to shift from a basic concern for mere survival and economic independence (although most did not possess the latter) to a concern for the human condition, that is, human dignity, optimum living and working environments, and improved physical, mental, social, and moral health.

More specifically, the efforts of the recreation movement were directed toward alleviating the environmental plight of the disadvantaged children living in the urban slum areas. Supported in part by contemporary developments in educational methods in Europe, a new social attitude toward play as both necessary and useful to the well-being of children began to flourish. Even though puritanical attitudes toward play and recreation existed, it was only a matter of time until the benefits (at least moral and social) of various adult recreation activities became publicly condoned as worthwhile. Sports, dancing, and outdoor activities began to receive much attention.

As strong opposition to the value and need for play and recreation lessened and the effects that recreation programs were having on the lives of many people became more apparent, additional private and governmental support became available. Organized recreation programs became more in demand. This was especially true in the 1930's, during and following the great Depression.

THE BEGINNING OF ORGANIZED RECREATION
PROGRAMS IN HOSPITAL SETTINGS

A highly significant factor for both the development of community recreation programs and for recreation programs in institutions was the impact of World War I and the provision for recreation programs in stateside military bases. Included in these bases were military hospitals. The American Red Cross, in 1918, was designated to provide basic entertainment and active recreation programs for military personnel in hospital wards and in convalescent homes. These Red Cross efforts represent some of the earliest examples of organized recreation programs in a community as well as for a special population of ill and/or disabled.

> The prospect of an early return of American wounded from overseas during W.W.I, and the constantly increasing number of men in the training camps, with a consequent increase in hospital populations, made very evident the need for a comprehensive and organized scheme to replace the rather incidental recreation activities which the Red Cross had undertaken up to that time. As a result, a standard program of recreation activities, adapted to the requirements of base hospitals, was developed and put into effect.[15]

The early Red Cross programs in the military hospitals consisted of active and passive activities. The latter were provisions for entertainment which consisted of movies, theatricals, musical productions, etc. The active phase of the program had as its goal self-directed recreation participation. This phase was viewed as important more for its curative function than for its entertainment value. The range of activities was diverse and included sports, arts and crafts, table games, dramatic and musical groups, and dances.[16]

Following World War I, the Red Cross was requested to provide services to ex-servicemen who had been hospitalized in facilities operated by the Public Health Services. From that time until 1931, the American Red Cross provided recreation services in the Veterans hospitals. An administrative directive, in October 1927, referring to the efforts of the Red Cross in the Veterans hospitals, acknowledged the value of the recreation programs as a necessary therapeutic contribution.[17]

The recognition of the therapeutic value of recreation activities continued to spread. In 1931, the Veterans hospitals established their own recreation services. About the same time, a recreation service was established in St. Elizabeth's Hospital in Washington, D.C. Recreation services were seen as providing therapeutic experiences for patients who were withdrawn, for those who were depressed, and for those who needed wholesome outlets for their energies. Trained recreation leaders began to replace nontrained and volunteer personnel, and many of these trained leaders had previously been with the American Red Cross.

Organized recreation programs were gradually being established in a variety of medical settings during the period from 1920–1940. Also, during this period, a concern for formal college level education for community recreation personnel was developing. This resulted in the establishment of recreation curricula in a few major universities in the latter part of the 1930's.

Pre-World War II recreation services in state institutions for the mentally ill, for the most part, consisted of entertainment and diversional programs adapted to the custodial nature of these institutions. These programs were provided through volunteer efforts. The pattern for the development of recreation services in state hospitals following World War II was being established concurrently in private psychiatric settings during the 1930's.

In an article written in 1937, William Menninger and Isabelle McCall described the value and use of recreation therapy at the Menninger Clinic. The clinic was one part of the Menninger Foundation established in 1925. One must remember of the state institutions for the mentally ill, especially prior to the 1950's, were understaffed, overcrowded, custodial care operations which essentially served the lower socioeconomic and destitute populations. The private psychiatric hospitals or clinics, on the other hand, usually employed better trained personnel, operated with a higher staff-patient ratio and served a more affluent population.

At this early period, prior to 1937, recreation therapy at the Menninger Clinic was equated with hydrotherapy and occupational therapy whereby patients were provided necessary, individualized therapeutic treatment. Recreation activities were prescribed for the individual patient by a psychiatrist. The Menninger staff recognized the value of recreation and play for its relaxation, amusement, and physical fitness benefits. But these were not the basic underlying reasons that warranted a good recreation therapy program in a mental hospital. The clinic staff saw play and recreation activities as an essential arena in which a person, child or adult, had an opportunity to work through unresolved conflicts. Play and recreation activities offered pliable mediums in which the participant could learn skills, master situations, and become the doer rather than the receiver of actions. In short, one could create a situation that was tolerable and which afforded need satisfaction. More specifically, the recreation program was seen to contribute to the resocialization of the patient, to help make reality more pleasant, and to provide an outlet for aggression and self-expression.

The ultimate focus of the Menninger resocialization program was to get the patient back to an adult (or appropriate) level of functioning. Resocialization activities were sequenced from the more simple, supportive activity with a therapist, to participation in group activities. Further, patients were allowed to leave the hospital, with or without a therapist, in order to participate in a variety of activities. Each succeeding step or activity required more individual responsibility and self-direction on the part of the patient.[18]

Successful functioning at an adult level requires many skills and abilities. Today we generalize this concern for the diverse complex of living skills and abilities under the heading of rehabilitation goals and objectives. Recreation in the Menninger Clinic was seen to contribute directly to these efforts. This early program was not limited to an intramural program. The ultimate test of their treatment-education program was how well the patient could cope with living in the "outside world." Recreation activities provided an arena for the initial "adjustment to the outside" phase of the program. This transition was usually entered into with fear and anxiety, but, with repeated experiences, self-confidence developed and fear diminished.

Although the Menninger Clinic and the Veterans hospitals felt that recreation was an important factor in the re-education process of the mentally ill, few state institutions during the period from 1920–1940 shared this view. The nature and purpose of these state institutions contributed to this divergent viewpoint. As mentioned earlier, the custodial care oriented state institutions rose out of the dilemma of overcrowding, professional pessimism toward curability, and ingrained public attitudes of fear and rejection toward the mentally ill. The years following World War II marked the beginning of new advances and perspectives that would bring about the breakdown of the custodial care institution, restore optimism regarding the treatability of mental illness, and begin the dismantling of misconceptions about the mentally ill.

POST-WORLD WAR II DEVELOPMENTS
IN MENTAL HEALTH PRACTICE

Post-World War II developments in psychiatry, psychology, and other mental health professions led to new viewpoints regarding mental illness and its treatment. Psychiatrists were beginning to consider the psycho-social aspects of emotional disturbances rather than emphasizing the disease aspect. The efforts of psychology in the area of learning and behavior were being received with more credence. Researchers were investigating the effects of long term institutionalization as a compounding cause of disability. In 1953, drugs were introduced which had a significant impact on institutional life and contributed to the reduction of community fear by controlling much of the patients' agitated behavior.[19]

Following the second world war the country became increasingly concerned about the problems of mental illness and the needs of the mentally ill. The federal government and private groups realized the necessity of preventing mental illness and providing services to those who were ill. Although some progress was being made in research and treatment practices, the introduction of these new developments into state hospitals was slow. In part this was due to the lack of financial resources and, consequently, a shortage of the necessary trained manpower. These were almost insurmountable obstacles, especially in view of the enormous patient populations in the state institutions.

Although slow, changes began to appear. Individual and group psychotherapy, vocational rehabilitation, and behavioral modification approaches were being introduced. The basic premise of "custodial care" and "incurability" were under attack. A renewed humanitarian concern for the plight of the institutionalized mentally ill was evident. Programs began to focus on attempts to return patients to their home, family, and community. Treatment efforts were being directed toward preparing the patient to assume a place in community life. At least the primary focus was no longer entirely concerned with adjustment to a permanent residence in an institution. Although these trends were in evidence during the period from 1940 to 1955, they were by no means representative of all state institutions.

Throughout this period the negative aspects of state hospitals were repeatedly noted. The internal operations of the institution were criticized, as well as the practice of "putting away" patients for society's convenience. Internally, the institutional "modus operandi" was no longer that of overt cruelty and disinterest; but rather there was an attempt to provide an atmosphere of well-meaning kindness and pity which, unfortunately, often had disabling effects. There existed rigid daily routines, depersonalization, personal neglect, forced dependency, and the expectation of incompetence. This state of affairs brought on aggressive, regressive, and otherwise inappropriate behavior which was not necessarily part of the illness but, rather, a by-product of the institutional environment.

Although some progress was being made, the domination of the "institutional" approach persisted. As a result the "out of sight, out of mind" attitude continued. Treatment programs that were oriented toward returning the patient to the community were impeded and hospital populations continued to increase.

POST-WORLD WAR II
ORGANIZED RECREATION SERVICES IN
INSTITUTIONS FOR MENTALLY ILL

The post-World War II period was significant also in respect to the development of organized recreation programs in state institutions. Actually, recreation activities such as dancing, sports, games, and music were recognized for their beneficial effect on disturbed or melancholic persons as far back as the ancient civilizations of Greece, Egypt, and Babylonia.

Significant also was the rise and influence of the professionally trained recreator. By 1937 five college-level programs in community recreation had been established. The 1950's witnessed the establishment of curricula to prepare recreators to work with persons in institutional or medical settings. During this period an identity of a recreator who worked in the medical setting was becoming established. By this time the public had come to accept and value recreation, but their attitude toward the professional recreator was not as clear. If the attitude was not negative, it was limited to an occupational category of limited status and debatable essentialness. In the past ten to fifteen years the stature of the recreation professional has grown measurably both in community and rehabilitation settings. Recreators have begun to see themselves, and in turn are being viewed by others, as playing an important and essential part in contributing to the health, education, and welfare of people and society. Less and less are recreators stereotyped as persons who "bounce balls in boxes." Later in this chapter we will return to the issue of the roles and functions of the recreator in modern society. First, let us look at the development of the organized recreation service in state institutions after World War II.

Keep in mind that the institutions in which organized recreation services developed were established and operated on the notions of custody and care for incurable mentally ill persons. As noted earlier, these notions began breaking down in the late 1950's. The internal concerns of the institution were on orderly management and intramural adjustment more so than on therapeutic intervention and quick return to home and community. Institutional policies and procedures were means to maintain management control. Institutional administration and program direction was vested in the medical practitioner who was not always a psychiatrist. This situation resulted in part from the earlier notion that mental illness was a physical disease and, thus, the domain of the medical doctor.

The identity of the "hospital" recreator and the organized recreation service (the recreation department) was formulated and developed within this traditional model of the mental institution and was circumscribed by it. The purpose and value of recreation and the functions of the recreator were defined and interpreted within this setting in accord with the nature and purpose of the institution, the prevailing conceptions of mental illness, and the existing practices in the care and treatment of the mentally ill.

The institution was a complete, autonomous social system. Policies and procedures governed all aspects of living and working within it. It contained its own system of rewards and punishment. This system maintained its own levels of patient and staff status which reflected its values on human and professional worth. All hospital personnel were differentiated, one from another, through clearly defined primary role assignments. This also applied to the various departments and services in a physical-structural sense.

The recreator was clearly understood to be the one who played softball with the patients. It was the recreation staff who planned ward parties, ran the movie projector, conducted bingo games, and provided the checkers and cards. Various areas and structures in the institution were the sole domain of the recreation department: the ball field, picnic area, gymnasium, social hall, etc. Other professionals and departments had their primary role assignments, areas and/or physical structures through which they were identified and received recognition. This type of structure did afford security and provided whatever status that was to be had. One knew clearly who he was, what he was to do, and where he belonged.

Generally, the earlier organized recreation programs were conducted by untrained personnel. Leaders could teach skills and conduct recreation activities. This level of proficiency was in keeping with the overall institutional program inasmuch as the concern was oriented to custodial care and intramural adjustment. Within this context, the recreation program provided opportunities to be with others, to release excess energy and to overcome some of the many hours of boredom. The above goals may have been laudable in themselves and programs for these purposes were necessary, but they represented an incomplete notion of the needs of people, mental illness, the significance of play and recreation, and the potential contribution of the recreation professional.

As post-World War II developments began to filter into state institutions for the mentally ill, programs and services were likewise affected. It should be recalled that during this period such attitudes as incurability, disease, and custodial care began to be replaced by more optimistic expectations, i.e., that patients could be treated, could return home, and could function successfully. The various disciplines and services began to interpret and define their efforts in light of these new orientations, although many institutions remained medically directed and the practice of in-house programs was dominant.

Even though the eventual return of the patient to his home or community was gradually becoming a primary concern, institutional recreation personnel had little or no professional work involvement with community programs or agencies. Activity programs were confined to within the institution or the patient living areas. Generally, recreators worked with large group activities. Trips to community recreation areas and participation in community programs were unheard of in many places. Working with small patient groups or individuals was just as rare.

Medical prescriptions were usually required for patient participation in recreation activities. Often these prescriptions were general in nature, i.e., allowing participation but not designating any specific activity. In some cases the opposite was true. Often times mention was made about specific activities which were not allowed. These kinds of decisions were made by the medical practitioner.

Basically recreation program objectives consisted of three major concerns: 1) to assist the medical staff to meet emotional and physical needs of the patient; 2) to assist the patient to make an adjustment to hospitalization and to make life as enjoyable as possible; 3) to assist the patient to develop proper attitudes toward leisure and to acquire skills that could be useful after discharge.

In many cases the recreation programs were limited to diversional and entertainment programs. The recreator's function consisted primarily of planning and carrying out activities for patients. The recreator was only tangentially concerned with the treatment of the patient and preparing him for discharge. He was not viewed as a therapist in the medical sense of the word, nor was recreation viewed as a legitimate form of therapy.

As the new notions about mental illness and new perspectives on methods of treatment began to be implemented, various disciplines and professions began a process of introspection and evaluation. This process resulted in new interpretations of professional purpose and practice, acceptance of other forms of treatment, and newer concepts of "what was therapy" and "who was a therapist."

A variety of postures were taken by recreators themselves. Some ascribed to the traditional medical model interpretation given above. Others definitely felt that a recreator was a therapist and that recreation was a therapy. Some argued that recreation could only be considered an end in itself while others contended it was a means to other more important learnings or behaviors. All traditional notions of recreation's nature and purpose came into question and review. At present a more eclectic attitude seems to prevail among most recreators regarding these issues. (Selected readings of articles listed in the bibliography at the end of the chapter will provide the reader with further information regarding the nature and purpose of recreation and therapeutic recreation).

COMMUNITY MENTAL HEALTH PERSPECTIVES OF THE 1960's

The pre-World War II rate of change in mental institutions was much slower than the accelerated post-war rate, which continues today. Change has not been limited to particular settings or institutions. All of society has been influenced by increased knowledge and technological progress.

In the treatment and care of the mentally ill, the sixties can be singled out as having ushered in history's most significant and far-reaching changes. These changes have brought about the demise of the custodial-care institution in principle and promise to eliminate it in fact. State institutions comprise only one of many sources providing services to the indigent mentally ill; community-based mental health services today are a reality. Public and social policy and legislation no longer reflect the earlier attitudes and notions of isolation, segregation, fear, and rejection of persons suffering from emotional disturbance. People have become more sensitive to the needs of the mentally ill, and are more willing to attempt to rectify conditions that cause emotional illness.

The roots of the new perspectives in mental health of the 1960's are found in the efforts of many individuals and agencies during the 1940's and 1950's. The new perspectives reflect divergent beliefs about the etiology of mental illness and its treatability. The post-war focus in state institutions shifted from "custodial care" to a "total institution" program, in which there were two primary concerns: provision of continuing institutional care or recovery of the patient followed by return to the community. The 1960's ushered in a shift from "total institution" to community-centered mental health programs, in which the state institution was only one of a network of services to persons suffering from mental illness. Implicit in the community mental health concept is the notion of a continuum of services: diagnosis, treatment, aftercare, and prevention. The broad conceptualization of rehabilitation can encompass all of these terms. In both cases, prevention is a major focus whether one is concerned with preventing the recurrence of emotional disturbances or preventing their first onset. The latter conception of prevention has implications for all facets of society: family, school, government, and all other private and public institutions.

In 1946, the United States Congress enacted the National Mental Health Act through which financial assistance was made available to the states for developing mental health programs outside the state hospitals. Two important types of treatment facilities began to appear which contributed to the community-based focus of the 1960's: outpatient clinics and psychiatric units in general hospitals. In 1954, New York enacted a Community Mental Health Services Act. (By 1964 there were twenty states that had this type of legislation enacted.) President Kennedy appointed a cabinet-level committee to review the report of the Joint Commission on Mental Illness and Health. This review culminated in the governmental publication *Action for Mental Health* (1961). In February 1963, President Kennedy sent to Congress the first message of its kind by any president in behalf of the mental health movement. Eight months later, on October 31, the 88th Congress enacted Public Law 88-164, the "Mental Retardation Facilities and Community Mental Health Centers Construction Act of 1963."

Public Law 88-164 specified that to qualify for federal funds, a community mental health center must provide at least five essential elements of comprehensive mental health services: 1) inpatient services; 2) outpatient services; 3) partial hospitalization services; 4) emergency services (provided 24 hours per day within at least one of the three above services; and 5) consultation and educational services available to community agencies and professional personnel. Adequate services also included five other components: diagnostic services; rehabilitative services (including vocational and educational programs); precare and aftercare services in the community (including foster care home placements, home visiting, and halfway houses); training; and research and evaluation.

These events, early in 1960, focused nationwide attention on the new perspectives in mental health practice. They also won much needed financial support for states to implement new mental health practices on a broad scale. Illinois and New York were two of the first states to begin construction of community mental health facilities and to establish state mental health and retardation services patterned on the new legislation which embodied modern mental health practice viewpoints. Implementation of these new perspectives led initially to reorganizing and restructuring of the state institutions for the mentally ill and retarded. This was no easy task and placed extreme pressure on the professions and disciplines working in these state institutions to internalize the new directives, reinterpret their programs and, then, deliver services that were consistent with these new trends.

Throughout the last half of the 1960's (and even presently in many places), state hospitals were going through the transition from custodial care to a therapeutic, community orientation. Translating the notion that "mental illness is treatable" into action necessitated many changes in state hospitals. Important in this period was the reorganization of centrally organized state hospitals to unitized or decentralized systems. Also important within this reorganization was the extramural focus rather than the traditional "in-house" or intramural focus. Continuity of care was a major concern. Also implicit in this reorganization schema was that administration, program planning, and delivery be vested in interdisciplinary teams. The development of team-directed, decentralized programs in state institutions made obsolete the role and functions of the departmental system which had been traditional in state institutions. It had been the role of departments to administrate, plan, and deliver particular specialized services within the institutional programs. As these changes occurred, customary sources of identification, security, and status were threatened if not lost entirely. One other change that was introduced, and which by no means has been worked through, was the shift to the "generalist" role of mental health workers as opposed to the traditional specialist orientation. The philosophy of despecialization, more pronounced in the field of mental health, is running counter to trends in society, although more uneasiness toward ultra-specialization is evident today.

IMPACT OF MENTAL HEALTH PRACTICES
OF THE 1960's ON RECREATION
AND RECREATOR

For many persons in recreation the impact of these new developments on recreation programs and recreators was severe,* but in the opinion of this author, they provided an immense opportunity for professional growth, both for the recreation movement and the recreation professional. Recreation can now be viewed as directly contributing to an individual's physical and social development by providing opportunities and an environment conducive for exploring capabilities, nurturing and using abilities, and acquiring new skills and interests. The concern and focus today, especially in mental health, is on the total life space of people, i.e., all those phases of life that affect the individual including his work, his family life, community life, his leisure, etc. The recreation movement must again see itself concerned with contributing to the basic aspects involved in living wholesome and adjusted lives. It cannot retreat to an isolated and limited focus on leisure concerns. The physical, social, and psychological parameters of self-directed, wholesome use of leisure are not different from those parameters that are prerequisite to meeting other life demands in an adjusted, independent, satisfying manner. These kinds of concerns seem to be basic to the preventative focus currently emphasized in mental health practice. Therefore, the challenge is directed to all individuals and institutions in society, not only those in the field of mental health.

Likewise, these new viewpoints and practices in mental health have contributed to the expansion of concerns and functions of the professional recreator. No longer can providing diversional, intramural adjustment programs be the sole or primary function of the professional recreator. Making the patient happy and helping him to forget his problems can no longer be the only justification for professional involvement. One

* Further discussion of the problems of decentralization and unitization is available in the *Unit Plan,* a conference transcript published by the Mental Health Association of Southeastern Pennsylvania, 1963.

might ask, "what advantage is there in being 'happy' at play and failing at everything else in life?" Maybe a better question would be, "what potential does play and recreation have for providing the kinds of real life experiences and learning from which a person can acquire the skills, interests, and attitudes that contribute to meeting his life demands and, thereby, contributing to a richer, fuller, and more satisfying life?"

The implication here for professional recreators is the necessity of being cognizant of the process of growth and development and the process of acculturation, which directly reflects societal values and attitudes, and indicates what living in our society requires for an independent and satisfying life. The recreator must then translate this information into programs and opportunities that will employ forms of play and recreation best suited to accomplish these ends. The focus is clearly on people and the provision of experiences that will provide for their optimum development and success in life's encounters. All other professional concerns and involvement are means to this end. As such, recreation is not an end in itself. Traditionally, we have tended to view recreation experiences only for the recuperative value, i.e., the restoration of balance after imbalance had occurred. This notion is akin to the idea of secondary prevention which is necessary and praiseworthy, but primary prevention should take precedence.

Many more recreators today are attempting to study the impact of play and recreation activities as vehicles for motor and social learning. The focus of concern is motor and social development. Many aspects related to successful play and recreation participation in the motor and social realm, for example, are directly related to success in other areas of living: the ability to receive and express language symbols (communication); to be able to use the physical body as a mode of expression and to accomplish tasks; and to gain competence in a variety of social roles such as the giver, receiver, leader, follower, etc. Other recreators are involved in analyzing play and recreation activities in terms of their potential as learning experiences by determining levels of physical and social skills and abilities necessary for successful entry into these activities. In no way have these recreators lost sight of that fact that recreation and play should be enjoyable to the participant. They are well aware that effective learning and desire to participate again are dependent upon enjoyable and positively reinforced experiences. Basically, their actions seem to be based in the belief that play and recreation activities are a medium through which motor and social development occur and provide a matrix in which one's personality is formed.

These kinds of notions are not really new even in the field of recreation. Some of the early leaders of the recreation movement viewed play and recreation in much the same way. It is believed by the author that, for the most part, this kind of focus has been relegated to a secondary concern as the recreation professional focused on establishing acceptance of recreation. Unfortunately, all too often recreation came to be seen as an end in itself.

As a result of modern understandings of how man learns, of new viewpoints on the causes of illness and of a revitalized concern for man and his environment, programs in mental health institutions have been focused on preparing the patient to return to society. Very early it was realized that even the best efforts within the institution would be doomed to failure unless the society or community to which these persons would return could maintain them and contribute to the prevention of their returning to the hospital. The latter is a secondary prevention focus but, actually, the line between secondary and primary prevention may indeed be fine or nonexistent in terms of community service provisions.

The recreation literature of the 1960's constantly trumpeted the concern for "bridging the gap" between institutions and the community agencies. This concern came about as recreators in the institutional setting realized the necessity of developing programs that began the treatment or rehabilitation process in the hospital and that continued in a community directed focus toward self-directed independent living out of the hospital. It became evident that the traditional intramural programs were insufficient to accomplish rehabilitative goals. The actualizing of this programmatic continuum required community-based programs and resources necessary for implementing initial transitional activities. It also required recreation opportunities following discharge that would afford a supportive and stabilizing environment which could contribute to preventing a return to hospitalization.

RECREATION PROGRAM ORIENTATION

These new directions were interpreted into various types of program organization. Some of the more common ones included activity therapies, rehabilitation services, education therapies, etc. In all of these programs, recreation was seen as an essential activity of daily living, although the manner in which recreation was interpreted and used varied. A therapeutic recreation service which was philosophically eclectic was developing. It embodied various uses of recreation activities and focused on the rehabilitative goals of self-directed, independent community living.

Basically, four phases of program focus are evident today, although all aspects may not be contained in every program. These phases have differentiated meaning for the recreator although not necessarily for the participant. The four phases of program focus include: 1) evaluation and remediation (treatment); 2) intramural recreational program—patient-planned activities; 3) transitional activities; 4) post-discharge recreation participation.

Evaluation and Remediation Activities

The primary concern of the recreator is to determine the strengths (abilities) and weaknesses (disabilities) of the patient in a variety of areas: physical, social, and behavioral. This information is provided by testing and observation methods. The recreator also tries to determine various interests and attitudes of the patient. On the basis of staff or staff-patient formulated goals, an activity program is established which is best suited to meet these ends. The starting point of a remediation or treatment program varies with the individual patient. For a patient who is extremely fearful of others, one might begin with object-related activities in which, initially, the patient does not have to contend directly with people. In this situation the intention of the recreator is to sequentially, through various activity experiences, bring about a one-to-one personal contact with the patient followed by a gradual movement into situations involving more than two people. Recreation activities must be employed that allow for this kind of social sequencing (object-related to people-related) and which provide favorable experiences for the patient. Recreation activities are also used in this manner to teach skills necessary for independent living. Sewing arts and various other home art activities are examples. Activities, let's say in sewing arts, can be used to provide a sequence of experiences along the social continuum as well as to allow the learning of various skills that are useful in the person's life. The particular activities and sequences used will vary according to the characteristics, needs, and rehabilitation goals of the patient.

As the reader might imagine, this aspect of programming can become quite complex and demands constant planning and evaluation. The intention is to change certain behaviors, provide necessary skills, and foster attitudes and interests that will help prepare the patient to progressively accept and meet demands of independent, community living. Activity analysis is essential as well as the knowledge of the variability of impact that given activities have on different individuals.

Patient-Planned Intramural Recreation Program

Basically, this aspect of programming provides opportunities to learn skills and acquire interests in a variety of recreation activities. It provides opportunities to participate in activities which the patient himself can determine. There exists a good deal of discretionary time in most residential settings. Traditionally, these time periods were "filled" by staff-planned activities to occupy the patient's time. This should not be the intent of the intramural recreation program. Rather, the intent should be to encourage and motivate the patient to self-direct his recreation behavior. This is not easily accomplished. The recreator must function as a catalyst for individual or group action. Social group process techniques have been employed with great success in this respect.*

It is important that the activities available through this aspect of the program be realistic, i.e., they should be generally available within the community setting or environment from

---

* References to the social group process include: (1) Campbell Loughmiller, *Wilderness Pond* (Austin, Texas: The Hoag Foundation for Mental Health, University of Texas Printing Division, 1965); (2) Gisela Konopka, *Social Group Work: A Helping Process* (Englewood Cliffs, N.J.: Prentice-Hall, Inc., 1963).

which the patient comes. Further, the activities should be consistent with what people usually do. These will vary according to available resources—both personal and community, as well as local and familial values, mores, and customs.

This kind of program is operable in decentralized, unit operations with or without internal, centralized resources. In situations where more central resources exist (i.e., a gymnasium, speciality areas for arts, crafts, woodworking, and home arts) and are available to a number of decentralized units, the organizational pattern of the central resource area can function analogous to a community center. In this situation, program planning originates with patients and staff of the individual unit or combination of units. The central resource area, within its own limitations, becomes an extension of the unit program, just as community resources are an extension of the family constellation. In many cases community resources also may be utilized and can contribute to the transitional focus of the third aspect of the program.

Transitional Activities

The transition we are concerned with here is the movement of the patient from the residential setting back to the community. It results in logical sequence from the treatment remediation aspect of the program. It is not necessarily patient planned and determined as is the intramural recreation program. Its focus is clearly on exposing the patient to community situations for the purpose of re-acquainting and re-educating him to community life and for providing real life experiences in which the patient can test himself. A supportive, encouraging, expectant posture is taken by the recreator in this phase of program. Here too activities can be sequenced according to the tolerance and coping ability of the patient. Usually a patient in this phase of program can already function reasonably well in a group of peers, i.e., with other patients. Large group excursions to parks or bus trips usually are some of the early transitional activities. Group trips to museums, shopping, etc., would probably precede individual or small group ventures to various community settings. The latter may well be without staff supervision, whereas the former would probably have institutional personnel in attendance.

The availability of community-based experiences is necessary in this phase of the program *and critical* in the fourth phase: post-discharge recreation participation. Joint planning and cooperation between mental health and community agency personnel is prerequisite. This state of affairs can only exist if both parties recognize a responsibility in this regard and are willing to work together. The inability of these two parties to communicate—to jointly determine each other's responsibilities and to agree upon a course of action—seems to be the most crucial issue in the development of needed services for the mentally ill as well as all ill and disabled groups.

Within the field of recreation itself, there has been divided opinion regarding the necessity and responsibility for providing community services for the ill and disabled. The recreators working with these special groups feel that the community recreator has a responsibility to provide these services. The community recreator feels that it is the responsibility of the therapeutic recreator because the community recreator has the "responsibility of servicing the majority of people" (and the ill and disabled are not the majority). Ironically, these efforts to "bridge the gap" have served, in some cases, to widen the gap and to emphasize the differences between the therapeutic recreator and the community recreator. Fortunately, in spite of these differing points of view, they are not universal. Many positive developments have taken place in the past ten years that have contributed to more effective working relationships between these two groups of recreators. Actually, the basis for the separation of these two groups can be found in the historical separation of the ill and disabled from the rest of society. There is no real basis for this separation in the goals, objectives, or original purpose of the recreation movement. As the problems and needs of the ill and disabled are increasingly viewed as a community concern that must be dealt with in the community (which is the trend of public policy today), the differences between the therapeutic recreator and community recreator should and will become nonexistent.

The joint efforts of the American Park and Recreation Society and the National Therapeutic Recreation Society have been encouraging and timely. Truly, their efforts only parallel the efforts of recreators on the local level who are planning and developing community programs that include the ill and disabled. Increased visibility of ill and disabled individuals in the community, increased public support for programs, and a broader conceptualization of the value and purpose of recreation for the ill and disabled have contributed to the progress being made within the recreation profession.

Only with the increased availability of community program resources will the transitional programs really be effective in preparing a person for discharge. Then, and only then, will the last phase of programs be possible and become an available and effective rehabilitative measure that could contribute to the prevention of a return to hospitalization and, at the same time, provide a first line of defense against emotional disturbances.

Post-Discharge Recreation Participation
(Development of Community Recreation Services)

The concern here is the development of recreation or leisure resources that are available to the ill and disabled. To be effective these community programs must be sensitive to the needs and abilities of these individuals. Self-directed independent life styles are not generally the modus operandi of most of these persons. In fact, many "normal" persons operate on varied levels of self-directedness and independence. These programs must attempt to reach out to people rather than wait for people to come to the program. These programs must epitomize constructive tolerance and acceptance of a variety of individual and group differences, focusing on inclusion rather than being prone to exclude.

Programs must be accessibility-conscious in order not to overlook the timid, fearful, unskilled, or persons who otherwise need help and encouragement to participate. (Accessibility is a notion that applies to eliminating human as well as architectural barriers to participation).

Recreation programs that provide opportunities to be included, to be understood, to be accepted, to learn skills, to receive recognition, and to gain self-esteem not only contribute to aftercare services for the discharged patient but also provide an atmosphere that is conducive to basic mental health. The recreation program with these characteristics is also focused on a primary prevention strategy.

Briefly, we have seen the importance of including community recreation programs in the network of services for persons who have become mentally ill and are in the process of regaining stability and adjustment to community living. They are essential parts of the broad rehabilitation program. As our knowledge and understanding of the causes of mental illness increases, it becomes clear that environmental conditions do affect the course of our growth and learning as well as our general ability to meet life demands. Individuals who do not possess the level of physical, social, or psychological skills and abilities to cope with the myriad of tasks necessary to live in today's rapidly changing, stressful, selective, achievement-oriented society must be provided with opportunities to gain these skills. Persons with permanent disabilities must be provided with opportunities to pursue a satisfying, meaningful life within the limitations of their abilities. Opportunities to work, to play, to be a part of something, to succeed, to be recognized must be available to all persons.

No one is immune to mental illness, although some persons may be in greater risk of encountering emotional disturbances than others. Mental health is an important factor in "the good life" that seems so basic to our recreation philosophy. In a sense, recreation programs and services directed toward providing those experiences that are prerequisite to mental health are also providing opportunities that contribute to worthwhile, wholesome living.

Today we are witnessing the rapid development of community programs for the mentally ill, the retarded, the physically handicapped, and other disabled or disadvantaged groups. Although not totally, individuals in these groups represent some of the most likely ones to experience emotional ill health sometime in their life. The families of these individuals can also be considered high risk groups. The many programs being developed for these groups contribute directly to mental health objectives. These programs, representing differing purposes and goals, focus on various aspects of life concern: work, physical restoration, social adjustment, education, and leisure. Examples of these community programs include halfway houses, sheltered workshops, daycare centers, comprehensive mental health and mental retardation centers, special education programs, and municipal recreation programs for the ill and handicapped.

For the most part, the public, private, and commercial

agencies concerned with community recreation services are only beginning to develop programs for these high-risk groups. The critical need today, in order to continue and promote further growth of community recreation programs, is well-trained recreators who are knowledgeable of the growth, development, and maintenance needs of people and the contribution that play and recreation can make to the acquisition of skills, abilities, and attitudes necessary to live in today's society.

NEW ROLES FOR RECREATORS

Typically, today, the ill and disabled and many others are disadvantaged by being deprived of opportunities to grow and to learn through play and recreation experiences. The recreator has the opportunity to assist these individuals in overcoming these areas of deprivation. To accomplish this task, he will be called upon to assume roles and functions within the community matrix somewhat different from his more traditional manner of operation.* The traditional functions of recreators have been related almost exclusively to activity leadership and administration. Usually these efforts have been confined to intra-agency programs. As we professionally focus our concern on people, their environment, and their ability to live in society in a worthwhile, satisfying, and healthy manner, new tasks and challenges become evident. These tasks and challenges can only be met through different and varied approaches.

* Further references on new functions and service models: (1) John A. Nesbitt, Ed.D., "The Mission of the Therapeutic Recreation Specialist," *Therapeutic Recreation Journal*, IV, No. 4 (1970), 2; (2) John A. Nesbitt, Ed.D., "The Therapeutic Recreation Specialist as a Change Agent," in *Recreation's Role in the Rehabilitation of the Mentally Retarded*, ed. Larry L. Neal (University of Oregon: Rehabilitation Research and Training Center in Mental Retardation, 1970), pp. 33–40; (3) H. Douglas Sessoms and Lee E. Meyer, eds., *Occasional Papers on the Role of Recreation in Service to the Handicapped Child*, a collection of seminar papers presented at UNC–Chapel Hill in Spring 1969, supported by the Bureau of Education for the Handicapped, Office of Education, Department of Health, Education and Welfare; (4) Fred Humphrey, "Therapeutic Recreation and the 1970's: Challenge or Progress?" *Therapeutic Recreation Annual*, VII (1970), pp. 8–13.

As we learn more about the impact that play and recreation activities have as vehicles for learning and acculturation, and as our concern for providing experiences that contribute to a person's healthy development increases, the necessity of functioning as a clinical-teacher will become evident. Recreators have begun to function in this capacity, usually in clinical or special education settings. The concern has been on the correction or remediation of developmental disorders. Disorders in motor, perceptual, language, or social areas directly affect the normal development of play skills and generally retard the individual's play behavior. It is being demonstrated that play activities, properly sequenced and adapted to individual skills and abilities, directly contribute to learning in all the areas related to the play situation. It is not unreasonable to imagine this kind of focus in our recreation programs even for those who are not classified as ill or disabled. The intent in this situation would be to promote and insure proper physical, social, and psychological development. Mild disorders could be recognized earlier and remediation programs established. More severe or multiple problems could be referred to appropriate agencies.

Since work weeks are being shortened, and since many nonemployeds are faced with large amounts of forced unobligated time, recreators must provide services to accomplish worthwhile, self-directed use of this time. Multiplication of the current practice of staff-planned programs and activities is not wholly the answer. Unless these programs and activities are directed toward learning skills, interests, and attitudes that directly facilitate independent, self-directed behavior, we will fall short of our goal. Programs of this nature cannot be limited to intra-agency operations. These programs must touch base with the families, schools, churches, and other community agencies who jointly provide other necessary life services. Broader-based conceptualization of community recreation programs is necessary.

Recreators must also function as leisure or recreation counselors. The formulation of this function took place in residential settings for the ill and disabled. The concern of the counselor was the integration or reintegration of the ill or disabled person back into the community setting. This problem of integrating into community life is faced by many who are not hospitalized. Participation in recreation activities can assist this process, but, without assistance and guidance, it may never come about.*

Another function of recreators, which is critical to everything that has been said earlier, is that of introducing systematic changes in our community agencies and institutions in order to provide the basis from which effective and meaningful services for all people can be realized. This process involves many skills and is a function required of recreators at all levels of involvement. Throughout this chapter reference has been made to societal attitudes toward the mentally ill. These same attitudes prevail toward other special groups in society. We have mentioned or implied that individuals, institutions, even professions are resistive to change. Much of this resistance may not be conscious or intentional, but it does prevent progress toward the delivery of necessary services to people who need them. The recreator must take on the responsibility of being an agent of change. This is no simple task; he must be knowledgeable of what needs to be done, must be skilled at how to best go about introducing changes and counteracting resistances,† and must be able to provide consultation and direction as new programs are implemented. To accomplish this function the recreator also must be an effective educator, trainer, and demonstrator.

The challenges to the field of recreation and to recreators, implicit in our concern for the mentally ill and for the mental health of all people, provide for us immense opportunities to demonstrate the value and significance of our profession and the necessity for well-trained and qualified practitioners. If you are in the process of preparing yourself to serve people or are presently serving people as a recreator, your best effort is required. Your complete commitment is a prerequisite.

* References to recreation counseling include: (1) Gerold S. O'Morrow, Ed.D., "Recreation Counseling: A Challenge to Rehabilitation," in *Rehabilitation Literature*, Vol. 31, No. 8 (August 1970), 226; (2) Gerold S. O'Morrow, Ed.D., "Recreation Counseling for Handicapped Children," in *Occasional Papers* . . . , eds. H. Douglas Sessoms and L. E. Meyer (Seminar Papers).

† For a more indepth discussion on the systematic change process refer to Donald C. Klein, *Community Dynamics, and Mental Health* (New York: John Wiley and Sons, Inc., 1968), pp. 123–139.

FOOTNOTES

[1] David Mechanic, *Mental Health and Social Policy* (Englewood Cliffs, N.J.: Prentice-Hall, Inc., 1969), pp. 1–2.

[2] David Mechanic, *Mental Health and Social Policy*, p. 5.

[3] Bernard H. Hall, ed., *A Psychiatrist for a Troubled World: Selected Papers of William C. Menninger, M.D.* (New York: the Viking Press, 1967), I, 607–608.

[4] James C. Coleman, *Abnormal Psychology and Modern Life*, 3rd ed. (Glenview, Ill.: Scott, Foresman and Company, 1964), pp. 167–538.

[5] Leonard P. Ullmann and Leonard Krasner, eds., *Case Studies in Behavior Modification* (New York: Holt, Rinehart and Winston, Inc., 1965), p. 9.

[6] David Mechanic, *Mental Health and Social Policy*, p. 21.

[7] Karl Menninger, M.D., et al., *The Vital Balance* (New York: the Viking Press, 1963), pp. 125–152.

[8] Leonard P. Ullman and Leonard Krasner, eds., *Case Studies in Behavior Modification*, pp. 15–28.

[9] Joint Commission on Mental Illness and Health, *Action for Mental Health* (New York: Basic Books, Inc., 1961), pp. 25–26.

[10] Joint Commission on Mental Illness and Health, *Action for Mental Health*, p. 27.

[11] Joint Commission on Mental Illness and Health, *Action for Mental Health*, p. 29.

[12] Joint Commission on Mental Illness and Health, *Action for Mental Health*, pp. 29–30.

[13] David Mechanic, *Mental Health and Social Policy*, p. 52.

[14] Joint Commission on Mental Illness and Health, *Action for Mental Health*, p. 65.

[15] Lillian Summers, "Development of Recreation Service by the American Red Cross," *Intercom*, Vol. IX, No. 11, May 1956, pp. 1–2.

[16] Lillian Summers, "Development of Recreation Service by the American Red Cross," *Intercom*, p. 2.

[17] Lillian Summers, "Development of Recreation Service by the American Red Cross," *Intercom*, p. 3.

[18] Bernard H. Hall, ed., *A Psychiatrist for a Troubled World*, pp. 296–302.

[19] Joint Commission on Mental Illness and Health, *Action for Mental Health,* pp. 35–40.

BIBLIOGRAPHY

Brand, Jeanne L., "The United States: A Historical Perspective," in *Community Mental Health,* eds. Richard H. Williams and Lucy D. Ozarin. San Francisco: Jossey-Bass Inc., 1968.

Deutsch, Albert, *The Mentally Ill in America.* New York: Columbia University Press, 1949.

Farber, Bernard, *Mental Retardation: Its Social Context and Social Consequences.* Boston: Houghton Mifflin Company, 1968.

Joint Commission on Mental Illness and Health, *Action for Mental Health.* New York: Science Editions, 1961.

Kline, Donald, *Community Dynamics and Mental Health.* New York: John Wiley and Sons, Inc., 1968.

Mechanic, David, *Mental Health and Social Policy.* Englewood Cliffs, N.J.: Prentice-Hall, Inc., 1969.

Nesbitt, John A., Paul D. Brown, and James Murphy, eds., *Recreation and Leisure Service for the Disadvantaged.* Philadelphia: Lea and Febiger, 1970.

Recreation in Treatment Centers. Washington, D.C.: National Therapeutic Recreation Society, Vols. I–VI, 1962–1969.

Rehabilitation Literature. Chicago: National Easter Seal Society for Crippled Children and Adults (a monthly Society publication).

Susser, Mervyn, *Community Psychiatry: Epidemiologic and Social Themes.* New York: Random House, 1968.

Therapeutic Recreation Annual. Washington, D.C.: National Therapeutic Recreation Society (the new annual professional publication since 1970).

Therapeutic Recreation Journal. Washington, D.C.: National Therapeutic Recreation Society (a quarterly professional publication since 1967).

7   Recreation
and the
Alcoholic and Drug Addict

Courtesy International Paper Company

H. DOUGLAS SESSOMS

For millions of Americans the use of alcohol and drugs is directly related to their recreation behavior. Although they do not consider themselves drug addicts, they do accept the moderate use of stimulants and depressants as normal and a part of their recreation scene. They serve coffee to their neighbors when they drop in for a chat, drink beer at baseball and football games, and go to cocktail parties on the weekend. More recently, some have substituted marijuana for alcohol, but the setting of the weekend party is the same.

Approximately 70 million Americans consume alcoholic beverages. Of this group, less than one in twelve drinks to the point where he is identified as an alcoholic. Our national expenditure for wine, beer, and whiskey is in excess of nine billion dollars; many health people consider alcohol abuse as the number one health problem.[1] Most people, however, consider drinking alcoholic beverages to be a part of the American way of life and become concerned only when alcohol abuse enters the picture.

Statistics on narcotic and drug use are more difficult to obtain; consequently, it is almost impossible to determine the number of narcotic users in the United States. There are so many forms of drugs and so many socially acceptable reasons for taking them that many addicts go undetected or are never described as addicts. If nicotine (cigarettes), caffeine (coffee), and theobromine (colas) are drugs, in the social sense, most Americans are chronic drug users. It is estimated that between 500 thousand and a million people use hard narcotics (the opiates), whereas between 5 million and 15 million periodically use stimulants, depressants, and hallucinogens for nonmedical reasons.[2]

The history of drug use and abuse is an interesting one. Drugs have long been associated with religious ceremonies. Among some American Indian tribes, the chewing of peyote is as much a part of the worship as is the drinking of wine in the celebration of the Lord's Supper in some Christian churches. Drugs have also been used as stimulants to production. In earlier days in South America, the Indians working the copper mines in Bolivia were given cacao leaves to chew. Today, we encourage workers to take coffee and coke breaks. Then, some athletes have been known to use stimulants to improve their performance. Finally, and with few exceptions, national holidays and festivals have been legitimized as a time for abandonment, that is, freedom from obligation, and this is often accompanied by the use of drugs.

Play and drugs have an increasing and long-standing relationship. According to Roger Caillois,[3] the use of narcotics as play is consistent with one of the four play patterns found in all societies. When the pattern of Ilinx (vertigo) is dominant, games of rules and order are secondary and the society tends to be more primitive; patterns of immediate gratification are highly desirable and minimal technological advances result. Abandonment is the major characteristic of the Ilinx play; the loss of orientation is its goal. The taking of drugs certainly facilitates it. As a group becomes more civilized, its play becomes less turbulent and more ordered. The desirability of Ilinx activities, including drug use, diminishes. The decline of a civilization is characterized by a move toward the Ilinx play pattern.

Most recreators would not consider taking drugs as a recreation activity. The idea is contrary to our belief that recreation is good, a wholesome experience. But when we look at our definition of recreation as activities entered into for the pleasure derived therefrom, there is nothing there which says an activity must be wholesome. For millions, drinking and drug use are recreation behavior. The moral and legal questions of "ought" are not considered or are soon forgotten by the user. He enjoys the use of the drug and it becomes a part of his life pattern. Inasmuch as he considers it a pleasure, it may be viewed as recreation. The late Dr. Paul Haun discusses the facet of recreation in a paper entitled *The Pathology of Play*.[4] He said that not all recreation behavior is socially acceptable nor is it healthy. Some forms of play are pathological and may result in the destruction of the individual and society. The question of the recreational nature of drug use is further complicated by the addictive process.

THE SOCIAL ASPECTS OF DRUG USE

Probably more germane to the problem of recreation and narcotic use is the social aspect of drug addiction. Very few individuals begin the pattern of drinking or drug use by themselves. These experiences normally occur in a group situation where the peer pressure to conform and the security of having others sharing the experience dominate reason and rationality. One learns to drink and to smoke grass. The initial experience is often physiologically unpleasant, but the psychological and social overtones more than compensate for the discomfort felt. As one learns to acquire a taste for the beverage or drug, he needs less of the social stimulant to reinforce his pattern of use.

According to sociologists, approximately two-thirds of all addicts are introduced to drugs by other addicts. Rarely does the nondrinker of non-narcotic user introduce the "goodies" to someone else. Group-sharing of drugs takes on a cult quality similar to some hobby groups. For example, the more skillful members teach the less skillful the rituals of use, thereby increasing the allure for the beginner. As one becomes more sophisticated with drug use, he finds opportunities to share his knowledge with the novice, and this gives him additional feelings of accomplishment—as is true in many recreation situations. Many basic social needs are met, and a drug-centered lifestyle emerges. The social effects of the drug culture on the larger society are most noticeable, especially in the language area where terms such as grass, high, stoned, and trip have been accepted as a part of our everyday speech.

Likewise, a network of social relationships develops around the use of drugs. Addicts know whom to contact, where to go for the best buys, and which bars or pushers to avoid. Certainly the risk of doing something illegal and the satisfactions which come from having beaten the system add to the pleasure of narcotic use. Being "in" with the language and having mastered the skills of social drinking or marijuana smoking frequently are seen as symbols of adult status. Some addicts become quite creative in their mixing of drugs or development of new forms of getting a "high." Of course, once one is addicted, the social aspects diminish as the psychological and physical needs for the drug become the user's master.

Interestingly, the acceptance of a given drug as part of the normal lifestyle of Americans generally occurs during periods of affluency. Although alcohol had been consumed for generations by adult males, the question of prohibition and its legality was not raised until the 1920's. Popular use by both males and females, and the excitement of running contrary to convention helped usher in its legal acceptance and reduced the public's concern of alcohol as a narcotic. The same pattern held true for the use of cigarettes. Smoking formerly was restricted for adult use only, but liberalization of institutional policies and state laws during the 1940's ushered in a general acceptance of cigarette smoking, even among early teenagers. The same shifts may be now occurring with the use of marijuana; at least, the arguments posed for its legalization are very similar to those used by earlier anti-prohibitionists.

Once a drug has become socially acceptable and may be used legally for purposes of pleasure, the public seems to ignore it as a drug regardless of its negative consequences. The question becomes one of drug abuse rather than drug use. Alcohol provides a perfect illustration. Society is concerned about the alcoholic, not the social drinker. Legal controls and programs are secondary to the medical ones; the issue of morality declines as action is taken to prohibit drug abuse.

In getting at the problem of the role of the recreation professional in working with drug addicts and alcoholics, those who have been identified as abusers of drugs, several questions come to mind. Who are the drug addicts? Who are the alcoholics? How are they being treated? Is drug abuse preventable? Does recreation have a role in the prevention and rehabilitation process? The remaining portion of this chapter deals with the answering of these questions.

BASIC DEFINITIONS

The World Health Organization defines drug addiction as

> a state of periodic or chronic intoxication detrimental to the individual and to society, produced by the repeated consumption of a drug (natural or synthetic). Its characteristics include: 1. an overpowering desire or need (compulsion) to continue taking the drug and to obtain it by any means; 2. a tendency to increase the dose; 3. a psychic (psychological) and, sometimes a physical dependency upon the effects of the drug.[5]

There are literally thousands of drugs used by narcotic addicts. They are generally classified as stimulants, those drugs which give one a feeling of excitement and energy; de-pressants, those drugs which depress the central nervous sys-tem thereby relaxing the user; and hallucinogens, the so called mind-expanding drugs.

Of all the drugs used for social purposes, none compare with alcohol. It is derived from a variety of fruits and grains and has been in existence since prehistoric times. Taken in full strength, this colorless, volatile, inflammable liquid is an irritant to body tissue. It does not require digestion and is quickly absorbed into the blood. It has the pharmacological properties of a depressant and an anesthetic. Intoxication is said to occur when the alcohol concentration in the blood is .1 percent but this is only a legal definition. Actually, drunkenness varies considerably as individual biochemistry and food pat-terns as well as the amount of alcohol consumed affect this condition. Death may occur when the concentration of alcohol in the blood is .4 percent or higher.

Although many individuals begin drinking when they are in their teens, one is rarely diagnosed as an alcoholic until he is an adult. At that point, the pattern of excessive drinking and alcohol addiction is usually well established. Alcohol has ceased to be a part of the individual's lifestyle; it has become the cen-tral focus of his existence.

There are three general classifications or types of drink-ers. First, there is the social drinker who tends to drink in moderation. He rarely drinks to excess; drinking is a part of the social convention. Secondly, there is the excessive drinker, who, like a social drinker, drinks for purposes of congeniality but tends not to allow alcohol to interfere with his life processes. Finally, there is the alcoholic who drinks because of some emo-tional dependency on the effects of alcohol. His drinking behav-ior does interfere with his social relationships; he is habituated to the beverage and is unable to give up drinking without assistance. The pattern of the alcoholic may be that of a spree drinker who frequently goes on binges but, between periods of drunkenness, abstains from alcohol, or it may be a pattern of continuous plateau drinking in which there are no peaks or ex-cessive consumption. In the latter pattern, the individual is in a drunken condition most of the time.

According to some students of alcoholism, there is a differ-ence between the alcoholic and the alcohol addict. The difference is a subtle one and is related to the ability of the individual to respond to treatment: the alcoholic seems to benefit from care while the addict does not. Alcohol addiction is characterized by the compulsive and obsessive desire to drink alcohol. Of the 70 million Americans who consume alcoholic beverages —beer, wine, and distilled spirits—less than 6 million have problems of excessive drinking (alcoholics). Of that number, a fourth (1.5 million) are diagnosed as alcohol addicts.

The effects of excessive drinking are generally quite pronounced in the alcohol addict. From a physiological view the most serious consequence of alcoholism is malnutrition. The chronic alcoholic tends not to eat enough and does not eat that which properly nourishes him. Alcohol provides him with energy but lacks protein. His appetite diminishes, and this is often accompanied by morning nausea which leads to giving up breakfast. The low energy level reinforces his pattern of passivity. He may develop cirrhosis of the liver or suffer from gastritis (inflamed stomach).

The psychological effects of alcohol are also distinctive. As a depressant, alcoholic beverages affect the central nervous system thereby reducing sensory perception and the ability to react. Latent emotional problems such as anxiety and anger may be more outwardly expressed as the effects of drinking reduce the inhibitions of the individual. Hallucinations and phobic fears may accompany excessive drinking and the alcoholic's increased psychological dependency for the effects of the beverage render him unable to function without it.

Whereas alcoholics normally are diagnosed during the adult years, drug addiction is more prevalent among the young. Over one half of the narcotic addicts currently being treated for addiction are under the age of twenty-five years.[6] There is another interesting difference between drug addicts and alcoholics. Alcohol users are classified according to the type of drinker. With drug addiction, classification of use is based upon the type of drug consumed, rather than the type of user. The three basic classifications are: stimulants, depressants, and hallucinogens.

Stimulants are sometimes referred to as pep drugs and are best known for their ability to combat fatigue and sleepiness. Often they are medically prescribed to assist in weight reduction, though they have not conclusively been proven effective in this capacity.

Stimulants create within the users feelings of alertness, self-confidence and well-being. The "high" of the stimulant is generally followed by a "down" or depressed feeling. The loss of sleep and food accompanying stimulant use results in jitteriness, irritability, and confused thinking. The most heavily used stimulants are amphetamine (Benzadrine), dextroamphetamine (Dexadrine), and methamphetamine (Methadrine).

Stimulants normally are taken as pills but can be taken in liquid form. The practice of shooting stimulants directly into the vein, known as "speeding," greatly increases the drug's effects. Under the effects of stimulants, individuals become highly active and feel exhausted when the drug is no longer in full force. The user may ingest or shoot more to retain his high or may rely upon a sedative to aid him in his period of depression.

The sedatives or depressants relax the central nervous system and give the user a calm feeling. They tend to reduce the heart rate and to lower the blood pressure. The individual under high dosage resembles the alcoholic with his confused speech and staggering. Probably the best known of the sedatives are the barbiturates. They are commonly referred to as barbs or goof balls and range from a short-acting, fast-starting drug such as secobarbital (Seconal) to the long-acting, slow-starting phenobarbital (Luminal).

The barbiturates are addicting. A physical need for an increased dosage or for more frequent use accompanies the prolonged use of the drug. Barbiturates tend to heighten the effects of alcohol; consequently the combination of the two may be lethal. If the drug is withdrawn abruptly, the user may suffer many of the same symptoms of the opium addict during withdrawal period. These symptoms include cramps, nausea, and convulsions.

Both amphetamines and barbiturates are readily accessible. They are chemically produced and, until recent times, were often indiscriminately prescribed by medical personnel. Their potential misuse and abuse were acknowledged but not given serious thought, as the opiates and other "hard" narcotics were held to be the major drug culprits. By 1966 this view began to change as thousands of cases of acute drug addiction among the young appeared with most of them involving the use of "uppers" and "downers." Efforts to tighten control of their legal use were taken. The effects of the efforts, however, have been less than many desired especially when the pressure of the drug culture exerts itself.

Traditionally, drug addiction has been viewed as narcotic addiction, specifically, opium addiction. The opiates are the most powerful group of drugs used by addicts and are the most addicting. They are derived from the seed of the poppy plant and are taken orally, intravenously, chewed, or are inhaled. They produce a euphoric feeling and a state of well-being. Morphine and heroin, the latter of which is illegal even for medical use, are its major derivatives. The profits associated with the sale of opium are fantastic, as a pound of raw heroin produced in Turkey at $10.00 per pound may gross up to $60,000 in the U.S. black market. The relationship between drug-pushing and organized crime is well established.

According to the Medical World News, heroin was the leading cause of death among teenagers in New York City in 1969. Of the 900 heroin deaths that year in New York, 224 were between the ages of 13 and 19 years. It is estimated that over 100,000 teens in the city are opium addicts. The rehabilitation rate among these addicts is the lowest of record, probably no better than 2–10 percent of those treated. Nearly all drug legislation and treatment efforts have been to curb the use of the opiates, but the problem still exists and with the growing use of other drug forms, the need for corrective action is even more critical.

The hallucinogens are the third classification of drugs. They are often referred to as the mind-expanding or mind-affecting drugs. They are noted for their ability to distort sensory inputs which may result in bizarre behavior. Marijuana and LSD (lysergic acid diethylamide) are the most frequently used hallucinogens. Mescaline and STP are other forms of these drugs.

Society's experience with the hallucinogens is somewhat limited. Other than the smoking of marijuana, there was little involvement by drug users with the hallucinogens until the 1960's. The ability of the drugs to distort sensory perceptions may give the individual a feeling of exhilaration or despair.

Their effects on the same individual differ from time to time, consequently the user does not know what kind of experience he will have when he takes his "trip." Psychotic reactions are characteristic of LSD and peyote use. Marijuana tends to have a much milder effect, leaving one with a feeling of well-being and relaxation.

The use of the hallucinogens among college students, teen-agers, and servicemen has shocked public officials. It is esti-mated that up to 30 percent of college students use marijuana and that many highly educated people consider it no more harmful than alcohol. To paraphrase Shakespeare, "to smoke or not to smoke grass, that is the question." Historically, it was believed that marijuana was used primarily as a lead to the hard drugs (the opiates). There is some evidence today to support the notion that maijuana smokers may limit their use of drugs to marijuana and may further restrict that to specific social occasions. The widespread use of marijuana is so recent that data are not available to support a modification of our cur-rent approach to its control.

There is a distinction between drug addiction and drug habituation. Technically, one is said to be addicted to a drug only when there is a physiological dependency upon the drug. The opiates and barbiturates do create a physiologic depend-ency. By this, it is meant the user must either take the drug more frequently or increase the amount of the drug consumed in order to maintain the same level of feeling and to avoid with-drawal symptoms. Psychological dependency may occur with the use of any drug. This dependency is referred to as drug habitua-tion. Persons who are addicted to the opiates may also experi-ence drug habituation. The problem of treatment is one of breaking the drug habit more than freeing one from his phys-iological dependency on the drug. Drug habituation and drug abuse are the major problems related to excessive drug use.

The recreation professional should be aware of the char-acteristics of drug users although he may not work directly in a program for the rehabilitation of drug addicts. He may fre-quently see young people under the influence of drugs par-ticipating in his programs. He may mistake the hyperactive youth on amphetamines for a kid with a lot of energy, having a good time. He may encounter marijuana smoking on the premises and be confronted with what to do. The problem of alcohol and teenagers and recreation has been with the administrators of organized recreation services for generations and has yet to be resolved.

For the student preparing to work with the alcoholic or drug addict in programs of prevention and rehabilitation, it is extremely important that he understand the etiology of these diseases. He will need to look at both the social and psychological factors which may have encouraged and supported drug abuse. His will be the task of developing recreation programs to fill the void which exists when drugs are taken from the user.

THEORIES OF ADDICTION

Why do people become alcoholics or drug addicts? There is no single answer to this question. With alcoholics there seem to be three dominant explanations for addictive drinking. They may be classified under the headings of physiological, psychological, and sociological theories.

Some students of alcoholism contend that alcoholic addiction results from biochemical imbalances. They hold that some individuals, because of their metabolism and neurological makeup, are highly susceptible to alcoholism. The presence of alcohol triggers chemical changes which create a physical dependency on alcohol. Others hold the disease to be strictly psychological in its origin.

Within the grouping of psychological theories there are two dominant explanations for alcoholism. The first holds that the alcoholic suffers from deep feelings of insecurity and finds compensation when he is under the influence of its effects. Drinking gives rise to his fantasies of self-importance and abilities. The other theory holds that the male alcoholic has an unresolved Oedipus complex. He drinks in order to suppress his latent feelings of homosexuality. This theory states that the alcoholic tends to marry a female much like his mother and thereby intensifies the conflicts of the unresolved Oedipus complex or he will seek out a woman who complements his illness with her martyr needs.

ᵻA number of studies have supported the psychological approaches to alcoholism; in fact, an "alcoholic personality" has been described. The alcoholic is seen as one who suffers from extreme feelings of inadequacy and anxiety; he is passive and excessively dependent upon others for support and direction. The same characteristics have been attributed to narcotic addicts and other habitual drug users.

Sociological explanations of alcoholism suggest that illness results from the dynamics of society. The disease is a product of the culture and its social organizations which create and maintain such inner tensions as culturally induced anxiety, guilt, and suppressed hostility. These theories are supported by studies of the rate of drinking and alcoholism among various ethnic groups. It is believed that the attitudes of these subgroups either support or discourage drinking and intoxication as an acceptable means of relieving these inner tensions. If one consumes alcoholic beverages for purposes which are socially unacceptable, the guilt and anxiety accompanying the drinking behavior would only encourage more dependency upon the drug for the suppression of guilt and anxiety. A vicious cycle is established. If drinking is a part of the normal social customs of the group, it is less likely to produce or be used as a means for escaping these tensions.

Nearly all the theories of alcoholism regard stress as a precondition of alcoholism. Stress may be of either the physical or psychological nature, but the inability of the organism to adapt to stress is of paramount importance.

Drinking and narcotic use have specific social class relationships. A higher percentage of the more affluent drink than do those in lower income brackets. This may be directly related to the ability to purchase alcoholic beverages but it may also be related to the social class's perception of alcohol, its use and misuse. Among the more affluent, alcohol is accepted as a social beverage, not as the "drink of the devil."

Residence and religious affiliations also tend to influence drinking behavior. Those who reside in rural areas are less likely to drink than those who live in the city. Then, too, those subscribing to a more fundamental interpretation of the Bible are less likely to drink than those who subscribe to the social gospel approach. If a member of the former group does drink, the problems of guilt and misuse are greater than are those of the latter group.

Finally, the type of alcoholic beverage consumed is related to the social class and income. Beer tends to be the beverage of the poor or the young of the more affluent groups. Middle-class and upper-class adults tend to drink distilled spirits and wines. The consumption of illegal alcohol is generally restricted to the poor, the rural, and the young.

Similar social class relationships are observed with drug use. Until the late 1960's, hard narcotic use (heroin) was primarily restricted to lower-income groups residing in major urban centers. Marijuana was smoked by various subgroups but rarely used by the mainstream of American youth. It was a drug associated with those seeking artistic expression, new frontiers, the underworld, or those wishing to escape the "unbearable" life in which they found themselves. Habituation to the stimulants or depressants generally resulted from abusive health practices rather than the taking of the drug for social or psychological kicks.

According to police and medical statistics, over half of the users of hard narcotics in 1960 were under the age of twenty-one. They were primarily the urban black and Puerto Rican groups. This picture has changed radically as middle- and upper-class youth are experimenting with a variety of drugs. However, narcotic consumption has not been restricted to the young; the use of marijuana and stimulants is becoming as fashionable among the intellectuals as has been alcohol among the social elite. Many explanations have been given for the drug phenomena, including the media's constant appeal for Americans to consume pills and beverages, but no single explanation appears to explain the phenomenon.

Possibly one of the reasons why drugs have become so popular among the young is their availability. As stated earlier, drug traffic is illegal and consequently an open market for organized crime. Tremendous profits are available for those willing to run the risk of arrest. The typical heroin habit runs between $40 and $60 per day. Many users resort to theft and prostitution as a means of supporting their narcotic habit. To encourage the use of addictive drugs, narcotic pushers often use feeder drugs to develop their clientele.

Drug use, whether it be consumption of alcoholic beverages or the taking of narcotics, is related to many social dynamics. In many ways, it is a social phenomenon. As stated previously, rarely does one experiment with drugs alone; he generally begins the drug use process in the company of other drug users. Once it becomes a part of his lifestyle, he may use alcohol or narcotics alone or with someone but for the most part, he does not become dependent upon drugs for life support. That occurs only with the addict.

The recreation professional should be aware of the relationship of drugs to various forms of social behavior. He will encounter many rationalizations for drug use based on these relationships. Among the more frequently observed are the relationships of drug use to artistic expression, to the rebellion of youth, to crime and accidents, to physical illness, and to social identity and individual purpose.

DRUGS AND SOCIAL RELATIONSHIPS

It is argued by some that drug use, particularly of the mind-expanding ones, allows for greater freedom of artistic expression and consequently should be legalized. It is true that drug use has been more prevalent among pop musicians and pop artists than among similar related occupational groups, but there is no concrete evidence to support the notion that drugs allow creativity to be expressed. Drugs do tend to reduce inhibitions, but creativity and abandonment are not synonymous processes and should not be confused as such.

There is a definite relationship between narcotic use and criminal behavior. This is not to say narcotics cause crime although the narcotic addict is very likely to commit crime in order to support his habit. Then, too, those under the influence of drugs, alcohol, narcotics or otherwise, are more likely to be involved in automobile accidents than are nondrug users. The depressing effects of some drugs and the distorting effects of others are directly related to these accidents.

Inasmuch as the use of alcoholic beverages is restricted to the adult segment of the society and the social use of narcotics is illegal, alcohol and narcotics have become symbols of rebellion and "growing up." It is not surprising to see young men, under the age of twenty-one, indulging in alcohol for the simple purpose of demonstrating their maturity or to find hard narcotics a welcome avenue for rebellion against authority.

When narcotic and other forms of drug use are romanticized in movies and on television, their desirability as symbols of rebellion and sophistication are enhanced.

To those habituated to the use of drugs, drugs are necessary to complete life. Many drug users who will not admit to themselves that they are habituated to drugs argue that drugs make them feel complete. They say drugs are dispensable and therefore not harmful, and, since they exist, they make life more satisfying. This is indeed a difficult argument to refute since there is no standard definition of what is the good life. To answer it, one must return to his value system and compare the merits of it in his life style with those of the user.

There is a definite relationship between the use of drugs and recreation behavior. As stated previously, for many, drugs are taken during non-work hours and are a part of their free-time expression. In the case of alcohol, its use is sociably accepted among adults. In the case of narcotics, there is peer approval, even if society disapproves. Stimulants may be taken to heighten one's reactions during a competitive event, while alcohol is used as a trend setter. It is difficult to determine if drug use results from the habituation qualities of the drugs or whether it stems from society's acceptance of it as one of the ingredients of the experience or event.

In the final analysis, society determines whether drug use is acceptable or not. For some drugs, social use is legitimate. For others, it is illegal. The determining factor seems to be society's view of the harmfulness of the drug and the number of persons who are using it. When drugs such as caffeine are used by the majority of the population, with few negative consequences of use, the drug achieves approval. On the other hand when the drug is used by a small group and it seems to have negative consequences, it is disallowed. The test question appears to be: "Does the drug prohibit the individual from fulfilling his socially prescribed responsibilities?" When the answer is yes, the drug is usually not allowed or is restricted to certain settings and under specific conditions.

The problem is one of drug abuse with abuse being defined in terms of the drug's effect upon the individual and his ability to perform. To prevent drug abuse from occurring, society has enacted laws prohibiting the sale of many drugs except for medical purposes. This makes the use of those drugs illegal and subject to criminal action. Yet psychiatry tells us that alcoholism and narcotic habituation is a sickness and those who abuse these drugs are to be treated as patients, not criminals. Society's moral and social-welfare feelings become intertwined and add to the confusion surrounding these problems.

In many ways it is much easier to work with the alcoholic in providing rehabilitation than it is with the narcotic addict. Alcoholism has been recognized as a disease, and it is no longer illegal to consume alcoholic beverages in most states. This is not true with narcotic use. The narcotic addict is engaged in an illegal activity when he procures narcotics without prescription. Society is still somewhat hesitant to accept narcotic habituation as a medical problem. However, to most students of alcoholism and narcotic addiction, the two are similar and both are illnesses. The legal aspects complicate the problem, but do not alter approaches necessary for the treatment of the addict.

APPROACHES TO TREATMENT
AND REHABILITATION

Essentially, the treatment approach is twofold. First, the alcoholic or addict must be isolated from the addictive drug. Frequently this means institutionalization for a period of time. The addict must be removed from the drug environment where he can physically reestablish a non-drug equilibrium. Once he has been "dried out," the process of rehabilitation begins.

Rehabilitation is the key to drug treatment. It is in this area where recreation may make its major contribution. Rehabilitation consists of re-education, altering personality dynamics, behavior, value modification, and skill development. In order to overcome addiction, the addict must undergo psychic changes. Drugs must cease to be the dominant quality of his lifestyle. Something must be offered to the addict to fill this void or he will return to his previous pattern as soon as the opportunity affords itself.

Various treatment techniques are used in the rehabilitation process. As addiction is a social phenomenon, group therapy is often prescribed. Individual counseling and psychotherapy sessions are also used. A variety of educational and skill development programs constitute a phase of the rehabilitation process. If the addict is vocationally unskilled, he may be placed in classes where he can find meaning through work. The development of nonwork skills must also be developed, as the free time problem is critical. The addict's use of leisure and his attitude toward recreation may determine the degree of success he will experience through the rehabilitative efforts.

RECREATION'S ROLE

Recreation may serve as a force in the modification of behavior, but it also may be used as a reinforcer or reward for behavior changes resulting from other efforts. The role assumed by the recreation specialist and the use he makes of activities and opportunities will vary according to the philosophy of the rehabilitation agency and the sequence of rehabilitation stages. Rehabilitation is not a straight line activity. It is a sequence of experiences, and the role recreation may play differs according to each sequence.

What are some of the roles recreators may assume in the treatment of the addict? As a rehabilitation team member, the recreator will be expected to act as both a generalist and specialist. In his generalist role, he should contribute to the team's overall understanding of the patient when he is in a recreation setting, support the patient as an individual, and aid in the day-to-day routine of agency functioning. As a specialist, the recreator will be called upon to assist the patient to develop the skills and attitudes necessary to cope effectively with his free time. He will be involved in the task of building the patient's ego and providing opportunities for the emergence of a new lifestyle. Recreation counseling and the development of referrals for the continuation of satisfying leisure activities are a part of his specialized functioning.

The role of recreation in the treatment program will vary according to the type of addiction. As stated earlier, alcoholics are generally adults whereas narcotic addicts are teenagers or young adults. The age factor and the legal aspects of the drug used may suggest a different set of responses as the recreator carries out his specialized task. The lifestyles—peer awareness, family affiliations, income, etc.—and self-concepts are certainly different among teenagers and middle-aged adults.

The recreator must understand these differences as he moves to meet the needs of the patient.

A further complicating factor in treatment is the place in which treatment occurs. Is the addict being rehabilitated in an institutional setting or is he being served in the community through an out-patient clinic? The problems of institutional dependency and bureaucratic procedures may plague those working in institutional settings, whereas the problems of the addict's peer pressure and his personal freedom hamper those working in the community. There are advantages and disadvantages with both settings.

A variety of institutional approaches to rehabilitation have been used. In the area of narcotic addiction, the federal government has operated two prison hospitals: Lexington and Fort Worth. Recreation has been a phase of the treatment program of each as it is true with the many state hospitals which have special wards for narcotic and alcoholic addicts. Several states have established special institutions for the rehabilitation of alcoholics. Activity therapy and group therapy tend to be predominant modes of treatment at these institutions. More recently, special units for the alcoholic and narcotic addict have been created at state hospitals. These programs are patterned after those pioneered at the special hospitals. Out-patient clinics for drug addicts and alcoholics are more frequently found in urban settings. The role of the recreator in the out-patient clinic has not been fully explored or defined.

Most addicts treated in the institutional setting are there as the result of some legal action. Although alcoholism is not illegal, the alcoholic is often referred to the treatment center by the courts. With the narcotic addict, institutionalization is often an alternative to prison. Seldom does the narcotic addict or alcoholic voluntarily seek admission to these institutions as the nature of their illness prohibits such behavior. Consequently, the addict is at an institution because of the actions of someone else. The problems of motivation are paramount and complicated by this fact.

In trying to develop an effective recreation program in an institutional setting, many considerations must be made. First, the recreator must understand the nature of the illness which brings the patient to the institution. Alcoholism and narcotic addiction are most frequently classified as personality disorders.

The alcoholic and the narcotic addict are of the dependent personality type. They are passive and frequently emotionally non-expressive. One of the goals of the treatment plan is to modify this behavior so the patient becomes more aggressive and self-expressive.

The second major consideration in program development is the recognition of the stage of rehabilitation in which each patient finds himself. As stated earlier, the role of recreation will vary according to the stages of treatment. The recently admitted patient who is undergoing the drying out process has different needs and will respond differently to the recreator than will the patient who is in the process of terminating treatment and is facing the apprehensions of returning to the community which supported his illness. In some instances, the treatment program would have recreation playing a diversionary role where in another phase, the plan would have the recreator involved in attitude and skill development.

A third consideration is to recognize the normalcy of the patients. The same forces which condition all of us are at work with the addict. Among these forces are age, sex, social class orientation, educational experiences, family status, previous recreation exposure, and the like. According to the limited research in this area, addicts participate in about the same activities as do nonaddicts.[7] Their rate of participation is much less, but the proportional participation from activity to activity is essentially the same. It would be unusual to expect addicts to pursue recreation activities uncommon to their age or economic orientation.

In addition to these three special considerations, there are additional ones which affect program development. They deal with the specific objectives of the agency. Is recreation viewed as therapy or is it an ancillary service? Are recreators expected to function as counselors and group therapy leaders or are they to simply offer activities and operate the program? Are recreators to observe patient behavior and provide feedback at team meetings or are recreators expected to disassociate themselves with the medical aspects and work primarily to keep the patients busy when they are not in treatment? If the recreator is expected to play a treatment role, and increasingly this is the situation, what activities does he offer to cause or support the behavior modification and an improved self-image?

Understanding the function of activity and the relationship of one experience to the total rehabilitation process is absolutely essential. The recreation program in the therapeutic context must be in harmony with the other rehabilitation efforts underway. As a diversion, it must be compatible with, but not necessarily a part of, the treatment effort.

Addicts are emotionally passive. Consequently, recreation may be one of the tools used to stimulate a more aggressive behavior. To facilitate this, activity skills may need to be taught or refined. In some instances, the addict should be required to participate in skill development classes. When this is done, he should be told this is a part of his re-education program. These experiences should not be called recreation although they may lead to recreative expressions.

In a sense, the recreation department serving the addict has two responsibilities. The first is to develop a skill and possibly the attitudes necessary to engage in recreation. It is an educational-rehabilitative enterprise. It may be achieved through classes or other forms of formalized instruction. The second is to provide opportunities for the addict to participate in recreation at his own volition. These opportunities may be an extension of the skill development experiences or they may be any occasions, as perceived by the addict, to do whatever he enjoys. Regardless of what they are, they should not be limited to any set time period, such as the recreation hour between 3 and 4 o'clock in the afternoon, nor restricted to a specific area such as the "rec" room. The occasion should be timeless and result from the provision of facilities and opportunities for their pursuit, not from a schedule or set pattern of activities and designated setting.

As the addict becomes more aggressive and overt in his expressions, his recreation pattern will change. Passivity and hours of consumptive behavior should give way to more outward forms of expression. Investment of self and appreciation of the worth of self should result from these expressions. It is at this point the recreator may play a critical role as teacher or counselor and reinforce and support the new learning of the addict.

The counseling role is a critical one both in the rehabilitation process and in the preparation for the addict's return to society. It should be coordinated with the other phases of treatment and should reinforce those efforts. The addict should be made aware of the progress he has made as well as the opportunities which exist in his community for the continuation of his new behavior. The counseling process may include the making of referrals or it may terminate at the time of discharge with no follow-up conferences as a part of it. In either instance, the process should aid in bridging the gap between the institution's program and the services of the community. After all, much of the addict's leisure behavior will be spent at home or in his immediate neighborhood, so preparation for discharge must begin the day the addict enters treatment. It is unrealistic to expect him to spend a preponderance of his free time in organized recreation programs in the community; the patient must be taught to stand on his own and seek those experiences which add to his fullness of life and these often occur in such "insignificant" settings as his neighborhood or home.

Ideally, the recreator should follow the addict into the community. The follow-up process should involve counseling, evaluation, and cooperative work with the community recreation agencies. If the institution's recreation department is unable to provide this continuing support, and few are, some of the recreation counseling might be achieved through the social worker or rehabilitation counselor who continues the addict's treatment once he is home. If this is the case, the recreator must work closely with these professionals or agencies serving them as a resource.

Every effort should be taken to provide opportunities for the addict to continue his new skills and practice new forms of time use. To achieve this, the recreator should not limit his concerns to the development of traditional recreation activity skills or work only in the sphere of organized recreation services. He should see volunteer services and social involvement as forms of leisure use and encourage and make available opportunities for those kinds of participation.

For many addicts, working as a volunteer or assisting in rehabilitation of other addicts (Alcoholics Anonymous and Synanon) are forms of time use preferable to participation in more organized recreation programs. These should be encouraged and used as building blocks. Participation as a volunteer, as a program instructor, or as a rehabilitation worker in the community not only becomes a meaningful use of the addict's leisure time but also enhances his self-concept and his status in the community. The success that Alcoholics Anonymous and Synanon has had is largely due to their involvement of addicts as people who know and can help other addicts. The peer pressure to refrain from addiction and the pride which comes from having succeeded and being helpful to others reinforces the rehabilitation process.

Recreation may serve to prevent as well as rehabilitate addiction. Leisure behavior is a good index of mental health and social adjustment. The need to escape through narcotics is certainly less when one is enjoying his life and is able to cope with problems as they arise. If his self-image is enhanced through the rewards he receives in his leisure expressions, he is less likely to turn to narcotics as a way of life. Also, group membership is frequently based upon activity interest. If one is in a group that disdains narcotics, for it sees no relationship between narcotics and its major interest, one is less likely to choose drugs. By providing a variety of recreation opportunities in the community and by offering opportunities for skill developments, the recreator may aid in the prevention of drug addiction.

Frequently, the recreator is in a position to identify drug use in its earlier stages and take corrective steps to avoid drug abuse. If the recreator sees an individual or group whom he believes is experimenting with drugs, he is in an excellent position to negate this behavior. He should do this in cooperation with other professionals as he will need their counsel and advice. The key may be the substituting of meaningful and rewarding recreation experiences for the drug experiences but "meaningful" must be viewed in terms of the participant, not the recreator, and the payoff must be more gratifying than the perceived rewards of drug use. Drug addiction and drug use are not the result of misuse of leisure time but a multitude of dynamics in the life of the individual. Consequently, the recreator cannot resolve the problem alone, but he can offer experiences which may counter some of the negative forces at work, while at the same time providing new satisfactions and meaning.

It is impossible to define meaningful recreation experiences in terms of specific activities. Most recreation activities have a potential for ego strength and growth. There should be enough variation in the program to allow people to find their way. Group approval is vital; the meaningful experience is often what the group says it is. The more opportunities one has to become involved in activities, to express himself in those activities, the greater the likelihood that he will find satisfaction and fulfillment without drugs.

With the increasing use of drugs in our culture, drug education and cooperative endeavors with other social service agencies are needed. Recreators will be expected to become a partner in community drug action programs. What will they offer to the addicts or to prevent addiction? Remember, addicts are members of the community and have had the same opportunities to participate in recreation programs as have had the non-addicts, but chose not to. Why? Is it the insensitiveness of the recreators and their programs or is it due to a lack of opportunity? Might it result from the kinds of recreation experiences afforded by the agency, or is it that the drug culture and the drug style of life are more exciting and more satisfying than the activities of the "straight"? The answering of these questions should provide direction for the development of the recreation program and for the educating of the staff in the area of drug addiction and drug abuse.

Alcoholism and narcotic addiction are medical problems. They are complicated by legal factors and moralistic views. They are dissimilar from most forms of illness, as they totally affect the lifestyle. The remedy is not simply the removal of a disease but the altering of an entire behavioral pattern. Group therapy has been proven to be the most successful form of treatment, but more than group reinforcement is required for these maladies. The addict needs to see himself as someone who can achieve. Recreation is one of those areas in which achievement can be realized. The breadth and progression of experiences in recreation may facilitate these goals. Often it is the limits placed on recreation by the recreators which deter recreation from achieving those goals, not the experiences themselves.

There is no magic remedy for addiction. One does not become an addict overnight, and likewise one is not cured in twenty-four hours. Many forces are at work in creating the addictive pattern and, consequently, many forces must be brought to bear to alter that behavior. Cooperation of the medical, health, legal, and social service personnel is essential. Recreators need to work with these interests. This is true both in the institution and in the community. The drug culture gives way only when the support culture does its job and recreation is an essential element of the support culture.

FOOTNOTES

[1] Joseph Thimann, *The Addictive Drinker* (New York: Philosophical Library, 1966).

[2] Robert K. Merton and Robert A. Nisbet, *Contemporary Social Problems* (New York: Harcourt, Brace and World, 1966), Chapters 4 and 5.

[3] Roger Caillois, *Man, Play and Games* (Glencoe: The Free Press, 1962).

[4] Paul Haun, "The Pathology of Play" in Herbert Brantley and H. Douglas Sessoms, eds., *Recreation Issues and Perspectives* (Columbia, S.C.: Wiry Publishing Company, 1969).

[5] United Nations Expert Committee on Drugs Liable to Produce Addiction, Reports 6–7, World Health Organization Technical Report Series No. 21 (New York: United Nations, 1950).

[6] Ernest Harms, ed., *Drug Addiction in Youth* (New York: Pergamon Press, 1965).

[7] H. Douglas Sessoms and Sidney Oakley, "Recreation, Leisure and the Alcoholic," *Journal of Leisure Research*, Vol. I., No. 1, 1969.

BIBLIOGRAPHY

In addition to the sources cited as footnotes, the following publications are recommended.

Alcoholism

Kessel, Neil, and Walton, Henry, *Alcoholism*. London: Penguin Books, 1965.

Pittman, David J., and Snyder, Charles R., eds., *Society, Culture and Drinking Patterns*. New York: Wiley and Sons, 1962.

Quarterly Journal of Studies on Alcohol. Editorial Office: Rutgers University Center of Alcohol Studies, New Brunswick, N.J.

Shepherd, E. A., and Barber, Mary R., *Teenage Alcohol Use*. Hartford, Conn.: Connecticut Department of Mental Health, Alcoholism Division, 1965.

Straus, R., and Bacon, S. D., *Drinking in College*. New Haven: Yale University Press, 1953.

Drug Addiction

Ausubel, D. P., *Drug Addiction: Physiological, Psychological, and Sociological Aspects*. New York: Random House, 1965.

Brotman, Richard, and Suffet, Frederick, *Youthful Drug Use*. Washington: U.S. Department of Health, Education and Welfare, 1970.

Chein, Isadore, et al., *The Road to H: Narcotics, Delinquency and Public Policy*. New York: Basic Books, 1964.

DeRopp, Robert S., *Drugs and the Mind*. New York: Grove Press, 1961.

Talday, Paul, ed., *Drugs in Our Society*. Baltimore: The Johns Hopkins Press, 1964.

8   Recreation and Persons with Physical Disabilities

Courtesy National Easter Seal Society for Crippled Children & Adults, Inc.

THOMAS A. STEIN

Perhaps one of the most frustrating and discouraging commentaries that can be made of organized community recreation in America is its failure to serve large segments of citizens. It seems paradoxical that on the one hand it is generally agreed by recreation professionals that opportunities for meaningful recreation experiences are a universal need and that programming should be designed to meet the needs of *all* of the people. This is particularly true in the public sector or in governmentally sponsored community recreation. Yet, on the other hand, such opportunities are not being offered to any great extent. Many practitioners are still defending their failure to provide for some—in this instance those with obvious and permanent physical disabilities—on the rationale that such persons require highly specialized leadership, equipment, facilities, and activities which are not feasible within the budgetary limitations placed on a recreation agency. This argument continues by implying that a public agency has the obligation to provide for the majority of the public. It should not attempt to dissipate its resources by trying to attend to the peculiar and special needs of those with orthopedic disabilities, deafness, blindness, chronic disorders, or other similar disadvantages. The expense for so many small groups with special leaders would be too great a burden for the community to absorb.

Such views are understandable when one recognizes that, except on an occasional basis, the majority of professionals in administrative or other leadership positions of community recreation have never been exposed to special populations either in their formal professional training or work experiences. Apprehension of the unknown is a normal reaction for most of us. We can envision a myriad of problems based on preconceived assumptions which would accompany any effort to serve all of the public. Many of these premises are based on myths. Therefore, our lack of knowledge about persons with physical disabilities, as well as biases founded on misinformation, accentuate a tendency to globalize disability to where an individual's potential and remaining abilities are either unknown or discounted.

The aim of this discussion is to attempt to assist the reader in gaining a greater sensitivity to the presence, needs and aspirations of persons with a physical disability. It is not our purpose to transform each reader into a highly trained paramedical expert in therapeutic recreation. Obviously a far greater academic experience, in addition to in-depth field training, would be required for that. Rather it is the contention of this writer that every generalist in the field of recreation should have an awareness of a degree of understanding about the people he will be serving. And such service should extend to all members of a community—whatever that type of community might be. To accomplish this mission the following discussion will offer:

1. A brief historical view of recreation for people with physical disabilities;
2. A review of terminology commonly related to this special population;
3. Some of the more critical physiological, psychological, and social problems that often accompany physical disability;
4. Some suggestions for recreation programming in both segregated and integrated settings.

Admittedly, the overriding hope is to minimize, or even eliminate, bias and the undercurrent of prejudice toward this segment of society.

BACKGROUND OF SERVICES

Recreation programming for persons with physical disabilities gained its greatest impetus and growth during and following World War II with the provision of diversionary activities for disabled servicemen in military and veterans hospitals. Prior to 1940, although some programs can be traced to earlier years, recreation programs tended to be a prelude setting the stage for the accelerated activities which accompanied and followed the war years.

In sheltered programs for children with disabling conditions, probably the most notable accomplishments were in residential camping opportunities. In the late 1930's Camp Daddy Allen in Pennsylvania and Camp Wawbeek in Wisconsin were established to provide a sheltered residential outdoor recreation experience. Although the principal purpose was to provide these youngsters with a few weeks in the out-of-doors—away from home, institution or hospital—a variety of side benefits resulted.

For many it offered a chance to develop a healthy physical, intellectual, and social proficiency under circumstances more conducive to such learning.

These camps proved to be the beginning "training grounds" for young people, many of whom would eventually enter career fields in the medical and paramedical professions. These camps were, as they continue to be, sponsored and operated by the Easter Seal Societies of those respective states. The next thirty years were to see these types of camps develop, expand and flourish until they are now found in virtually every state in the union. In many cases services have been extended to include adult camping. For example, Camp Wawbeek now offers six weeks of camping exclusively for adults. By the end of the 1960's there were over 100 residential camping programs serving individuals with physical disabilities.[1] Sponsorship has included various voluntary health agencies, community service clubs, and private groups.

Following the war years of the early 1940's, the Red Cross, the Armed Forces, and the Veterans Administration continued to provide recreation services for military personnel and veterans who were institutionalized. It was not until after the mid-twentieth century, however, that similar programs were found to any great extent in nonmilitary hospitals and institutions. And it was not until the late 1950's that recreators were offered specialized academic training to work in therapeutic settings.

Community recreation for persons with physical disabilities has yet to develop into a widespread movement, although isolated examples do exist. Where they are found, program activities invariably are segregated or sheltered, i.e., people with disabilities are grouped and thus separated from the able-bodied population. In all fairness it must be noted that segregation is not necessarily wrong or unhealthy. Most "handicap" adult social clubs and athletic groups have maintained a self-imposed restriction on membership which requires disability as a prime prerequisite for belonging. These types of programs are discussed later in this chapter. For children we do find some—though relatively few—sheltered playground programs, day camps and year-round swimming activities offered under the auspices of various community agencies or organizations. Yet, if we were to review community recreation programs nationwide, we would find that our disabled citizens are truly handicapped by a dearth of leisure opportunities.

UNDERSTANDING TERMS

Today in our society there is a tendency to use a variety of terms when referring to physical disability or when attempting to describe this special population. Some of these have descriptive value while at the same time suggest a minimum of stigmatizing or devaluing effect. Others are negative, devaluating terms which carry a connotation that is depreciating to any person with an obvious, permanent disability. It is essential that we become sensitive to some of the more common references used.

For a start, it might be helpful to eliminate the terms of "crippled," "maimed," and "defectives" when identifying this population. All of these terms tend to not only accentuate the disability but, in addition, tend to imply total uselessness. Most individuals with a permanent and obvious physically disabling condition are well aware of that condition. Yet, many of these same people, when their opinion is sought, are unhappy —occasionally angry—about being referred to as "cripples." They tend to find such terms as "disabled" or "handicapped" more palatable. For purposes of this discussion the following terms are defined: *

Physical disability.   Relates to the physical degeneration or loss to an individual that may have been caused by congenital or adventitious factors.

Congenital disabilities.   Usually relates to prenatal malformations, defects, or injuries existing at or before birth.

Adventitious disabilities.   Physically disabling conditions that are acquired after birth by traumatic or chronic events.

Traumatic disabilities.   Caused by a fast-moving or critical inci-

* All terms defined in this section are based on a review of three sources, including *The American Pocket Medical Dictionary*, 16th edition (Philadelphia: W. B. Saunders Company, 1941), *The American College Dictionary* (New York: Harper and Brothers, Publishers, 1957), and *Websters Third New International Dictionary*, (Springfield, Mass.: G&C Merriman Company, 1964).

dent such as accident, assault, war, or other similar episodes.

Chronic disabilities.   Usually refers to those resulting from diseases or conditions that may be slow-moving and progressive or in an arrested state, i.e., where the progression or worsening has temporarily or permanently ceased.

Another means of referring to physical disability is through the use of terms which relate to that portion of the body which is involved. Although it is not our intention to present a medical dictionary of terms, semantic references are relatively common, particularly among professional recreators who work with this population.

Paraplegia.   Paralysis and a loss of use of both lower limbs and lower part of the body, often as a result of spinal cord or brain injury. In cases where only the loss of use of arms are found, such as in some post-polio conditions, "paraplegic" is not usually used as a functional description.

Quadriplegia.   Indicates a general paralysis and a loss of use of all four limbs, usually as a result of brain damage or high spinal cord injury, i.e., in the cervical region of the vertebrae. Such loss of use, particularly in the upper extremities is not always total and the individual may have some functional use of his arms and hands.

Hemiplegia.   Paralysis and loss of use of one side of the body, a condition sometimes resulting from a stroke, brain damage, or lesion of spinal cord. Again, such functional loss is not always total.

Therefore, on occasion we may hear the reference that a particular person is a 5 C. Quad. This merely means that he has partial or total loss of use of all four limbs (quadriplegic) and that the spinal injury or involvement is at the fifth cervical vertebrae.

Handicapped.   This is a term that is used every day when referring to an individual but often it is used incorrectly. The word originates from the Anglo-Saxon phrase "hand-in-the-cap" which was a game of chance. Later it became "handicap" and was used to describe persons who were inferior in economic competition because of mental or physical disabilities. Later still, it was used to describe disadvantages in successful competition for any reason. Although it was intended to mean disadvantage due to disability, it generally became used to mean the disability itself; that the only difference between disability and handicap was possibly the severity of the disabling condition.

Handicapped still refers to people with disabilities but its current meaning has changed to describe persons with degrees of difference physically, mentally, psychologically, and socially. It no longer refers to the extent of the disability except as that disability limits that person competitively or in reaching a particular objective.

The extent of disability does not always determine the extent of handicap. Often the handicapping feature may not be a person's disability as much as it might be the way society visualizes his disability, or the way in which the individual himself views it. Consequently, failure to function in a given task may be the result of other-imposed or self-imposed barriers.[2]

Beatrice Wright suggests that using "shortcut" semantics such as "the handicapped" or "the disabled" carries a connotation of total handicappedness or total disability. It would be more realistic to refer to an individual within this special population as a person with a physical disability whereby the emphasis is on the person rather than the disability. Further, such a method of referral, though more cumbersome, implies that the individual has capabilities and abilities in spite of the particular disabling condition; a factor which is certainly true in nearly all, if not all, cases.[3]

As may have been noted, the preceding discussion has incorporated the more cumbersome terminology out of recognition of the merits of Wright's argument. However, for the present this writer is willing, though reluctantly, to accept the use of "disabled persons" on the admittedly weak rationale that it has extensive and common usage among various agencies and organizations serving this population as well as among those persons with physical disabilities. One outstanding example of this would be The Disabled Veterans of America.

As long as persons with physical disabilities are handicapped by a lack of recreational, educational, or vocational opportunities and by environmental barriers to full participation, they are truly handicapped. Conversely, it seems just as logical to assume that once opportunities are available, where such barriers are eliminated and where a person's disability is no longer impeding his involvement in a given activity, the term handicapped should no longer have application. An example of this notion in operation would be the following case:

John, who is a paraplegic and therefore cannot use his legs, may be required to gain mobility through the use of a wheelchair. He is undoubtedly handicapped in performing certain activities, such as mountain climbing or bicycle riding, because of his disability. Or he may be unable to gain entrance to places where activities take place because of such architectural barriers as steps and narrow doorways which prevent him from functioning in an independent fashion. However, where such barriers do not exist and where his disability need not be a preventing factor, e.g., archery or card playing, he still has the disability but he should not be called handicapped with respect to these activities.

To some readers this distinction may appear to be "nit-picking." Yet, the primary goal of rehabilitation, in all of its facets, is to assist the individual to develop the fullest use of his remaining assets and to eliminate, where possible, all handicapping features which bar the way to realistic educational, vocational, and recreational goals.

In summary then, every effort should be made to avoid using devaluating terms such as crippled, maimed, or defective when referring to persons with physical disabilities. As currently used, the terms disability and handicap are not synonymous. Whereas a disability relates to the specific loss of a physical function to the individual, handicap relates to a disadvantage in performing a given task as a result of the disability, society attitudes, environment, or self-imposed restrictions.

PROBLEMS OF DISABILITY

Keeping in mind the overall objectives of this book and particularly of this chapter, a discussion of problems relating to physical disability must, of necessity, be confined to those concerns which directly bear on an individual's capacity to take advantage of leisure opportunities afforded by special and general recreation agencies. It is fully recognized that other crucial concerns dealing with educational, vocational, spiritual, and other aspirations are not only essential to the total well-being of every individual, but may have an indirect effect on his capacity to gain maximum fulfillment from a recreative experience. However, the task of providing visability to these problem areas must be left to others. We do attempt to discuss some concerns that may not fall within the strict purview of a traditional approach to recreation services. By our citing of examples, the reader should come to realize that such problems often have a direct bearing on the rate and depth of participation in recreation programs as well as the degree of satisfaction that can be derived from the experience.

As recreators, it seems incomprehensible that we could ignore physiological, psychological, or social difficulties facing potential or actual participants in our programs. Nevertheless, this is probably the case in too many instances. Possibly we have been led to believe that if we provide an outstanding program with proper leadership, facilities, equipment, and activities people will clamor for admittance. Maybe this does happen on occasion. But most experienced recreators will recognize that often it does not, and we are left to wonder why. If we would take a moment to explore this further, part of the answer might be revealed. To what extent can a hungry child, who comes to us without having breakfast, fully enjoy a recreation experience? To what extent is an individual ready to enjoy a dance when he has never learned to dance? These and many more examples could be given as they relate to people who are considered able-bodied. Lack of readiness for a variety of reasons is also true for many persons with physical disabilities. Following are presented some modified cases intended to further our understanding. It should be kept in mind that these are actual cases extracted from research conducted by the author. Of course, names have been changed to maintain the anonymity of individuals.[4]

The Case of Fred

At the time of the study Fred was a 43-year-old chronic quadriplegic who had been diagnosed as have multiple sclerosis (a neurological disease) at the age of thirty-five. He was unmarried and lived with a sister and her family. Although unable to walk, he was able to move about independently with the use of a battery-powered wheelchair. He required help when arising from bed and retiring at night. Further, he needed assistance in attending to his toilet needs and, to some extent, when eating. For example, he had difficulty in cutting meat.

During an initial interview* he had indicated a particular interest in archeology and electronics. Although having only a high school education, he was an avid reader on these subjects. Prior to the onset of disability he had been employed in a paper mill until no longer able to perform the tasks required of that job.

He was given the opportunity to attend a two-week residential camp for physically disabled adults. Camping was an experience he had not had since youth. He arrived at camp on a Sunday afternoon and, following a regular check-in procedure, was assigned to a counselor and immediately "wheeled" to his living quarters.

During the first few days of the camp session it was observed that Fred did not participate in any of the planned camp activities although encouraged to do so by members of the staff. He was usually seen sitting just outside his living quarters or on the sundeck of another facility watching other campers in swimming or playing table games. After three days of this nonparticipation he was asked to discuss his experiences to date and how he felt about camp.

He pointed out that when he first arrived, his first inclination was to "turn tail and run." With over one hundred other campers present having all types of disabilities, his previous self-image was apparently shattered. He indicated that at that moment he had said to himself "My God—am I like these other people?" He possibly carried the same stigmatizing impressions of "crippled people" as do many of the rest of society.

Another factor that made Fred's case so interesting was his comment that when he first arrived at camp he couldn't have cared less about the various activities available. His major concerns were who would help him to get out of bed, to get dressed, to shave, to go to the toilet, to shower, to eat, and to

* It should be kept in mind that the pre-camp interview was not a regular procedure of the camp administration, but was a part of the research technique of the writer.

go to bed at night. Even though all of these physiological concerns had been anticipated by the staff and were, in fact, handled by his counselor, it was only when Fred had had this care demonstrated to his satisfaction that he was prepared to participate in the general camp program. Further, only when he became acquainted with other campers—a slow process for Fred—whereby they became individualized as people first and disabled second, was he prepared to join them in activities and to begin enjoying the benefits of the experience.

Near the end of the first week, apparently as the result of a discussion with a staff member on the subject of electronics, Fred was encouraged to start a radio club. A few other campers expressed an interest and some Army surplus "walkie-talkies" along with a used transmitting set were located. From this point on, Fred not only became an acknowledged leader of an activity but this critical incident, resulting from a chance conversation, seemed to transform him into one of the more popular campers. His self-acceptance appeared to be greatly enhanced as well. There is a rather important footnote to this case. During a follow-up visit to Fred's home it was found that he had acquired the necessary receiving-transmitting equipment and was studying for his amateur radio license.

In reviewing Fred's experience we can learn a great deal about working with people with a physical disability. First, we cannot merely assume that every individual who moves into a recreation setting is immediately ready to fully participate. We should do everything within our power to eliminate all feelings of concern or threat—whether real or imagined—as quickly as possible. It seems logical that a pre-camp or pre-activity interview for beginning participants be conducted to dissipate all apprehensions of that person as well as those of concerned family members. Perhaps visual aids could be helpful in familiarizing each person with the facilities, general program, and the personal care to expect. Also we should be sensitive to possible feelings of alienation on the part of a participant whenever he enters into a strange and sometimes forbidding environment. The sooner that such a person feels at home, the sooner he will be ready psychologically to gain a truly recreative experience.

Second, most of us have initial feelings of discomfort when first beginning work with people with physical disabilities. Certainly many disabling conditions are awesome to behold.

We should not feel a sense of guilt because of these feelings. They are a normal reaction. What we probably don't realize is that these people often have the same feelings when thrust into a new situation with other persons with varying disabilities. However, if we take the time to allow individual personalities to emerge, i.e., get to know them as people, we will usually discover that the disabling condition is neither as overwhelming nor as important as we previously thought. Although the disability cannot be ignored, it is confined to its facts rather than extended to encompass the total person. At this time we are prepared to work effectively with that person.

Third, if we have some advance awareness of an individual's interests or aspirations, we may be in a position to suggest activities which can build on these interests—activities that are feasible within the remaining potential of that person. Yet, what that potential might be is often a very difficult question to answer. Perhaps it is one of the greatest problems facing a recreation leader when working with this special population. Some may have a tendency to place too severe restrictions on "potential" based on preconceived notions of the limiting factors of disability. Here the leader's expectation level may be much lower than the facts of the case warrant. Consequently, there is utter amazement when a person with a disability is able to perform at a higher level than had been anticipated. Usually we hear such a comment as this: "Isn't it amazing what Mary can do—in spite of her handicap."

On occasion we may place a too high potential evaluation on an individual when the physical facts of a disability may require some restrictive measures. Should a person with a severe speech impediment be encouraged to continue her aspirations to become a speech therapist? Probably not any more than we would encourage a double leg amputee person to become a high jumper. Yet on rare occasion we have found well-meaning advisors providing this type of counsel, possibly on the rationale that you can be anything you want to be—a judgment which is probably not true for any of us when our potential is totally ignored.

In recreation, as we view expectations, it is suspected that the overriding inclination is to underestimate potential—perhaps to act in an overcautious way. This should be avoided. However, it is essential that, before we encourage an individual to participate in activities that might possibly be overextending physically or totally inappropriate from a medical point of view, we gain proper clearance from a physician. Although it is conceivable that he too may be overcautious, he is the doctor; we are not!

Finally, in our leadership role in recreation, we should be constantly on the alert for a critical incident or occurrence which may open the way for a new-found activity interest. This happened to Fred when a conscientious staff member was able to help convert a chance discussion on electronics into a new camp activity. What is perhaps more important was that similar elements of this interest—a radio club—were transferred to the home situation into a year-round activity that was full of meaning and continuous opportunity for growth. Unfortunately for most other campers, lack of guidance or a lack of concern for transfer of interests resulted in, "that's what I did at camp" and "that's what I hope to do again next year at camp." It is essential that recreators assume a counseling role—whether in a camp or in a community recreation center—and suggest ways in which a given general interest might be continued away from the group situation.

The Case of Bob

One of the major problems we face in our association with persons having physical disabilities is a tendency to extend an observable disability to a point where it encompasses the total individual. Wright refers to this psychological aspect as "spread."[5] Although this phenomenon was alluded to earlier in our discussion, the following incident will, hopefully, add the needed emphasis to this problem.

One day during an adult camp session, a group of women came to visit and asked to see the various facilities. I agreed to be their guide. As we left the camp office we noticed a group of adults—some in wheelchairs and some sitting on a bench—socializing and from all appearances enjoying each other's company. One of the women said, "Oh isn't that a shame, to be so crippled and to be mentally retarded too!" I asked her what she meant. She pointed toward the group and indicated that she was referring to one particular young man.

Bob, the subject of her pity, was about thirty years old and had cerebral palsy to the extent that he was in a wheel-

chair. He tended to sit on his hands to prevent them from fly-
ing about in an uncontrolled fashion—something that occurred
when he was excited. He had some oral communication difficulty
although his speech, in my opinion, was quite easy to understand.

I suggested to the woman that she meet Bob and, although
seemingly reluctant, she followed me to the group of campers.
Introductions were made and Bob was quite cordial to her. He
closed the conversation by stating that he hoped she would
enjoy her visit. Apparently our visitor had difficulty in understanding Bob because, as we reached her group of ladies, she
again said, "What a pity; what a shame!" I asked her, "You
don't still think he is mentally retarded do you?" She replied,
"Well, that's obvious." I then told her that she might be interested in knowing that Bob had just received his Ph.D. from
a midwestern university and that he was currently employed as
the clinical psychologist at a large health agency in a nearby
city. He was not in camp as a camper but was visiting some
of his clients. With that, one can imagine how her jaw sagged
in disbelief. She had placed an immediate evaluation on another person without knowing that person or without requesting
more information. She had spread the disability to the total
person without knowing anything about the potential of that
person.

To summarize this discussion, suggestions have been
made with regard to developing healthy, realistic attitudes toward disability:

1. Recognize that initial feelings of discomfort when first interacting with persons with disability will usually evaporate
   quickly;
2. Be careful not to allow our preconceived notions to dictate
   prematurely what we can expect in the way of performance
   from any individual;
3. Avoid the tendency to spread disability to the total person
   based on the knowledge of one obvious disabling condition.

There are other problems which tend to handicap persons with
disability such as curiosity, unsolicited expressions of pity or
sympathy, and unrequested help. Some people in this special
population have learned, through training, how to handle these

situations, while others have not. If healthy relationships between able-bodied and disabled are to develop and flourish, it is imperative that persons with disability accept a part of the responsibility. Yet, those of us in leadership positions in recreation can be more effective in our roles if we are sensitive to problems which accompany disability and learn how to deal with them. The reader may realize from the following comments that treatment of people with disability should be essentially the same as treatment of nondisabled people. In either case, good judgment and common sense should prevail.

A group of adults with varying types and degrees of disability were discussing the topic "The Disabled Person's Responsibility to Society." The conversation at one point turned to the problems they face when interacting with able-bodied people—problems which are germane to our theme.

One ambulatory girl of about 22 years of age who had cerebral palsy mentioned that she tended to stagger slightly when she walked. She disliked walking down the street in her home town because people would either stare at her as though she were someone "from another planet" or else they would turn away—even cross the street to avoid meeting her—as though trying to "block out" her presence. At one time she was even stopped by a policeman who thought she had been drinking. "Frankly," she said, "I would just as soon stay at home than to put up with that." Others in the group verbally "spanked" her by noting that they all had run into the problem of curiosity but that the only way it could be overcome would be for all handicapped people to get out into the community so that their presence would become commonplace. Then other people would not only get used to seeing them but would probably not even give them a second look.

As a vivid example of this phenomenon in action, the author had the opportunity to revisit the University of Illinois campus which has a sizeable number of wheelchair students. Everywhere we went wheelchair students seemed to be in abundance. It was soon noticed that the students with disabilities were being treated much like all other students. Some could be observed in casual conversation with able-bodied students, who may have been boyfriends or girlfriends. Others appeared to be "wheeling" to or from classes—some in a hurry, others in a more leisurely fashion—just as one would find students moving on any campus. It was quite obvious that the students and faculty at the University of Illinois had become quite used to wheelchairs, white canes, crutches, and other prosthetic devices. One had the feeling as he watched that there was a great deal of empathy or understanding present but absolutely no pity.

Another member of our discussion group complained that he was extremely annoyed when someone, whom he didn't know, started to offer unsolicited sympathy because of his amputated leg. It seemed to him that such people are not as sympathetic as they make out to be and probably forget that he even exists as soon as they part company. Others in the group expressed similar concerns while one person noted that she didn't mind discussing her physical problem if it was with someone she had come to know and who indicated a desire to understand. ". . . But as soon as they get syrupy, I just turn them off in a hurry."

Perhaps the best procedure to follow with respect to discussing an individual's disability is to allow that person to broach the subject. If he does, accept his comments on face value without trying to evaluate or minimize them. For example, if a person tells you that he has difficulty in speaking clearly when it is clear that he does, do not say that you haven't noticed. Of course you have. If his speech is comprehensible you can tell him so. Be understanding but don't be dishonest in your discussion. An astute person with disability will usually quickly pick this up. It will not help the relationship. Don't be too anxious to change the subject, but if that person wishes to close the discussion, allow him to do so.

Another member of the group pointed out that he wished people would be a little less eager to assist him when he is traveling about in his wheelchair. "Sometimes, when I'm going up a ramp which I would like to navigate alone, some well-meaning person will come along and grab my [wheelchair] handlebars and begin pushing without even asking." The girl with cerebral palsy interrupted to say that on occasion she loses her balance and falls down. Often people rush up to pick her up and put her back on her feet. "It's embarrassing and I'm perfectly able to get up without help." All of the group agreed that on occasion help is not only needed but essential. However, it would be best if people would ask to help rather than to impose it on someone who may not have wanted it.

It should be kept in mind that many, if not most, persons with disability are anxious to be as independent as possible. When we give assistance where it is not needed, we unintentionally rob these individuals of a chance to achieve a degree of independence. Dr. Anne Carlsen suggests that we "Offer help when it looks as though it might be needed but do not insist on it if the individual refuses aid. . . . When a handicapped person falls, take it easy. Wait for him to give you a cue. If he can get up by himself, he may prefer doing that; if he needs a lift, he will tell you which is the easiest way to get him back on his feet. . . ."[6] It should be added that if your help is accepted, do not make the person feel that he should be eternally grateful to you. Sometimes we do this, albeit unintentionally.

ENVIRONMENTAL BARRIERS

Previous discussion has considered some of the important psycho-social problems which face persons with disability. Further, it should be realized that a great deal of effort has gone into physical restoration programs whereby individuals have been given treatment needed to develop optimum use of their remaining physical attributes. Yet professionals in the medical, paramedical and rehabilitation service fields have become increasingly frustrated. An individual may be prepared to use his remaining capacity—to develop mobility, to gain meaningful employment, to gain an education, to participate in recreation—and still be blocked from these experiences. Here, the problem is not so much the person as it is his environment. Part of the environmental problem of course is that of community attitude which has been alluded to in previous discussion. Another important and much more tangible aspect is the problem of architectural barriers. Such barriers are those which prevent persons with physical disability from independently leaving their homes, crossing streets, entering buildings and facilities which are intended for public use and, where the person is fortunate enough to be able to enter a building, functioning once inside. If each reader could, but for a few hours, be a wheelchair traveler, he would have a first-hand experience that would provide visible evidence to this concern.

In presenting the specifics of architectural barriers, it should be noted that they do not only affect persons in wheelchairs. They are also a problem for all people who have a mobility problem including the blind as well as those with less severe visual defects. For example one small, unobtrusive step can lead to serious injury for persons wearing bifocal glasses. People with arthritic conditions, heart impairments, and the many millions who are among the elderly population for whom mobility is an increasing concern, are also affected. Professor Timothy J. Nugent, possibly the principal pioneer in the attack on architectural barriers, indicated that approximately one of every seven people in the United States has a permanent physical disability and that most of these are affected by architectural impediments.[7] If we added the vast number of people who are temporarily disabled at any given time, the magnitude of the problem would be further increased.

For our purposes architectural barriers are those manmade physical impediments which prevent any individual from functioning as independently as his disability will allow. They include:

1. Unramped curbs at crosswalks;
2. Parking spaces too narrow to allow persons who drive their own cars from transferring to a wheelchair;
3. Steeply pitched walkways;
4. Stairs without an accompanying ramp;
5. Lack of properly designed handrails at steps or ramps;
6. Narrow door openings at entrances and within buildings;
7. Doors that revolve or are difficult to open;
8. Multiple-storied buildings without elevators that can accommodate a wheelchair;
9. Too high telephones and drinking fountains;
10. Inaccessible toilet and washroom facilities.

There are many other barriers, but these tend to be the most critical.

A growing awareness of these impediments has resulted in a concerted effort to eliminate existing barriers and to prevent new ones from being incorporated into new buildings.

In 1959 a special committee of the American Standards Association* was formed under the sponsorship of the National Easter Seal Society and the President's Committee on Employment of the Handicapped. With the cooperation of some fifty other organizations concerned with the problem, a plan was formed to develop a set of specifications which could assure access and function of all persons in buildings intended for their use. The prime responsibility for conducting the needed research was given to the University of Illinois and was supervised by Professor Nugent. In 1961 these standards were developed, approved and adopted by the ASA committee and the American Standards Association. They are titled "American Standards Specifications for Making Buildings and Facilities Accessible to and Usable by, the Physically Handicapped A117.1-1961.†

Beginning in 1961 a national architectural barrier elimination and prevention program was launched by the National Easter Seal Society in close cooperation with the President's Committee on Employment of the Handicapped. The major focus was not to only create a broad awareness and understanding of the problem but to also enlist the active participation of state and local leaders. As a result, many thousands of persons from all walks of life became engaged in the effort. Architects and other members of the design fields often played leading roles. By the end of the 1960's, impressive results had been achieved.

Forty-four states had taken some type of official action on the prevention of future barriers through the process of legislation, building code revision, or administrative order. According to a 1967 survey conducted by the National League of Cities, Department of Urban Studies, and reported by the National Commission on Architectural Barriers,[8] action to eliminate barriers was reported by 95 cities with populations of over 50,000 and by 42 metropolitan counties. Of particular importance to our discussion, this meant that, at least within these governmental jurisdictions, new publicly owned recreation buildings

* Now called the United States of America Standards Institute.

† These Standards are available from the United States of America Standards Institute, New York, N.Y., or The National Easter Seal Society for Crippled Children and Adults, Chicago, Illinois.

and facilities would have to be designed to accommodate persons with physical disabilities.

Although many thousands of barrier-free buildings and facilities are now in existence, to say that the problem of architectural barriers has been resolved would be a gross overstatement. Accomplishments, though gratifying, are tempered by the recognition that probably many more structures continue to be built with inaccessible features than are being constructed without barriers.

Professional recreators have, in some instances, accepted their responsibility by assuring that new recreation facilities are totally accessible. In addition, professional recreation and park publications have added visibility to this concern and have suggested specific means of resolving it within their own programs. Those of us in the field of recreation are in a unique position to give effective leadership to our communities by first determining that our buildings and play areas are accessible to all of our constituents. We are then in an excellent position to encourage other public, private, and commercial agenies to follow our example.

Environmental barriers also include the problem of transportation whereby public vehicles for land or air travel—busses, trains, aircraft, etc.—are designed primarily for agile, able-bodied persons. Some progress has been made here as well, although it has not been as dramatic as in the architectural barrier program. Concerted efforts, under the leadership of the President's Committee on Employment of the Handicapped, did not begin until the late 1960's. These include the requiring of proposed rapid-transit systems for metropolitan areas to design stations, boarding platforms and vehicles for use by wheelchair travelers. A few urban bus systems have indicated intentions of adding busses which can be used by disabled persons. Major passenger airlines have developed criteria for accepting and transporting passengers with physical disabilities. However, even where our recreation and park facilities are designed for total accessibility, the problem of getting this special population to these areas is generally unresolved, particularly where public transportation is required.

The basic philosophical view that has been taken is that persons with physical disabilities have an equal right to recreation opportunities as all other members of the community. If we accept this basic assumption, then it is logical to assume that persons with a disability should be able to reach our recreation facilities, gain entrance to and be able to function within them, and should be served in any available organized or unorganized activity where their disability does not overly handicap them or other participants from a satisfying experience. If there must be restrictions, they should be the result of careful and objective evaluation of the facts of disability and not by environmental barriers—attitudinal, architectural, or transportation.

PROGRAM CONCEPTS

When providing recreation opportunities for persons with disabilities there is a need for both sheltered and integrated experiences. Sheltered programs are important for the following reasons:

1. They provide a protected environment for children as well as some adults to develop social and activity skills—skills which may not have been developed in the normal growing-up process in the home, school, and neighborhood;
2. They will probably always be required for some children and adults with severe degrees of disability who may never be able to function in an integrated situation because of the extensive handicapping features of their disability;
3. Just as other children and adults occasionally enjoy being in a group with other children or adults who have similar interests, backgrounds, and skills, many individuals with disabilities enjoy the opportunity to continue friendships that may have developed in sheltered settings—in school, camp, or therapeutic programs. The growing popularity of so-called "adult handicapped clubs" is an outstanding example of this self-segregation.

Except for some notable exceptions, recreation for people with physical disabilities usually begins and ends with the segregated program. As important as sheltered activities are, they should not be considered the ultimate objective in our programming efforts. Rather they should be another step in a continuum whereby the ultimate goal is involvement of the individual in a vast array of integrated opportunities. Consider that the same person will be required to intermingle and compete with the rest of society in his education, vocation, and religion if he is to ever become a productive member of the community or to lead a meaningful, self-fulfilling life. So integration should be an ultimate aim in his recreation as well.

The following program ideas are intended to be suggestive and are not to be considered all-inclusive. The discerning reader will, hopefully, be able to view these as a point of departure for his own program ideas. As will become quite obvious, the purpose here is not to offer specific how-to-do-it activity suggestions which are readily available in other texts. However, on occasion and where appropriate, new or unique activity suggestions are made.

SHELTERED PROGRAMS
IN THE COMMUNITY

A major difficulty when attempting to provide experiences for children with disabilities is their general lack of skills in leisure pursuits. These youngsters have often been growing up in comparatively isolated circumstances. They have probably spent a great amount of their early life in therapy programs, and, on occasion, have tended to be overprotected by concerned parents. Some community agencies have created "homebound" recreation programs in which a recreation leader visits the home and works with both the child and the parents. In this way, newly learned activity skills might be continued without the professional leader's presence. This one-on-one, leader-participant ratio can be most effective in the first stages of moving such a child into community recreation or in cases where an individual is bedridden. However, the obvious drawback to this program is one of cost. Possibly this is one situation where the public recreation agency could develop a cooperative relation with a voluntary health agency such as the United Cerebral Palsy Association or the Easter Seal Society. Volunteers of these groups could be trained by professional recreators to teach skills and to work with the disabled. The volunteers would then make the home visits.

Another approach that would be valuable in the beginning

of each child's recreation experience is to establish a weekly activity program in which the child is taken from the home environment for a few hours and transported to a community recreation center. In this situation he could be involved in a sheltered activity with other children having disabilities. Activities might include swimming, parties, short trips to interesting places or to sports events. Besides the benefit of moving the individual out of isolation, opportunities to begin developing healthy socialization skills and activity skills could be most valuable.

A major deterrent to any program which removes the child from the home is the reluctance of some parents to "let go" of the child. Their concern for the welfare and care of their offspring is one that neither can nor should be ignored. It is essential that a home visit be made to explain the program to the parents and to do all possible to minimize anxieties. Once they have given their approval and after a few successful experiences have been accomplished, these same parents can often be a positive influence on other concerned mothers and fathers.

After the child has developed the needed social and activity skills, he may be ready to participate in a program of longer duration. This might be a sheltered or semi-sheltered summer playground program in which the usual playground activities are provided under organized supervision. The semi-sheltered playground has been quite successful in some communities such as Oconomowoc, Wisconsin. That program which began in 1960, included both disabled and able-bodied children. One concern of the city recreation director was that the able-bodied youngsters would be overprotective of their disabled counterparts even though they were essentially healthy children. However, as he later verbally reported: "All it took was for one handicapped child to trip an able-bodied child with his crutch and we had a 'normal' playground program."

It may be that a city recreation board or commission will be reluctant to provide the necessary finances to begin a playground program. They may not be aware of the number of disabled children and adults in the community and cannot visualize any need. Too, in their trusteeship of public funds, they are attuned to the concept of the most good for the most citizens. A relatively small number of persons requiring facilities, equipment, and leadership may be difficult to justify. Where this attitude exists, some public recreation departments have acquired funds from nonpublic agencies to inaugurate a sheltered program. These funds, usually in the form of "seed monies," are made available for a reasonable period of time until the program is established and visibility has been given to need. At that time it is expected that program expenditures would be planned for within the department's regular budget.

With respect to adults having physical disabilities, it should be reemphasized that many of these persons have the potential to participate in a number of ongoing recreation activities. It should be obvious by now that nonuse of legs should not in itself be a handicapping feature in arts, crafts, music, dramatics, or a myriad of other traditional leisure pursuits. However, in addition it would represent little additional cost to sponsor a club for disabled adults or some similar organization for those who might be interested. We are doing this for other homogeneous groups such as senior citizens clubs, boys clubs, girls clubs, etc. However, when selecting a recreation leader to work with such a group, it should be someone who can readily recognize that these people are as intelligent as any other group of adults and should never be treated as children. The following example might be helpful in bringing home this point.

A club for adults with physical disabilities was formed in a small midwestern city and it was found that many members were no longer attending meetings or various planned activities. One of the members, a woman of about fifty years of age with multiple sclerosis who was a wife, mother, and grandmother, was asked how she enjoyed her club activities. She said that she didn't bother going anymore. When asked why, she commented, "That woman from the recreation department must think we are all a bunch of idiots because she treats us like children. We have nothing to say about planning our own activities. She does it all for us. We have club officers and even an activity chairman but not once has she ever asked for our ideas. We complained to her and then to the Director but nothing ever changed so I quit going."

It is important that an agency provide leadership to such groups. However, it is equally essential that such a person function in the background and primarily as a coordinator and resource person. Only in this way, in the author's opinion, can such a leader be effective.

SHELTERED OUTDOOR
RECREATION PROGRAMS

A distinction should be made between a summer playground program and a day-camp program. A number of programs which are essentially of the playground variety, whereby activities take place on a community playground or park area, are called day camps. However, for purposes of this discussion, the term day camp is reserved for a program carried out in a natural setting which may have all of the advantages of a residential camp except that participants return to their homes each evening. Because of transportation problems, these are usually located on the periphery of an urban area whereby too much time is not lost in moving participants to and from the camp setting. Although day camping has been found to be a meaningful program for all children as a prelude to a residential camping experience, it is probably even more necessary for children who are socially disadvantaged or who have a history of overprotection. It is here that they can begin to become familiar with nature and to gain elementary skills which they will need in a residential setting. At the same time this program offers another gradual step away from the frequent isolation of home. Frankly, it allows parents to have an opportunity to get used to not having these children with them continuously.

A valuable adjunct to a children's day-camp program is a period of the summer set aside for adults. The Milwaukee Recreation Department has been quite successful in their adult day-camp efforts. Remember that many of these people were raised in greater isolation than most of today's youngsters who at least have been involved in special education and therapeutic activities. We still have many adults within this special population who have had little formal education and are socially incompetent. Consequently, they are often unemployed and unemployable. Life for them, from our point of view, is one of existing rather than "living." Unfortunately, because they have learned to assume that this is all they can expect, they may overtly appear to be relatively satisfied. Although recreation cannot be expected to resolve all of their disadvantages, it can give greater meaning to vast amounts of present unobligated time. In a day-camp setting it is possible to instill a sense of meaning to their lives through the development of activity skills which have carryover possibilities. As we increasingly recognize the need for adult residential camping, the day-camp program can provide the same preparatory experiences for adults as it does for children.

The residential camp program is where the camper may spend from a few days to a full summer in a camp setting. Such camps are usually operated by agencies other than the public recreation department. They provide permanent facilities for sleeping, cooking, and program activities. In sheltered residential camps for persons with physical disabilities, participation is usually on a coeducational or corecreational basis. The reason for this is because many of these children and adults have suffered from social isolation in the past. We can probably all agree that relating to the opposite sex in social situations is an important part of social development for everyone. Because it is often an unmet need for this population, camping can help to resolve the problem.[9]

Within the camp program the primary emphasis should be on recreation, even though many educational and rehabilitational by-products can accrue to each participant. On occasion you may hear of a camp program where the major goal is therapy and where enjoyment of an outdoor group experience is secondary. One example of this was a case where children in camp were required to spend a period of each day in speech therapy. The therapists had difficulty holding the attention of these youngsters because just outside the therapy room window other children could be seen participating in recreation activities. In the opinion of this writer, such use of camp facilities is tantamount to taking a clinic out to the woods. And if we think of camping in terms of program rather than facilities, such a clinical approach is not camping. Fortunately this use of camp facilities is on the wane and perhaps dying out.

Even though primary importance should be given to recreative experiences, it is not suggested that physical needs of the individual be ignored. Attention should be given to at least maintaining the physical health position of each person if not enhancing it through activity participation. Camp nurses, along with a visiting physician, are essential members of a camp staff. During orientation, it is recommended that paramedical professionals, e.g., physical, occupational, and speech therapists, be utilized to teach counselors and program leaders proper means of handling campers and to provide safe supervision.[10]

In developing a camp program of activities, efforts should be made to avoid overmodification of activities. The rule should be to modify only where necessary and only to the extent required to allow inclusion of an individual. Much will depend on the severity of disabilities present as to the extent of modification needed. In some situations none may be needed while in others lack of adaptation may result in elimination of excellent program opportunities.

In one special camp the facilities were located on about 13 acres of land while the remaining woods and fields of the total 400 acres of land were, in effect, out of bounds for wheelchair campers. As a result, the nature study program, with its field trips, suffered. Yet, with modification, this program was opened to all campers who were interested. Not only was the nature program expanded, but also wheelchair campers could now participate in the overnight primitive camping activities—activities which many participants felt they would never be able to do. The answer was found in the construction of a specially designed "trailmobile" which could carry approximately ten wheelchair campers and a similar number of those not so confined. It was pulled by a tractor and the many dirt roads, some already in existence for maintaining the total area and others constructed for program purposes, became the paths for these groups. The trailmobile was designed so that the rear gate could be unfolded forming a ramp. In addition the top of the vehicle was covered with a wire mesh to protect occupants from falling branches and other debris as well as to provide a structure for a canvas cover in case of sudden rain storms. The writer recalls the misty eyes and excitement of some adults immediately following a first venture into the woods at night to hear the night sounds. Surely the effort to modify this activity was most worthwhile.

Dependent to some degree on the background and skills of individual staff members, thought should be given to such activities as camp shows, with staff and campers participating together, and to offering discussion opportunities with varying themes from politics to social and ecological concerns. Discussion groups are particularly popular with adults who are often intellectually starved. For some it may be one of the few times in their lives when they feel free to debate their views and, more important, when they are being heard. It is important that as leaders we do not underestimate the knowledge of these persons. Many spend extensive time with television and radio and are quite familiar with current events.

These are but a few ideas that deserve attention and can be readily extended through the ingenuity of recreators and the willingness to try. It will be through these as well as the more traditional experiences that greatest meaning can be given to residential camping. Activity skills and social skills can be enhanced provided there are possibilities for each person to move from the simple to the complex—from a beginner's role to more advanced opportunities—where full potential can be realized.

TOWARD INTEGRATED RECREATION

Perhaps a rough measure of the advances made in theoretical concepts and demonstration programs in therapeutic recreation has been the introduction of nonsheltered programs during the last fifteen years. Although not as yet to the extent provided other special populations, professional recreators are concerning themselves with the need to deal with the total healthy part of a person—to be concerned with his psychosocial and physical needs as well as his leisure needs. Experiences in the milieu of a recreative setting are uniquely suited to providing the means for individuals to play out various social roles, e.g., the give and take required in both competitive and cooperative activities. One major facet of this interacting is the ability to relate effectively to other persons, no matter what their station in life or ability potential might be. This is just as true for people with physical disabilities as it is for other members of a general society. Consequently some attempts have been made to provide integrated opportunities for the physically disabled. Although other examples undoubtedly exist, two are presented which have been in operation for a number of years. One is in an urban community setting while the other is primarily in outdoor recreation. However, the objectives of both are quite similar: to provide a vehicle for physically handicapped children to enter and participate in integrated social-recreational opportunities.

In 1959, the New York Service for Orthopedically Handicapped began a project that would bring physically disabled children and able-bodied children together in recreation activities. Community Centers and settlement houses in the various burroughs of New York City have been the locale used for these programs. The stated purposes of the project were:

1. To prove that the functioning of orthopedically handicapped children will be improved through participation in groups with nonhandicapped children;
2. To demonstrate the effectiveness of community centers and settlement houses as resources in aiding the mental health of orthopedically handicapped children.[11]

In addition, a number of secondary aims were also presented. These included the determination of how the program would affect "normal" children, the studying of program and leadership techniques, the development of an effective case finding and referral service and the development of a guide which might be useful to other communities.

At the time of the interim report, over 150 children had attended integrated recreation programs in 25 community centers and settlement houses. Cooperation had been received from various other youth-serving agencies. A major effort had gone into educating the total community through the use of mass media, meetings with school, parent, and hospital groups, and personal contacts with influential leaders to interpret the program and enlist support. Tentative evaluation of the program based on structured interviews with the children, parents, and group leaders was reported as most encouraging. Richard Kraus, in discussing this project, offers some vivid examples of the benefits that have accrued to individual children which the reader would find helpful.[12]

The Easter Seal Society for Crippled Children and Adults of Connecticut has been embarked on an integrated social-recreation program for children since the early 1950's. The aim is to provide physically handicapped children with a gradual transition from highly segregated to fully integrated programs. The technique apparently involves individual evaluations and a determination of readiness for each youngster before he moves to a more complex group experience. A five-stage system has been devised to accomplish the transition.[13]

In stage one, children with physical disabilities are taken out of the home situation and brought into a community recreation setting for various planned activities. This is done on a weekly or biweekly basis. In this sheltered program children have the opportunity to begin development of activity skills and to learn to relate to others in a social environment.

Stage two involves moving those children who have demonstrated a readiness into a sheltered day-camp program in which they spend the day in camp and return home each night. More advanced skills are practiced while new activities are introduced. Social development continues while at the same time the child is partially weaned from the constant care of a parent and the isolating elements of home.

Stage three is represented by a sheltered residential camping experience in which those children who are ready are away from the home and community for a more extensive period of time. Again new activity skills are introduced while old skills are enriched. The child has the opportunity to sharpen his social abilities and to further realize that he is required to give to a social experience if he is to reap the benefits. His social world is expanding as new friendships are made.

In stage four a buddy-type residential camping program is provided whereby a disabled child is paired with a non-disabled youngster. The beginning of integration of program activities and social relationships is primary. Perhaps the benefits which result are as valuable to the able-bodied child as the disabled in that he can gain a greater sensitivity to disability and realize that many imagined differences are really nonexistent.

Finally, for those who can "graduate" from this program and who have disabilities that no longer handicap them, opportunities are provided for movement into regular camping programs. The Connecticut Easter Seal Society has successfully developed cooperative relations with a sizeable number of youth serving agencies and private camps whereby many children and youth with physical disabilities have had the benefits of being fully integrated into regular programs.

It must be reemphasized that great care is taken in evaluation to assure that each child has an excellent chance for success. To what extent such integration carries over into the home community is not known by this author but it is reasonable to assume that these children and youth could never be satisfied with an isolation that possibly would have happened had they not had this opportunity.

These are only a few examples of what can be accomplished by recreators who have a sensitivity to the needs of this special population and who are willing to make the effort to get involved.

This chapter has offered a brief background of recreation services to persons with physical disabilities, defined terms commonly used and has presented some of the major physical, psychological and social problems which often accompany disability. Although the illustrations were largely drawn from the camping aspect of recreation, the program concepts are applicable to all facets of recreation—whether in the sheltered-segregated setting or in the integrated environment.

FOOTNOTES

[1] National Society for Crippled Children and Adults, *Directory of Camps for the Handicapped* (Chicago: National Society for Crippled Children and Adults, 1967), pp. 1–53.

[2] Valerie V. Hunt, *Recreation for the Handicapped* (Englewood Cliffs, N.J.: Prentice-Hall, Inc., 1955), pp. 44–48.

[3] Beatrice A. Wright, *Physical Disability—A Psychological Approach* (New York: Harper and Brothers, Publishers, 1960), pp. 7–8.

[4] Thomas A. Stein, "Some Affective Outcomes Accompanying a Camping Experience of Physically Handicapped Adults" (Doctoral Thesis, University of Wisconsin, 1962).

[5] Wright, *Physical Disability*, p. 118.

[6] Anne Carlsen, "Tips on Dealing With the Handicapped," mimeographed handout sheet, N. D. Dr. Carlsen is Superintendent of the Crippled Children's School, Jamestown, North Dakota.

[7] Participants in National Facilities Conference, *Planning Areas and Facilities for Health, Physical Education and Recreation* (Chicago: The Athletic Institute and American Association for Health, Physical Education and Recreation, Rev. 1965), p. 238.

[8] National Commission on Architectural Barriers, *Design for All Americans*—A report of the National Commission on Architectural Barriers to Rehabilitation of the Handicapped (Washington: Rehabilitation Services Administration, Department of Health, Education and Welfare, U.S. Government Printing Office, December, 1967), p. 5.

[9] Task Force on Special Camping, *Easter Seal Guide to Special Camp Programs* (Chicago: The National Easter Seal Society for Crippled Children and Adults, 1968), p. 2.

[10] Task Force on Special Camping, *Easter Seal Guide*, p. 51.

[11] Harold W. Robbins, "Let Us Belong," a paper presented at the 46th National Recreation Congress (1964). Report on project "Integrated Social-Recreational Experiences for the Orthopedically Handicapped Child," sponsored by the New York Service for Orthopedically Handicapped.

[12] Richard Kraus, *Recreation Today—Program Planning and Leadership* (New York: Appleton-Century-Crofts, 1966), pp. 363–364.

[13] From a lecture given by L. Paul Murray, Executive Director, Easter Seal Society for Crippled Children and Adults of North Carolina and former staff member of the Easter Seal Society of Connecticut (1970).

BIBLIOGRAPHY

The following books can be valuable resources in developing a program of specific activities for persons with physical disabilities as well as other disadvantages.

Chapman, Frederick M., *Recreation Activities for the Handicapped*. New York: The Ronald Press Company, 1960, p. 309.

Hunt, Valerie V., *Recreation for the Handicapped*. Englewood Cliffs, N.J.: Prentice-Hall, Inc., 1955, p. 340.

Fait, Hollis F., *Adapted Physical Education*. Philadelphia: W. B. Saunders Company, 1960, p. 332.

Kraus, Richard, *Recreation Today: Program Planning and Leadership*. New York: Appleton-Century-Crofts, 1966, pp. 298–366.

Pomeroy, Janet, *Recreation for the Physically Handicapped*. New York: The Macmillan Company, 1964, p. 382.

Task Force on Special Camping, *Easter Seal Guide to Special Camp Programs*. Chicago: The National Easter Seal Society for Crippled Children and Adults, 1968, p. 103.

9 Recreation and the Visually Impaired

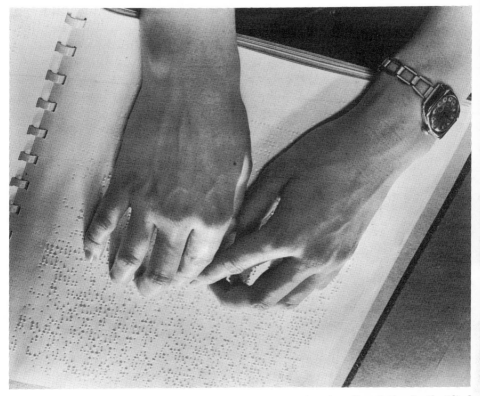

Courtesy American Foundation for the Blind

ELLIOTT G. YOUNG

INTRODUCTION

This is a chapter about recreation for the visually impaired and it seems unlikely that one should have to justify recreation. However, nearly every recreation leader will occasionally encounter the slightly amused attitude that recreation is not really important. Many consider it a suitable and respectable time-killer for children, the aged, and the disabled but certainly not justified for the so-called normal healthy person. It is believed by many that if a man enjoys his work he would not need to spend idle time playing games. But, were recreation not rewarding for the normal healthy adult, it would certainly not be valuable to the young, old, or therapeutic for the disabled.

There is a grudging recognition of the fact that the young learn to cope with the world of reality through their play.[1,2] There has been much done by psychologists in child's play. Jean Piaget[3] differentiates between exploration and the play process. Exploration involves sensory receptors as it does with the visually impaired child. Play begins when the object is taken over and assimilated into motor activity. Piaget[4] states that play involves the ability to make the stimulus over into something else; he calls this transformation. It is during this period the child is able to put a problem into focus by reducing it to his own size in a play situation. During play begin the muscular coordination and body development, which become necessary in an activity.

Play requires imagination and fantasy, with adults we call it creativity. So does learning, and a child who does not know how to play will probably be tomorrow's dropout.[5]

The adult has often been brought up to believe that all pleasure should come from his work and each person would have a greater sense of fulfillment if he could find more of his creative drive satisfied in a work situation. Our present society, with its pressures, tensions, and frustrations on the job as well as off the job, often prevents a person from finding full satisfaction.

Recreation properly selected can relieve the emotional deterrents built up in a work schedule. It can give the sedentary worker a chance to improve his physical, emotional, social, and intellectual conditions. The person who does physical labor needs a chance to extend the intellectual, social, and emotional aspects of his life. Everyone needs a change of pace to recharge his batteries, to give the body and the mind an opportunity to rest.

An example of proper selection of a recreation activity occurred with a professional who worked with drug users. He had been an athlete in college and had knowledge of and played most sports, therefore he saw no challenge in learning any special sport. He set out to analyze his job frustrations and became aware that the great frustration in his work lay in the fact that, 1) there was such a high rate of recidivism in this field, and 2) even if the drug user was able to kick his habit and have a normal life, the professional never knew about it. He saw only the failures.

Adding this up, he decided that a truly satisfying recreational activity would be one in which he could see immediate success or failure and in which the failure could be discarded rather than remain to produce agony. So he turned to baking, and thoroughly enjoyed his successful cinnamon rolls, eating them and sharing them, basking in approval of his accomplishment. The soggy Danish pastries were flung into the garbage with great satisfaction and showmanship. The immediate satisfaction was the exact thing lacking in his job situation.

Therein is the real key in recreation, supplying the factors lacking in the daily routine of life. For some it is social contacts; others, intellectual stimulation; and with others, physical involvement. This is what the visually impaired may learn through therapeutic recreation.

When we think of rehabilitation of the visually impaired, we automatically center our thoughts on vocational rehabilitation. Teaching only work skills to the young, the middle-aged and the old, and ignoring their needs for recreation is of the old era, a carryover from the industrial age and puritanism. Rarely do we consider the ways in which the visually impaired are to spend their leisure time. Since the industrial age there have been changes even in the concept of recreation. Formerly recreation was considered a waste of time and energy and suitable only for the wealthy but not for the poor. Living in an electronic, computerized society in which there is a longer lifespan due to advanced medical techniques, we are approaching an era of abundance of free time. Too often our concept of recreation lags behind in the industrial and puritanical era. Now recreation must afford an opportunity to satisfy one's social, intellectual, physical, and emotional needs. The visually impaired also have an abundance of free time and must be given the same opportunity to satisfy their needs. We also must face the fact that the visually impaired have been denied recreational services within their community.

Charles K. Brightbill[6] wrote about educating for leisure-centered living and questions our readiness to accept leisure as a way of enriching our lives and our society. Father Carroll[7] treats the losses inherent in visual impairment, including the loss of recreation for the visually impaired. If there are losses that lead to unemployment then these same losses lead to lack of recreation opportunities. If we rehabilitate the visually impaired for employment, we should rehabilitate them for leisure-time activities. Total rehabilitation includes recreation. The physical, psychological, and social factors that prevent the visually impaired from finding employment of their choice are the same factors that prevent full participation in leisure-time activities.

Vision is one of the most vital sense receptors a person can lose in a sight-oriented world. It is an important sense receptor in recreation, for many enjoyable and pleasurable experiences depend upon sight. Sight is also important in many work experiences. Just as visual disability affects work, it also affects one's leisure-time activities. But the visually impaired can be habilitated or rehabilitated to successful employment by restoring the losses resulting from visual disability. Losses in integrity, self-esteem, social adequacy, perception of beauty, financial security, and independence are among those that can be restored. The visually impaired can also be habilitated or rehabilitated to enjoy an enriched life in a sighted world.

In this chapter we are concerned with the ability of the visually impaired to select those activities they enjoy and which are meaningful and constructive to them or their group or to society. In a democracy (and the philosophy of recreation is democratic by virtue of the freedom of choice) the visually impaired should have the opportunity to select those activities they feel will fulfill their social, physical, emotional, and intellectual needs. We will, then, deal with vocational, educational, or personal rehabilitation only as it affects the visually impaired's leisure-time activities. For rehabilitation does include the visually impaired's leisure-time activities and is affected by his mobility, communication, self-help skills, techniques of daily living, and psychological adjustment to his visual disability.

Rehabilitation of the visually impaired should be a team cooperative movement, that team consisting of a therapeutic recreation specialist, a social caseworker, a psychologist, a rehabilitation counselor, a mobility instructor, and other specialists responsible for total rehabilitation. When a staff team does a diagnostic appraisal of the visually impaired person, it should include the individual's vocational, personal, educational, and recreational interests and abilities. A therapeutic diagnostic appraisal of the visually impaired person's leisure-time needs should be part of the overall assessment. The work of the therapeutic recreation specialist is to assist in the planning of the visually impaired's leisure-time needs and an evaluation of his progress.

In programming leisure-time activities for the visually impaired, we must be cognizant that blindness is classified along the continuum from total loss of vision to the ability to read large print. Such awareness will serve as a guideline in planning the type of activities the visually impaired can normally pursue without further damaging the physiological condition of the eyes and determining the kind of adaptations necessary to participate in a variety of activities. Knowing the visual acuity enables one to devise effective recreation planning.

Terms such as "blindness," "the blind," "blind person," or "legally blind" are misleading to the public when referring to those who fall along the continuum of visual impairment. The public assumes that persons who are referred to as blind are totally without vision. The truth is that the percentage of totally blind persons and persons having only light perception is less than the percentage of those who are partially sighted. Terms become important because in the psychosocial development of the visually impaired, such terms shape the attitude of the public and the role the visually impaired plays in society. If the words, "for the blind" are used in the title of an agency, the client's dependency is reinforced and impedes his rehabilitation. The visually impaired's sense of independence is strengthened when we program with him rather than for him.

For the purpose of this chapter the terms, "partially sighted," or, "partially visually impaired," will be used rather than the term "blind" unless referring to those who are totally without vision or those who have only light perception.

We shall deal with both congenitally blind (those blind at birth) and adventitiously blind (those who lost their vision). However, it is generally believed that children who become adventitiously blind prior to five years of age have little recollection of their environment and therefore an extremely small amount of visual imagery. This chapter will treat physical aspects of visual impairment and the sensory receptors as they affect the visually impaired person's leisure time.

The sensory receptors are important to learning for they are the pathways to knowledge. We are aware of and perceive the environment through the visual, auditory, olfactory, labyrinthine, gustatory, tactile, and kinesthetic sense organs. The remaining sense receptors of the visually impaired enable them to perceive recreation experiences. Being aware of the remaining senses, the recreation leader can understand and develop recreation activities that are enjoyable, meaningful, and constructive for the visually impaired participant.

Persons who are blind or partially sighted have difficulties in fulfilling their leisure-time needs and face difficulties similar to those faced by people with other physical, emotional, and social disabilities. Disadvantaged persons are in themselves a minority group and are confronted with problems of social isolation, prejudice, and discrimination. In order to participate in recreation services, they must modify their activities and accept new approaches in fulfilling their leisure time. The visually impaired, with or without professional assistance, may recognize their disability[8] as a medical limitation and make the adjustment enabling them to fill their leisure time with activities that suit their particular interests, capabilities, and physical limitations.

On the other side of the coin, we may find the visually impaired person who sees his disability as a handicap,[9] that which is psychological or social, and he may gravitate to leisure-time activities that are not purposeful or constructive to himself, to the group, or to society. He may withdraw himself from community participation or submerge himself in complete isolation from recreation services. The professional recreation worker is charged with the responsibility of implementing the humanistic ideals which are part of the philosophy of recreation to enable the visually impaired to enjoy significant recreation services.

This chapter will treat the psychological and social factors that determine the role the visually impaired must play and the role the public plays in the use the visually impaired makes of his leisure time. These factors influence the programming of activities for the visually impaired.

The image the public has of the visually impaired reenforces the attitude they have of themselves. The psychosocial factors put the visually impaired into an inferior social status. They are eliminated from the routine competition of society and are subject to a downward flowing pattern of pity.[10] The recreation leader must cope with these factors in planning recreation services with the visually impaired.

The social revolution has made minority groups aware of their human and civil rights. Everyone wants to do "their thing." It is also true with the visually impaired. They, too, want to do "their thing" and be apprised of their human and civil rights. The problems of integration are many but similar to those of other minority groups. The problems of integration are a result of the psychosocial factors that formulate prejudices. Prejudices cause discrimination. The work of the recreation leader will be to deal with the prejudices and discrimination that have isolated many visually impaired from full community and commercial leisure-time services. This will be dealt with in the section on recreation.

The classical concept of leisure-time activities or recreation has changed, as has the social order. Society is in the midst of a social revolution. The social change has altered the meaning or concept of recreation. Recreation was considered "fun and games." Now that recreation is a profession, the professional's concept of recreation includes social contribution. Richard Kraus[11] has added another dimension to the meaning of recreation; that is, recreation should have an immediate sense or conviction of social purpose. This does not mean that one cannot use recreation activities simply for relaxation. Whether or not recreation is meaningful and constructive depends upon the attitude and intent of the persons who recreate. Nash,[12] in his illustration of the concept of recreation in the form of a pyramid, refers to the lower portion of the pyramid as "spectatoritis," or passive participation. Such recreation could be called "fun and games." "Fun and games" activities can be classified under three categories:

1. Destructive: a type of activity that involves acts against society, or activities engaged in by delinquents. Such activities may be stealing, vandalism, or street fights under the guise of fun and games,
2. Pathological: a type of activity which may result in self-destruction. Under this category come such activities as taking drugs for kicks, Russian Roulette, and games known as "chicken" (taking chances against large odds that might cause death),
3. Negative: a type of activity in which there is little or no personal involvement and little or no personal satisfaction so that the experience has little value to re-create. Such activities are engaged in to overcome boredom; other activities are those to kill time. Many of these activities become excessive: bar drinking, daydreaming, gambling, to mention a few.

This is not to say that these activities classified as "fun and games" are not recreation, for depending upon the attitude and intent of the participant, such activities may adhere to the classical definition of recreation. But to the professional recreation leader and to the profession of recreation, the concept of recreation means a great deal more. Recreation must be of social value. Adding this to the classical definition of recreation, we have the following definition:

> Meaningful and constructive recreation should be enjoyable and designed to meet goals that are constructive and socially worthwhile for the participants, for the group, and for society at large, or it can fulfill one, or any combination of the three goals.

The section on recreation goes into depth on recreation and its philosophy and definition. Understanding the philosophy of recreation produces better programming and can set the guidelines for involvement of the visually impaired. Before participating in general recreation or community or commercial recreation services, the visually impaired should have a knowledge of leisure-time activities that are meaningful and constructive, as well as activities that are relaxing socially, emotionally, physically, and intellectually. They should be able to select leisure-time activities that are within their capability and limits of their disability.

The section on recreation will treat the need for therapeutic recreation, its definition, and the leadership that is needed to implement the program. The success of recreation experiences greatly depends upon good leadership. Leaders function to get the disadvantaged to participate and to involve themselves in recreation services within their community. The task can best be accomplished with interdisciplinary teamwork: the psychologist, rehabilitation counselors and specialists, the social caseworker, and the community and commercial recreation leaders with the therapeutic recreation specialist, all working together.

PHYSICAL ASPECTS
OF VISUAL IMPAIRMENT

The term "legally blind" is administrative, serving to identify a visually impaired person who may receive governmental, public, or private services. A legally blind person is one whose sight is measured by Snellen's Acuity Chart to be 20/200 or less. Herman Snellen in 1868[13] developed the Snellen Visual Acuity Chart by measuring the visual acuity of an impaired eye in comparison with that of a normal eye. Snellen placed 20/20 as being perfect vision. Snellen's visual acuity was then measured in fractions, the numerator representing the distance the object could be seen by an impaired eye and the denominator representing the distance the object could be seen by a normal eye. Legal blindness of 20/200 means that the visually impaired eye sees at 20 feet an object which a normal eye sees at 200 feet.

Snellen then defined blindness as a condition in which central visual acuity is 20/200 or less with corrected lens, or a condition in which central visual acuity of more than 20/200 is accompanied by a peripheral field which has contracted to such an extent that the widest diameter of visual field subtends on an angle no greater than 20 degrees. Some states included up to a 30 degree angle as the widest diameter of visual field. Snellen's measurements were used to determine employment of adults and placement of children into schools for the visually impaired or for regular schools for the sighted. Later the test was used to determine who of the visually impaired would receive government assistance and service. In later years, with medical advances, visual acuity standards progressed, so that those with impaired vision measuring between 20/200 to 20/195 were considered functionally visually impaired, even though they could see and read newsprint either with or without visual aids. According to Snellen's definition, they would be classified as legally blind.

In any testing situation the effect of the variables is often minimized. In the case of Snellen and his determination of blindness, he minimized the variables in measuring visual acuity by assuming that many factors of the stimulus remain constant. Such factors were illumination, eye fatigue, contrast, angular size, pathology of the eye, light adaptation of the eye, state of muscle function, state of accommodation and convergence of the eye, the degree of refractive error, and degree of diffraction. Scott[14] and Lowenfeld[15] point out that the elimination of these variables has caused Snellen to grossly classify all persons of 20/200 or less as blind and has affected their role in society so that they are members of the blind population.

Many professionals in the field of visual impairment found Snellen's chart and method of measurement imprecise. Scott[16] presented psychological and social disadvantages in the use of Snellen's definition. He had found that declaring those who were functionally visually impaired, or partially sighted, those who would have measured between 20/200 to 20/195, as blind produced dependence on the part of some of these people and that they assumed the role of the blind. On the other hand, the stigmatizing effect of such a classification prevented others, who would be declared blind according to Snellen's definition, from reporting their condition to appropriate governmental agencies.

An example of a person classified as legally blind who did not wish to be was a student whose visual acuity was 20/200 but had been, through his ophthalmologist and optometrist, fitted for contact lenses. With the use of these lenses he is a senior in college and during the summer months drove an ambulance for a large private hospital. Another case was that of a two-year college student who dropped out of school. She has a job with a federal hospital and wears no glasses. When asked why she does not complete her degree, she stated she would have to wear thick lenses to read, and she felt this would indicate she was legally blind. She thus refused to complete her degree because it would humiliate her to be classified as legally blind.

Weymouth[17] points out measurements other than Snellen's acuity chart as a means of measuring an aging person's visual acuity. Lowenfeld[18] gives six classifications for visual impairment: 1) total blindness, which is congenital or adventitial before the age of five years; 2) total blindness, adventitial after five years of age; 3) partial blindness, congenital; 4) partial blindness, adventitial; 5) partial sight, congenital; and 6) partial sight, adventitial. Persons under the first four classifications can be grouped as blind and under the last two as partially sighted or visually impaired: these persons can see form, have object perception and travelling vision, and read large or small print with or without visual aids. Every effort should be made to encourage the partially sighted to make use of their remaining vision. Modern ophthalmologists and optometrists maintain that the use of one's remaining vision strengthens the ability to see; formerly it was believed that such use weakened sight. Visual aids, such as magnifying glasses, various thicknesses and shapes of lenses including telescopic lens for distant vision, have increased the use of vision.

POPULATION

There are no accurate statistics on the number of legally blind persons in the United States, since all persons who would be declared legally blind are not recorded. Unless a visually impaired person seeks government aid, the chances of his being statistically recorded are unlikely. Statistics are inaccurate also because many persons prefer not being classified as "legally blind." Aging, too, frequently causes gradual visual impairment. It is even more difficult to determine the age, sex, race, and cause of blindness because there is no systematic recording process.

There are efforts to centralize statistical reporting and to persuade ophthalmologists and optometrists to report to the State Commission all cases of those who are legally blind. The prevalence[19]—total number of cases at a given time in a population—of visual impairment in the United States is compiled by many organizations. The National Society for the Prevention of Blindness, Inc., jointly with the American Foundation for the Blind, have formed a Committee on Statistics of the Blind. The United States Public Health Service has made several reports on visual impairment by age, sex, race, and cause of blindness. In 1962 the National Institute of Neurological Diseases and Blindness of the Public Health Service formed the Model Reporting Area for Blindness Statistics. Their goal is to obtain the cooperation of all states in using their standardized method of reporting blindness. Forms for physician's reporting of eye examinations have been undertaken by the Subcommittee on Operational Research to gain more accurate information on prevalence and incidence.[20] As more accurate statistical data are gathered, the recreation leader can better plan long-range programs and facilities for the visually impaired.

The most recent figures obtained by the National Society for the Prevention of Blindness[21] estimated in 1969 that 2.14 percent of the total population in the United States, or 430,000 persons, were declared legally blind. The Binocular Visual Acuity Report[22] estimated that of adults between 18 years of age and 79 years of age 889,000 were visually impaired in 1962. Should one estimate the total number of visually impaired for the same age group in the United States for 1970, it would be over 1,000,000. The N.S.P.B.[23] reported children who are partially sighted, not including those who are legally blind, to be estimated at 97,900 in 1965. The American Printing House for the Blind[24] in their annual report in 1965 estimated 18,093 school children with visual impairment between the ages of 6 and 12. N.S.P.B.[25] in 1962 estimated 38,860 children under 20 years of age in the United States to be legally blind. There is some indication in the statistical reports that among children under six years of age there will be a greater number of multiple-disabilities, with visual impairment being a secondary factor of the disability.

These estimates on the number of visually impaired in the United States indicate the difficulty in gathering reliable data. We do know, however, that the largest group of visually impaired will be those persons who are 65 years of age and over. Over half of the visually impaired population in the United States will be over 65 years of age, and of that more than 50 percent will be new cases.[26]

CAUSES OF VISUAL IMPAIRMENT

The four primary etiological factors in visual impairment are prenatal influence or hereditary and congenital causes, senile cataracts, glaucoma, and diabetes. In 1962[27] prenatal influences, not including diseases the mother contracted during pregnancy, were estimated at 16.7 percent. Senile cataracts were 15.6 percent, glaucoma at 13.5 percent and diabetes at 11.2 percent. One of the most dramatic reductions in cause of visual impairment was that of retrolental fibroplasia produced in premature infants because too much oxygen was administered while they were in the incubator. When this was discovered the incidence of visual impairment due to retrolental fibroplasia dropped considerably. Retrolental fibroplasia was brought under control in 1954 after finding its cause.[28] From 1953 to 1960 it dropped from 5.1 percent to 0.[29]

Eye accidents are also a cause for visual impairment. Play or sports injuries accounted for the highest percentage of accidents: 67.3 percent. Household, traffic or transportation, school (excluding gym), and industry accounted for the remainder of eye injuries. These statistics were estimated in 1965.[30] The most frequent cause of accidents occurring during play or sports were blows that were either directed to the eye or eyes or blows on the head. Such blows normally might not be injurious to the body but are to the eyes.

THE SENSES

Man's impressions, his knowledge, and his perception of his surrounding environment depend upon his sensory receptor system.[31,32] The sensory receptor system is made up of sense organs with nerves leading into the brain. Sensory receptors are the main source of learning. This intricate interrelated sensory system transmits sensations produced by a stimulus, which may be in the form of a tree, to the brain where man forms his perception of objects. These sensations that are triggered by a stimulus become conscious experiences that follow immediately upon the stimulation of the sense receptors. The experience of an activity is a result of how skillfully one uses his sensory receptors, for the conceptual knowledge of man is the combination of sensations and images. The recreation leader's techniques in teaching and selecting activities for programming are enhanced by considering the remaining sense receptors of the visually impaired in his learning or re-learning skills and recreation activities.

The two most important sense receptors are hearing and seeing. Both of these sense receptors complement each other. You hear sound and you look to locate and identify it. Hearing also locates the direction from which the sound is coming. Smell and taste also complement each other. Many foods lose their taste when one cannot smell, and it is difficult to determine at times whether we smell the flavor or taste the flavor of food. The labyrinthine sense receptors complement the kinesthetic sense in balance, posture, and movement. The tactile sense receptors are extensions or tentacles of the kinesthetic sense organ. They determine the temperature, texture, and pressure of objects.

All or some of the sense organs send sensations to the brain at the same time depending upon what a person wishes to perceive. When one examines a piece of sculpture he will first see the object to identify it. He might touch the piece of sculpture to feel its shape and texture. The sculpture might be struck to hear the sound, indicating whether it is hollow or solid. He might smell the sculpture to perceive another dimension of the material. Watching children play you will notice that small children uninhibited by social custom will often seem to use all of their senses to experience an unfamiliar object.

The Eye

The eye has nine major parts: cornea, iris, anterior chamber, pupil, posterior chamber, lens, retina, vitreous, and optic nerve.[33] The cornea is the clear, transparent portion of the outer coat of the eyeball. It is the front window of the eye. Behind the cornea is the anterior chamber filled with aqueous, a clear watery fluid. The iris is a colored, circular membrane suspended behind the cornea and immediately in front of the lens. The iris regulates the amount of light that enters through the lens by changing the size of the pupil. The pupil is the shutter and a part of the iris. The posterior chamber is located behind the iris and in front of the lens which is filled with aqueous. The lens or crystalline lens is a transparent, colorless body suspended between the posterior chamber and the vitreous. It serves as the refractive medium and brings the rays of light to a focus on the retina. The retina is the innermost coating of the eye which is formed of sensitive nerve fibers and about 30 million rods and cones which are connected to the optic nerve. The functional part of the retina is extremely delicate and is where the sensation of vision is initiated. The optic nerve is a special nerve of the retina or visual sense organ that carries the sensations from the retina to the brain.

Any portions of these parts of the eye may be diseased or damaged and will affect the vision. There may be disease of the cornea, the iris, the lens known as cataract, or of the retina and optic nerve. The eyelid, although not a part of the eyeball, is a protection to the eye and may help in adjusting the amount of light that reaches the retina. The eyelid can be injured or diseased, the disease being termed conjunctivitis.

Auditory Perception

The perception of sound involves listening. Listening involves the ear which is a source of communication and socialization. The hearing receptors have the ability to recognize and identify the sounds that a visually impaired person must rely upon for mobility and the recognition of places and persons. The hearing receptors function as a discriminative screening device that selects out sounds the listener wishes to hear from those he does not wish to hear. Hall[34] considers hearing as one of the three distance receptors, vision and smell being the other two. The hearing receptors can locate sound but a more accurate localization is assisted by vision. With the loss of sight or an impairment of vision, the hearing receptors can be trained to increase the accuracy of locating sound.

There are three major parts to the ear: outer ear, middle ear, and inner ear. The outer ear is visible and can be recognized by its many shapes and sizes. The outer ear is called auricle or pinna but serves no acoustic purpose. The outer ear and the canal or passageway leading into the middle ear have been described as a sound box. The middle ear transmits sound energy to the brain. The inner ear with its intricate organic mechanism controls pitch and frequency, and functions as an amplifier for the auditory system. Only one-third of the ear is used for hearing.

Two-thirds of the ear or the inner ear is automatic pilot of the human body. The inner ear is called the labyrinthine sense organ and two major parts, the vestibule and semicircular canals, control bodily equilibrium. It also controls the sensation of speed, direction of movement, and postural control along with the kinesthetic sensory organs.

Kinesthetic Sensory Organs

The kinesthetic sense organs include the whole body, its joints, muscles, body frame, and the skin. With the visually impaired we think in terms of the tactile or touch sensations of sensory receptors. But the other parts of the kinesthetic sensory organs are as important for they deal with balance, posture, movement and one's relationship in space and to other objects. The awareness of the use and the sensitivity of the kinesthetic sensory organs can complete the task of the visually impaired in perceiving their immediate environment. The kinesthetic senses report to the brain sensations that occur within the body as well as those that occur without the body. It is therefore said that the kinesthetic senses receive both chemical and mechanical stimulation.

As one who with an outstretched hand receives added weight in the hand, the stretch receptors send the messages through the sensory nerves, relayed to the spinal cord to the motor command neurons and the muscle reflex is to counteract the overload and the hand continues to hold the additional weight. But if the overload is too heavy, the reflex reverses and the tendons send their message to the commanding neurons to relax the muscles and the overload falls out of the person's hand. This is known as mechanical stimulation. All such commands are acknowledged through the kinesthetic sensory organs in lifting, pushing, running, and walking. These performances are easier when vision accompanies the movements. With the partially sighted, and the blind in particular, such movements many times are taught and this becomes a learning situation. It becomes important for the therapeutic recreation specialist to include such activities and games as assist in the development of the kinesthetic sensory organs to improve body movement and awareness.

The hands are extensions or tentacles of the kinesthetic sensory organ. Feet are another extension that are seldom given proper importance, for in many ways their functions are as important as the hands. Although the feet are not as sensitive as the hands, watch children in their bare feet maneuver around the ground or woods. Shoes deaden much of the sensation of different textures under the feet, but with constant training one can become aware of grass, dirt, gravel, or stone walks. Another kinesthetic sensory receptor is the lips. Watch babies mouth objects as they play.

The tactile sense receptors are the most important. The hand grasps and fondles objects for texture, shape, size, to tell whether they are cold or hot. The fingers are sensitive, as is the skin on the body, to pain. Much of the visually impaired persons' contact with their environment is through their tactile sense receptors. Images are formed by handling them with the hands and the fingers.

Smell and Taste

Smell and taste have socialization characteristics. In recreation they are particularly useful in social contexts of eating and cooking, and in smelling the beauty of nature. It is difficult to tell which sense is used in distinguishing flavors, since many flavors are smelled rather than tasted. Both sense receptors complement each other, for the perception of flavors is a combination of the sensation received from the taste buds and the smelling sense receptors. These sensory receptors are assisted in discrimination of flavor by the kinesthetic sense organs that receive the pressure and temperature from the lips and the mouth. Aromas from food or other substances can reach the olfactory sense through the mouth as well as the nose.

Odors are gaseous forms and the number of odors distinguished by smell or olfactory sense receptors are in the millions. Taste or gustatory sense receptors have four distinct basic receptors: sweet, sour, salty, and bitter. Smell sensory receptors are located in the nose where sensory hairs or cells go to the brain. Taste is located in the mouth along the buds on the tongue and along the side of the mouth. Only the four basic taste receptors function without the assistance of the olfactory sense organs. Once the functions of the many sensory receptors are known it is possible to plan activities and assist the visually impaired to enjoy recreation and social activities more fully.

It should be kept in mind that if there is any doubt about the extent of vigorous activities that might further impair vision, the recreation leader should consult the visually impaired person's ophthamologist.*

PSYCHOLOGICAL AND SOCIAL ASPECTS OF VISUAL IMPAIRMENT

Those working in the field of recreation may wonder why some visually impaired persons function independently while others are dependent. There are those visually impaired persons who prefer socializing with others who are visually impaired while others choose to be with the sighted. The psychosocial factors define the role the visually impaired play in our society. They are, many times, the result of their own psychological development and of the attitudes and treatment by those within their own environment. Persons with strong psychological characteristics have often changed society's concept of them. Others find it difficult to change their role and the attitude society has toward them.

There are two major factors that determine the behavioral pattern of a visually impaired person, the psychological and the social factors. The psychological forces are the emotional and

* For additional information and a copy of "A Worker's Guide to Characteristics of Partial Sight" by Eleanor E. Faye, M.D., and Clare Hood, R.N., 1966, write to the New York Association of the Blind, 111 East 59th Street, New York, New York, 10022.

perceptual responses, memory, thought, judgment, attitudes and beliefs that are part of the way a person responds to stimuli. The psychological factors deal with the way one perceives himself, his self-concept, his self-esteem, his self-respect. The social factors are those outside oneself, the way people perceive another person and the way society responds toward another.

Social barriers usually result from many social factors. These are the factors that are instrumental in the role in which the visually impaired find themselves in a sighted world. Both these factors are so interrelated in their influence upon the visually impaired that it is difficult to determine which is the more dominant influence. Studies have indicated that when both factors are favorable, visual impairment may not cause maladjustment or the visually impaired person does not become handicapped.[35,36,37] Should the visually impaired child develop healthy emotional relationships and be able to use his remaining sense receptors in replacement of his vision or as learning pathways to the brain, his chances are good for accomplishing a normal life. He has overcome the psychological loss and can cope with the attitudes of society.

Father Carroll[38] stated that when a person has lost his sight, he has died because it is the death of a way of life. Loklin[39] treats the same subject by stating that the loss of vision at any age is a severe blow that interrupts one's accustomed way of learning, making choices, moving from place to place, and communicating with others.

In a sighted society vision becomes the dominant sense receptor for it synthesizes the sensations received in the brain from the remaining sense receptors. When we hear a sound, smell odors or touch an object, we verify these sensations by visual imagery. When a visually impaired person shows good object perception by walking into a room without bumping into the furniture or by singling out different sounds from a cacophony, he has adapted his remaining sense receptors in place of his vision. It is assumed that the remaining sense receptors compensate for the loss of vision. Such assumption is folklore, superstition, and stereotyped thinking that originated in the cultures of the past.[40]

The visually impaired person functions with the same sense receptors as those with vision. What appear to be supernatural sense responses are results of long, hard training and education. Any person may learn to develop skill in using his sense receptors by becoming more aware of his surrounding environment.

This was true of a recreation specialist who was teaching games to help a group of visually impaired to become more aware of the sounds around them. At the same time she was developing a keen sense of sound, so much so that the assault of street noise gave her a headache. There are, however, other visually impaired persons who are never able to improve the sensitivity of their sense receptors, just as there are among those who have vision. The congenitally blind, if taught at an early age, can develop such skill.

This was true of Jane whose visual acuity measured that of light perception. She was able to move about with no difficulty and used a cane only when absolutely necessary. During Christmas she would direct other visually impaired persons in the decoration of a room. Once while talking to a group she was able to recognize by name a staff member before he spoke. Her only explanation of this phenomenon was that her early training and the ability to select cues helped in her identification.

Dreves[41] tested the tactile and kinesthetic perception of blind persons and found that the blind were superior to the sighted. This does not mean the blind had supernatural perception; rather it means that they had developed greater skill and awareness in the use of their tactile and kinesthetic sense receptors. A game played with a group of children required them to identify the different kind of material under foot. Each child was asked to distinguish among slate, stone, gravel, dirt, grass, and brick.

Mobility and cognitive function are thought to be directly affected by the loss of vision. The loss of mobility means the loss of independence, causing feelings of being trapped, fixed and unable to move. The loss of mobility brings fears, anxieties, and frustrations. The congenitally blind child who has limited mobility is also limited in physical movement. Such limitations affect his psychomotor responses so that there are voluntary responses to a stimuli rather than reflex actions or involuntary responses. There is a lack of big muscle movement and fine muscle movement. Such deficiency and limitations affect the posture of the child; he may become awkward, clumsy, stiff, and erratic in his muscle responses.

A blind child's cognition is affected by the degree visual impairment prevents his learning opportunities. During the early years the child experiments and explores through play, which is an important factor in the process of learning. He learns to deal with things and people, and stores a reservoir of knowledge and images. It has long been theorized that the deprivation and lack of sensory stimulation in a child's early years influences his later years of intellectual development. The blind child is usually deprived of this opportunity to stimulate his sensory receptors. Since many parents are fearful of a blind child's mobility, they prohibit the child's desire to explore and experiment. Many are denied the opportunity to learn how to learn.

Further evidence of the psychological effects of blindness has been reported by Lairy[42] and Cohen.[43] They stated that the congenitally blind child becomes anxious, tense, and apprehensive of the world around him. The lack of vision causes him to depend upon others with vision. He develops fears as he encounters unknown situations which make him more conscious of the dangers that surround him. These fears are compounded by worries, warnings, and limitations placed upon him by anxious parents and people within his community. His emotions are sometimes characterized by blindisms. Blindisms manifest themselves in rocking, rubbing of eyes, or exaggerated facial expressions during an emotional experience.

When recreating with the congenitally blind, many of these psychological affects may be present and are results of the distortion caused by the absence of visual perception. On the more positive side, Kenmore[44] and Lowenfeld[45] report that blindness does not affect the scores in measuring the intelligence and achievement of blind children. Much of the psychological adjustment of the congenitally blind person depends upon his immediate social reaction toward his blindness. This is dependent upon his self-concept developed during his early years. The extent of his rehabilitation to a sighted world may compensate for the loss of vision. Rehabilitation includes psychological adjustment, sensory training, mobility, and techniques of daily living.

The adventitiously blind or the partially sighted, representing the largest group of those who are classified as legally blind, may face their psychological problems differently. If the adventitiously blind child loses his vision after the age of five, he has stored some concept of the world around him. He has formed some knowledge or imagery of his environment. With the partially sighted, their degree of restoration may depend upon their self-concept or how they perceive themselves in relationship to the blind and the sighted society. Lairy[46] states that some partially sighted children have been placed in sighted classes. The partially sighted live in two worlds but are part of neither world: neither that of the blind nor that of the sighted. This psychological effect may be that of never belonging to any dominant group.

Whether a person is blind or partially sighted, the legal definition of blindness encompasses the continuum from total loss of vision to the ability to read newsprint. Society makes little distinction between individuals who are blind and those who are partially sighted, and thus the visually impaired become enmeshed in the elaborate social system that molds the role visually impaired persons play. Lukoff and Whiteman[47] found that sighted persons' attitudes have a great influence on the self-concept and adjustment of the visually impaired. Society limits their chances of employment, friends, and access to many leisure-time services. They are placed in an inferior social status because of society's concept of visual impairment. The process of social action toward the visually impaired is the same as toward any minority group, the difference being the types of disability which are discussed in Allport's book, *The Nature of Prejudice*.[48]

The social contacts of the visually impaired begin at an early age. Parental care of a child should be the same as for the sighted child. Should the parents' actions toward their visually impaired child be that of a normal parent, the child has chances of developing a strong self-concept which strengthens his ability to cope with the attitudes of society toward blindness. Lairy[49] and Ayrault[50] mention the deep feelings of depression of parents concerning their visually impaired child, feelings which cause the parents to neglect giving the child the normal stimulations to produce emotional and learning growth.

Ayrault[51] lists a number of attitudes parents may have toward their handicapped child, which may well be the same as those of parents toward their blind child. There is the parent who wants his child to perform better than the child's disability will allow, the parent who may reject the child and exclude the child from family participation, the parent who makes an adjustment to the child's visual impairment and expects the child to do the same, the parent who is always looking for a miracle hoping sight will return someday, or the parent who is constantly criticizing every act of the child. All of these reactions toward the child influence his self-concept.

There are many social factors that separate the visually impaired from the sighted world. Those in recreation should consider, along with these social factors, the nature of prejudice that has stigmatized the visually impaired as "blind" and has reduced them to "second-class citizens." To a degree, we are what people think of us. It is true with the visually impaired, for if a visually impaired child is constantly reminded both in words and in action that he is dependent, he will be dependent.

Society has placed the visually impaired in a minority role by its attitudes toward visual impairment; a well developed stigma which has resulted in prejudice and discrimination. The visually impaired have reacted and in many cases performed according to what society has expected. Many of the elements that have determined the role of the visually impaired are those founded in prejudice.

Allport[52] gives three definitions of prejudice from classic times to modern times. Prejudice comes from the Latin form *praejudicium* meaning *precedent* or *judgment based upon previous decisions and experiences. The New England Dictionary* defines prejudice as feeling favorable or unfavorable toward a person or thing prior to or not based upon actual experience. Webster's *New Twentieth-Century Unabridged Dictionary* gives six possible definitions, some with modern emotional flavor, suspicion, intolerance, or hate of others or things.

Therapeutic recreation goals should be set toward integrating the visually impaired into their community life. As leaders, we should have some knowledge of prejudice and disorientation. By knowing the nature of prejudice and some social factors in its formation, better programming and placement can be made. A better life for the visually impaired can be unfolded.

The psychological factors that determine the visually impaired person's self-concept, or how he sees himself, have been discussed under psychological aspects of visual impairment. How the visually impaired person responds to the role in which society sees him depends upon the degree of self-concept.

Society has not kept abreast of the results of modern medicine and rehabilitation in the restoration of the psychological and physical deficiencies produced by visual impairment. Modern science has diminished the differences between the visually impaired and the sighted. As many visually impaired persons have stated, they are not sick but healthy normal human beings.

Without going into all causes of socialization of the blind, we may consider those that formulate prejudices and later discrimination against the visually impaired. Gordon Allport,[53] in *The Nature of Prejudice,* mentions causative factors that are common to those the visually impaired encounter.

Attitudes are basic to prejudice and attitudes about visually impaired are their dependency, docility, helplessness, and differences. In one situation, a sighted mother refused to allow her son to swim with the visually impaired because to her blindness was a contagious disease and her son would contract blindness. These attitudes built upon the mores of our society stigmatize the visually impaired until the attitudes become stereotyped beliefs. The stigma implies that blindness is a trait that discredits the visually impaired by spoiling both their identity and their respectability. It also carries moral imputations about their character and their personality.

Attitudes which the schools, industry, and recreational services have toward the visually impaired coalesce into a pattern that results in prejudice then discrimination. Even labels are important, for they form the linguistic factors that reinforce the attitudes encountered by the visually impaired. Terms such as "legal blindness" and "blind beggars" are a few linguistic factors that make the visually impaired different from the normal society. As stated before, we are what people believe us to be. This is what Allport[54] describes as a situational emphasis. It is the atmosphere theory that a visually impaired person growing up surrounded by immediate influences will soon reflect all of these influences. The visually impaired person who grows up surrounded by prejudice reflects these prejudices.

One important factor for recreation leaders to remember is the situation emphasis. If, in a recreation activity, a leader does too much for his participants rather than allowing them to do for themselves, they become dependent. With the loss of independence comes loss of self-respect, self-esteem, and self-concept.

Out of prejudice comes discrimination—discrimination in jobs, recreation, and other social and economical benefits. Discrimination is the acting out of prejudice. It is the overt form of a prejudiced attitude of rejection from the in-group represented by the sighted world. It is the "we" group against "them." It is formed on similarities in physical and attitudinal standards set by the in-group.

Many of the visually impaired minority group diminish the differences between them and the sighted—or in-group—and align themselves with the in-group. Those visually impaired persons who have had a normal development reject the role set by society and develop similarities that permit them to be accepted. They are the "unusual" ones or those who have made it.

Evidence that the visually impaired discuss ways of being accepted was overheard by a chauffeur driving them to activities. The visually impaired group discussed ways of obtaining hotel reservations without being rejected. If one has made it, then he must have some special information to help others make it.

Another example pertained to a group of visually impaired who found it difficult to get service at a restaurant. It was learned that over a period of years the restaurant had difficulty with a few visually impaired customers and all visually impaired customers were unwelcome.

Both incidents demonstrate the theory of visibility, that the visible visual impairment identified them and the prejudice caused discrimination. This is not typical of all visually impaired persons. The visually impaired person must be educated to enable him to develop self-concept, self-esteem, and self-confidence and to reject the role society has forced upon him. The public, too, must be educated to the knowledge of visual impairment and to reject superstitions, and folklore.

RECREATION

The recreation needs of the visually impaired are as great as, if not greater than, those of the sighted. The youth have less opportunity for full development and growth through play, an essential activity that broadens one's knowledge of his environment and methods for coping with it. The adventitiously blind adult who must seek other activities or develop new skills and relearn old skills in recreation to enjoy his leisure time, the aging person who must regain confidence and seek social outlets to keep emotionally, physically, socially and intellectually alive, need assistance to enjoy their leisure time—all these groups of visually impaired persons have leisure time needs that should be fulfilled.

The loss or impairment of sight does not mean that programming for the visually impaired to obtain the aims and objectives of leisure-time recreation should be different from those aims and objectives for the sighted. Activities can be adapted, special methods can be used, and techniques are constantly emerging to enable the visually impaired to fully enjoy their leisure-time activities.

Once the visually impaired are able to select recreation activities which they enjoy and which enrich their lives, the community should be made aware that the visually impaired can participate within their community and need not be relegated to separate and isolated leisure-time services. The special agencies that service the visually impaired have this added responsibility in educating the public to accept the visually impaired into their midst. The visually impaired must also be encouraged to venture out beyond the separate recreation services and become part of their community. Many visually impaired who have been so conditioned fear the involvement in a community program. The reasons for their hesitancy were explained under the section of psychological and social aspects of blindness.

There have been many social changes and with these social changes have come new concepts of recreation. In order to view programming for the visually impaired in perspective of the new concept of recreation, the philosophy and definition of recreation is warranted. Our social order and recreation are interrelated and affect each other. The sociological changes in society change our recreation philosophy. The fun and games type of recreation, predominant during the industrial era, met the needs of the working class. There was little time allowed for cultural improvement or even intellectual improvement.

Recreation activities were primarily social and physical; their contribution to society was not stressed. Now in the new electronic and computerized society where advanced medical science has increased our life expectancy, we have more free time or leisure time to fill with activities. The visually impaired have even greater free time because of society's limitation in employment and acceptance in community and commercial recreation services.

We have said that in recreation one must have the freedom of choice. But one can hardly have a wide range of choices if he is limited in knowing what is available. Unable to see the variety of activities that are available, he must learn of them through his other senses or be enlightened by descriptions given to him by those who are sighted or from reading material. Those who are sighted forget that activities are seen in action or on television and from visual stimulation the sighted can determine whether the activity might be enjoyable. It is the therapeutic recreation worker who should bring these varieties of activities into focus for the visually impaired so that they, too, have a variety of recreation activities from which to choose. In therapeutic recreation, the visually impaired individual should experience all activities or be exposed to all activities to register the experience for later selection. During this period he learns his limitations in respect to the activities and how to adapt to them.

These are additional elements in therapeutic recreation that make it different from general recreation. Knowing these differences, therapeutic recreation becomes a rehabilitative or restorative approach to leisure-time activities. Therapeutic recreation can be a catalyst in the team concept of treatment and rehabilitation. It can be the laboratory where the disabled or disadvantaged can experiment during their period of restoration.

Activities in therapeutic recreation become a means to an end rather than the end themselves. This does not mean that the basic elements in recreation are negated or replaced. There is still the element of free choice; activities participated in during free or leisure time have the element of self-satisfaction and fun experience and still are an individual inner personal experience. As a laboratory for the visually impaired under normal social conditions, recreation enables them to evaluate and experiment with the techniques of daily living under guidance and protection. The child who is learning to dress or tie his shoes must do so when going swimming or bowling. The adults who learn to use dinner equipment do so when on field trips to a restaurant. The visually impaired are able to test their skill in mobility as they participate in field trips. All these experiences are re-created or discussed either in a group or individually.

Programming with the visually impaired in a therapeutic or rehabilitation setting gives the visually impaired an opportunity to experience recreation activities that are unknown to them or that they might not experience in normal or recreation services in the community. The program should contain activities in which there is physical development. Such activities should help keep the body in tone and spirits high. The visually impaired should be able to use their creative talents for self-expression. The activities selected by the visually impaired give them a feeling of achievement and a thrill of accomplishment. There should be activities that are challenging, exciting, and adventurous. Through the use of activities, the visually impaired should experience the sense of giving service to others and the enjoyment of beauty.

There are many secondary gains from recreation that the visually impaired should experience: the ability and opportunity for self-expression, for social adjustment, for practicing democracy and citizenship, and for learning to work with others and have respect for others' beliefs.

Without stimulating leadership, the visually impaired may never learn the art of recreating or even why recreation is important to a well-balanced life. There are six roles a recreation leader plays that are important in therapeutic recreation. He becomes a stimulator, an educator, an advisor, an observer, a director, and a controller.

1) As a stimulator he generates positive interests and encourages the visually impaired with favorable rewards. When necessary he arouses others into an activity for which seemingly there is no desire. His enthusiasm and drive, his interest in people and their enjoyment is absorbed by the participants. It is his skill, his technique, and his patience that inspires favorable experiences within the visually impaired.

Several examples can explain the technique. Bingo can be a dull, routine recreation experience in which the winning is more important than the game. When there is no visual stimulation the other senses should be excited. A vibrant, clear, jovial voice in calling the numbers, jokes and humorous description of what is taking place or how the other players are responding, a showmanship recognition of the winner and the losers and patience with those that are slow in finding their numbers, all of which gives life to a dull game and brings more into the activity because of the fun of playing.

Another example is either at social dances or at table games where wallflowers are common. A recreation leader as a stimulator will be everywhere, beginning a game then asking a watcher to replace him, or dancing with those on the sidelines and introducing them to others to finish the dance. These techniques can be used in any activity to stimulate the motivation of participation.

2) The recreation leader as educator teaches new skills or re-teaches old ones. Principles of teaching techniques and methods are similar to the teaching of any activity or subject matter. The educator should know what the limits of the visually impaired are. Techniques in teaching the blind would not necessarily be the same as for the partially sighted. In either case the use of all the remaining sense receptors should be involved. With the blind the educator must be the eyes of the participant. Explanations should be descriptive, exact, and in detail. Instructions must also be exact and in detail, even to the kinds of materials used in an arts and crafts class, discussing the material's composition, and giving any information that might give the visually impaired person a better idea of the object with which he is working. Once he knows, his imagination and creativity will do the rest. The educator must assist the visually impaired in developing and adopting independent ways in a recreation activity, always trying new ideas and techniques to encourage independence. The educator is an important role in encouraging independence in the visually impaired.

3) The recreation leader will find he must take the role of advisor or counselor. This is a very necessary role if one is to learn how to recreate or where to recreate. It is an essential role of the therapeutic recreation specialist who should constantly counsel with the visually impaired to give reassurance and answer questions that might affect the visually impaired's

leisure time. This is done either in a one-to-one relationship or in homogeneous groups where the interests and conditions are similar. Such counseling may stimulate greater interest and knowledge of recreation possibilities and areas of exploration. It may function as one of the processes of learning, to verbalize one's experience. Counseling is becoming more important as a tool in therapeutic recreation and may be used as one of the many assessment tools in rehabilitating the visually impaired person.

4) The recreation leader may function in the role of an observer, i.e., one who assesses or records what is taking place. This may occur in evaluating an activity, a program, or a participant who is being rehabilitated. As an observer he makes no judgment; listens, but gives no direction. The recreation leader may be called upon to observe and record in his role as an advisor or counselor. As an observer the recording should be in terms of what is taking place, what action happens, and what a participant does. He should not judge.

5) Occasionally the leader must direct, but, hopefully, in a supervisory capacity. The role of a director with participants is rarely used, for a director allows little self-decision. The role of a director contradicts the goals established for the visually impaired. The goal to be accomplished is independent functioning in a recreation setting. Such a role as director tends to reinforce an attitude of dependence.

In a case where the role of director was taken, a group of older adults lost all desire for independence having everything from meals to their programs planned inside the agency. It was known as the "bread and circus" program. Later the leadership role was changed to that of stimulator, suggesting that they do the program planning, that they share in the cost of field trips, that they recreate with their sighted peers. The reaction was one of complete dismay, that they were being put upon, that the agency was "for the blind," and that they were not capable of doing for themselves.

After several months of group discussions, encouraging those who had leadership qualities to become group leaders, many began to enjoy the successful experiences of being independent. They encouraged the others to do things for themselves. They began to plan more activities that they wanted, more field trips into the community were requested, and the planning groups requested more responsibility in planning programs. The climax of this experience was when two older women who were fearful of going out into the community alone requested the director's permission to walk around the block by themselves. This happened to be in a crowded downtown section of a large metropolitan city.

6) The role of controller, in which the leader makes all the decisions, allows for little growth of the individual or the group, and is not in the best interest of the visually impaired. It tends to develop dependence or reenforces their feelings of dependence. This role should rarely be used by the recreation leader.

The recreation leader should have some evaluative tool to determine the extent of re-education or education necessary to enable the visually impaired to function independently or in the community. The following is a suggested evaluation tool to determine on what level of ability the visually impaired is currently functioning and to suggest some measures that might assist in fulfilling his needs.

Classification of a Visually Impaired Person According to Current Level of Functioning

1. Classification I

    a. Description: The visually impaired person is able to find satisfying social and/or recreation experience independently. He reflects good environmental adjustment and his socio-recreation activities indicate a healthy constructive adjustment to his total life pattern.

    b. Possible Services: Individuals who fall in this classification probably will not need direct recreation services from a rehabilitation agency offering therapeutic recreation. It may, however, be necessary to provide short-term counseling of a direct or supportive nature.

    Counseling may be on an individual or group basis. Assistance here may be short-term and may consist of giving direction and/or support to the individual's present use of leisure time.

2. Classification II

    a. Description: The visually impaired person demonstrates or communicates the need for minimum assistance in finding realistic, satisfying social and/or recreation experiences. He will display the following characteristics, good personal management, independent mobility skills, good physical health, good emotional health, positive self-image, self-confidence, positive attitudes towards visual impairment, well-developed interests and motivation toward exploring new socio-recreation activities and desires to learn new skills.

b. Possible Services:

    (1) Recreation Counseling for Guidance and Information.

        (a) On an individual basis at the agency giving special services to the visually impaired or in a community setting. Counseling at this level may be short-term and will be directed to providing information which the visually impaired persons can use in discovering and carrying out meaningful and constructive leisure time activities.

        (b) Group recreation counseling for the partially sighted or combined partially sighted and sighted at the agency giving special services to the visually impaired or in a community setting. This type of counseling could be designed to allow the visually impaired persons to ventilate their feelings and ideas in the presence of others with similar recreation problems. The exchange of thoughts and ideas in the group should be supportive as well as informative.

    (2) Temporary Assistance in Developing Recreation Skills, Habits, and Motivation Toward Making Use of Leisure Time.

        (a) Adult Education Classes at the agency giving special services or a community-based agency. The location of classes will be influenced by the type of skills required as well as by the attitude of those participating. Visually impaired persons who require a somewhat more sheltered setting would participate in education classes at an agency giving special services. The purpose of these classes would be to give the visually impaired person the opportunity to learn or improve upon recreation skills which he might use outside the agency giving special service. The emphasis would be on the method of doing, not the actual project itself.

(b) Combined recreation program for the partially sighted and sighted in a community setting with supportive individual or group recreation counseling for the partially sighted only. The supportive counseling may be offered either at agency giving special service or in the community setting.

Visually impaired persons in this classification are capable of participation in recreation activities with sighted peers but still require supportive counseling to improve self-concept and enhance self-awareness. The degree and extent of this counseling may vary from visually impaired to visually impaired, but hopefully will be of relatively short-term duration, resulting in independence from the agency.

3. Classification III

   a. Description: The visually impaired person demonstrates or communicates the need for extensive assistance in finding satisfying social and/or recreation experience.

Although the visually impaired person may display some of the strengths mentioned in Classification II, adequate functioning is inhibited by the visually impaired person's poor environmental adjustment, self-image, attitudes toward visual impairment, lack of self-confidence, lack of skills, motivation and purpose for living. The visually impaired person may be in poor physical health, exhibit lack of orientation and mobility skills, etc.

   b. Possible Services:

      (1) Counseling: the visually impaired person within this classification may require extensive counseling to improve attitude, self-image and self-awareness in recreation experience.

         (a) On an individual basis, either at agency giving special services or in a community setting.

         (b) Counseling for partially sighted or combined partially sighted and sighted at the agency giving special services or in a community setting. In both cases, the counseling should be on a regular basis structured so as to improve and enhance the areas mentioned above. Again the approach and content will be determined by the needs of the individuals involved.

(2) Temporary Assistance in Developing Recreation Skills, Habits, and Motivation Towards Making Use of Leisure Time: Visually impaired persons within this classification may or may not require some form of supportive transportation.

(a) Therapeutic recreation program for partially sighted at agency giving special services.

This would be a person-centered program designed to evaluate and teach recreation skills for the partially sighted only. Program emphasis would continue to be on carry over value for participation in a community setting.

(b) Therapeutic recreation program for both the partially sighted and sighted at agency giving special services. Similar to agency program for the partially sighted only as mentioned in (a) above with the inclusion of sighted peers.

(c) Therapeutic recreation program for the partially sighted only in a community setting. This program would be designed to evaluate and teach recreation skills but would be conducted in a community setting close to the visually impaired person's home in the hope that integration would be easier.

(d) Therapeutic recreation program for the partially sighted and sighted in a community setting.

Similar to (c) above with the inclusion of sighted peers. This program would be designed to lead, in a relatively short period of time, to a complete non-therapeutic or general recreation program participation.

(e) Therapeutic recreation program for partially sighted or both partially sighted and sighted in an agency giving special services or a community setting plus a community recreational program. This combination of programs would hopefully enable the visually impaired person to receive support and skill training in a person-centered program while attending a regular community program.

(3) Assist in Interest and Skill Development in the Home: A variety of techniques may be employed to increase skill ability and enhance the visually impaired person's interest for participation in recreation activities in the home setting.

(4) Assistance in Organizing Social Activities in Immediate Environment: Visually impaired persons who indicate the need for socialization may get assistance through counseling, group discussion and/or group participation in planning, organizing and carrying out social activities in the immediate environment. This may involve contact with neighbors, etc.

4. Classification IV

  a. Description: Visually impaired person communicates or demonstrates the need for intensive developmental assistance in establishing functional social and recreation experiences. Visually impaired person may be severely impaired emotionally, intellectually and/or physically.

Visually impaired persons included in this classification may have a great need for regular social contacts as emotional and psychological deterioration may be present.

  b. Possible Services: Most visually impaired persons within this classification will probably require long term intensive services. Success in achieving complete recreation independence will be limited. Services would be designed to maintain the individual at his present level of functioning with attempts towards a positive improvement in as many areas as possible.

(1) Recreation Counseling: Both individual and group counseling will be extensive and intensive and through necessity require involvement with the psychological department on a consultation basis to the recreation staff.

(2) Intensive Developmental Assistance Through Organized Recreation Activities: Visually impaired persons of this classification would in all probability require some form of transportation assistance. The ultimate purpose of this programming would be to prevent deterioration and maintain the visually impaired person's current level of function.

(a) Long-term therapeutic recreation program for blind and partially sighted at an agency giving special services. Through the use of organized activities, an attempt will be made to help each visually impaired person function and develop to his maximum potential. Some emphasis will be placed on improvement of self-image, self-awareness and attitudes.

(b) Long-term therapeutic recreation program for the partially sighted and the blind only or both the visually impaired and sighted in a community setting. This service would be designed similar to that described in (a) above, but the location would, it is hoped, aid in the maintenance of community contact and assist in the reintegration and/or maintenance process.

(3) Assistance in Interest and Skill Development in the Home: These services would include home counseling and instruction in recreation activities and possibly visitation on a regular basis by an individual capable of assisting the visually impaired persons in their home recreation projects, etc.

(4) Assistance in Organizing Social Activities in the Immediate Environment: This service would involve assistance in learning social skills on a limited basis, establishing means of contact with peers and the arrangement of visitation, either by peers, a recreation worker or a volunteer on an informal basis.

Another tool used to indicate areas in which additional training may be necessary before the participant is ready for community placement is the "Participant's Diagnostic Profile." This diagnostic tool may be used in determining the participants level of functioning. The areas considered are: 1) degree of mobility skill; 2) degree of communication skill; 3) degree of residual vision; 4) degree of techniques of daily living skills; 5) concept of leisure-time activities; 6) span of interest in recreation activities; and 7) degree of involvement with sighted persons or with visually impaired persons.

1. *Mobility skills.* How well does he travel alone? Does he use dog guide or cane travel? Can he travel at night? How well does he orient himself to new surroundings?

2. *Communication skills.* Does he read braille, use talking book

or tape recorder, or read printed material? Does he write or type?

3. *Degree of residual vision.* How well does he see? Can visual aid improve his vision? What is the condition of his eye—to determine whether physical activities may be restricted?

4. *Degree of techniques of daily living skills.* How well does he dress himself? Can he put away his clothes? Is he able to find them after he has put them away? How does he handle table utensils?

5. *Concept of leisure-time activities.* How does he conceive leisure time? How does he conceive recreation? What does he expect to gain from recreation or his leisure time? Does he like to socialize? What does he want to do with his leisure time?

6. *Span of interest in recreation* What activities was he interested in or did he pursue prior to onset of visual impairment? What activities is he now interested in and is now doing after onset of visual impairment? Is he interested in making things, doing things, acquiring things or learning about things?

7. *Degree of involvement with sighted persons.* To what extent does he associate with sighted persons? Does he prefer socializing with other visually impaired persons? Does he have any interest in participating in a community recreation program, or a public or private recreation service?

The summary and recommendations of "Participant's Diagnostic Profile" are in two parts.

I. Summary:

1. General observation (based upon appearance, conversation, behavior).

2. Evaluation results of the "Participant's Diagnostic Profile."

II. Recommendations:

1. Activities (give name of activity, purpose, relationship to life goals, etc.)

2. Services needed (recreation-education, activity programming and leadership, recreation-counseling, etc.)

Recreation for the visually impaired is found in many settings. The visually impaired may recreate in a private or public agency or a specialized agency serving blind and partially

sighted. In this section we will deal with three age groups—
youth, adults, older adults—in rehabilitation setting. This rehabilitation setting should have multiple services: social case
work, psychological testing, mobility, sensory training, techniques of daily living, medical, low vision service, and leisure-
time services. All or part of these services offered may be
necessary for the restoration of the person who desires to function fully and independently in community integrated leisure-
time services.

YOUTH RECREATION PROGRAM

There may be two approaches to a youth program for the visually
impaired, therapeutic and general recreation. In a rehabilitation
setting, the goals of a therapeutic recreation program are to
teach the youth how to use their leisure time, to assist in their
restoration, and to prepare them for full participation in community leisure-time services.

The program should be youth-oriented, meeting today's
needs and problems. Activities should be of a wide and varied
selection to allow for experiencing recreation through doing,
since visual experience is limited in their leisure-time education. It is not a question of whether or not they will use the
activity but to build a reservoir of knowledge of activities that
are available and to help in developing them physically, socially,
intellectually, and emotionally.

In selecting activities, special attention should be given
to the physiological condition of the eyes and the sharpening of
their remaining sensory receptors. Youth who have partial
vision should be encouraged to use their residual vision. Youth
with degenerative eye disease should be exposed to as much
of their environment as possible. Even if total loss of vision occurs, they will have stored in their memory images of their environment. Great care should be taken with those youths who
have retina disease or detachment or other physiological eye
disease of such nature that damage to the head or a quick
movement of the head might cause total loss of vision. Total
loss did occur to one youth who was dancing with vigorous
head movement. During the dance she had detached the remaining nerve fibres from choroid, which is the vascular tissue

that furnishes nourishment to the eye and is connected to the optic nerve.

A youth recreation program in a rehabilitation setting can be planned on three levels. The levels are a continuum to community participation, each level having a special objective.

Level I

The program should allow for the visually impaired to find themselves and to overcome some of the physical and psychological problems mentioned under psychological and social aspects of visual impairment. It is a period of education in leisure-time activities and how to adapt oneself to enjoy the activities in which one is capable of participating and the skill and knowledge of selecting leisure-time activities in later life. An arbitrary age range is 6 to 11 years of age. Activities for this age group should be planned to expose them to as many activities within their age group as possible. They should be allowed to explore, make mistakes and enjoy the activity and learn how to make adaptations. George Dennison[55] describes the kind of environment in which a child should be able to learn. The environment should have all the elements that will offer the child a sense of the skills and the varieties of behavior that will lead him to greater pleasure and greater security. These elements a visually impaired child needs, but the rewards for this growth should be immediate and intrinsic in the activities themselves.

It is during this period that greater learning in daily skills is practiced: dressing, tying shoes, putting away clothes and equipment, and exploring rooms and halls as they move from one activity to another. Activities should be selected not only for the age group, but also to develop muscle skills, coordination, and an awareness of their remaining sensory receptors. As they progress in skill and age, more responsibility is given and more independence is encouraged.

Level II

As they progress and seek more challenging experiences, they should be moved into the second level. The age group is approximately from 12 to 17 years of age. A child who is 16 or 17 years old and has the skills for level three should not be kept back. Nor should a child of the same ages or older be moved ahead if he does not have the necessary skills.

This level is a level of independence. There are youth counsels; activities and programs are decided and developed by youth with their advisors. The young people select the activities in which they wish further skills. This is a period in which they are permitted to experiment and try the knowledge they learned during the first level. During this period they prepare themselves for recreating in the community and competing with their sighted peers. These activities are mostly social, group activities and field trips. The youths are counseled individually and in groups during this level.

Level III

This is the interim period or community-based program. Those in this level are travelers who must be able to travel alone. This youth group makes all plans for their recreation within the community. Trips might be to community settlements, public or private recreation centers, and commercial leisure-time services. The young people are encouraged to compete, to mingle, and to make friends with their sighted peers. They are to learn how to adjust to the pressures of the sighted community. It is hoped during this period that the visually impared youth will find a place in the community and drop out from the group. It is understood that should there be any recreation skills that need improvement, they can be taught at the recreation rehabilitation center; however, these youth are encouraged to gain such skills in the community.

Activities

The visually impaired youth can participate in a great number of activities, some requiring adaptations, others depending upon the creativity and imagination of the recreation leader. Many youth have some vision, which broadens the number of activities available to them. When in doubt whether physical activities may be restricted, check with the youth's ophthalmologist.

Games

As in any activity in therapeutic recreation, the leader must consider the desired outcome for the participant in the game. The visually impaired young person should learn all that a sighted youth learns, such as: 1) taking his correct turn, 2) accepting the boundary limits, whether they be physical or personal behavior, 3) being able to accept defeat as well as victory gracefully, 4) being eliminated from the game for whatever reason, 5) accepting being placed in any position in the game, 6) learning new skills and improving upon old skills, 7) developing sportsmanship and respecting the rights and feelings of others, 8) improving the power of decision-making in situations that call for quick decisions, 9) developing leadership abilities as well as learning how to be a cooperative follower, and 10) playing fair by observing the rules.

With the visually impaired it is particularly important to improve his sight, that is, the use of his remaining sensory receptors. These sensory receptors are his eyes as well as the pathways to learning and enjoyment. It is through his remaining sensory receptors that the visually impaired will seek his leisure-time activities.

When selecting games for the visually impaired individual, consider his degree of vision and the type of eye disease or injury. Games that are active may be restricted. Use whatever device that will allow the youth to participate, pairing a partially sighted or a sighted youth with a blind youth, or using sound to direct them through the game. Such imagination can be adapted to most games. Whether the game is one that a child cannot play in a community center he should at least, under adaptive methods, be exposed to the fundamentals and experience of the game.

Games can be developed that require the visually impaired to use each of his remaining sensory receptors. Smelling games, games to detect odors and to identify odors are numerous. Games using taste: what do I taste, or what am I eating? There are a number of games in which hearing can be used. Different sounds of bells, one for bikes, for automobiles, trucks, subways, busses, horns, and a list of others. Many of these games can be adapted for sighted as well as the visually impaired to play together. Tactile games are unlimited and are as many as one's imagination can go: touching art objects, cooking and eating utensils, clothing, just to name a few. Some can be devised that involve the kinesthetic sensory receptors by using obstacle courses of many kinds made of chairs, tables, or gym equipment.

Relays are exceptionally good for visually impaired youth. They teach him the rules of a game and their elements. Their sensory receptors are used and it replaces hours of physical exercises that many do not like. The muscles are developed, body coordination developed, and an awareness that some exercises are necessary.

Games have certain patterns that the leader should know: those in which the arrangement of the players is fixed and those where the players are scattered over a large or small playing area with no special positions assigned. The fixed arrangement for formations used are: 1) single circle, 2) double circle, 3) single line or file formation, 4) leader and class formation or semi-circle, 5) spoke or star formation, 6) zig-zag formation, 7) relay formation, or multiple line, 8) line or rank formation, 9) shuttle relay formation.

Charles E. Buell[56] in his book *Physical Education for the Blind Children* has listed a number of games that the youth can play. Any circle dodge ball game can be played. The child in the center continuously making a loud sound by voice or mechanical instrument so that the children in the circle can locate the sound and throw the ball.

For the older youth, chess, checkers, and card games are all specially designed for the visually impaired. Regular cards can be used by attaching a braille number and suit on the end of the card. Special bingo boards and numbers are made for the visually impaired. Commercial games can be adapted by using braille instead of script or using large print for the partially sighted. Using ingenuity many games can be adapted so that the sighted and visually impaired can play together.

Recreation Sports

There are many sports the older youth can enjoy: swimming—including long-distance swimming, water polo, water basketball, and racing. They can either enjoy or participate in canoeing, row boating, speed boating, sailing, water biking and water skiing. Many are known to play golf.

Winter sports, where there is snow, can include games designed by using small or large banks of snow as guidelines. There is ice skating, coasting, making snow or ice sculpture, and skiing.

Field sports can be enjoyed; e.g., racing using guidelines or sound at the finish line, ball-throwing, baseball using a ball with sound placed on a stand and another sound to direct runners, rope-climbing, and ladder-climbing.

Performing Arts

Many activities in the performing arts are both for pleasure and physical, sensory and emotional development. Dance, drama, and music give the youth opportunity for expression physically and verbally and help in developing poise, balance, body coordination, body movement, and body awareness. For the visually impaired child, dance movement or rhythm band can be important in his training for mobility. The older teenager will need the finer skills in dancing, drama, and music to enhance his socializing in the sighted world.

Applied Arts

Recreation arts and crafts have few limits: sculpture, ceramics, woodwork, sewing, working with wire, paper, cloth, metal, beads and most any other medium in the crafts can be included. Teaching youth to use hammer, scissors, power tools, sewing machine, cook on electric or gas stove are all helpful. Many of these skills are further developed in rehabilitation, but before they reach rehabilitation they become familiar with tools used in recreation.

Again, imagination is used in developing techniques to perform the task independently: cutting out paper diagrams to follow in making designs in needlework or using pins as a layout or using raised or embossed material as guidelines. Many adaptations come from the visually impaired in developing techniques.

Special Events, Parties, and Outings

For the older youth, special events and parties are exciting. They get the opportunity to use the many skills learned in their performing and applied art classes—making their own designs, painting their own pictures, and being host and guest at their own affairs. Special events may mean activities in recreation sports, entertainers, or operating their own puppet show. Giving plays, musicals, or carnivals are special events where again their skills in the performing and applied arts are used.

Outings give the youth a better knowledge of their environment. These may be field trips to restaurants, theatres, movies, and places of entertainment. It can be educational as well as recreational. Boat rides, picnics, tours, and walking tours also are entertaining and educational. The visually impaired young people learn, under guidance, how to enjoy and mingle with others in the sighted world. They have the opportunity to experiment with their newly found skills in recreation.

ADULT RECREATION PROGRAM

An adult recreation program in a rehabilitation setting should make every effort to return the visually impaired person to the community. Assuming the youth have been fully rehabilitated, there should be little need of their attending an adult recreation program in a rehabilitation center. The clients who might need therapeutic recreation are the adventitiously blind or partially sighted persons whose onset of visual impairment occurred after twenty years of age. The objectives for leaders in an adult recreation program are to teach new recreation skills or re-teach old skills, assist in regaining the visually impaired person's confidence, self-esteem, self-respect, and self-concept in his functioning during his leisure time.

Some evaluation should be made of the adult prior to developing a program to meet his needs. The "Participant's Diagnostic Profile" and the "Current Level of Functioning in Recreation" may be used. Counseling is also important in restoring a visually impaired person. There are times when an adventitiously blind or partially sighted client may have unrealistic goals set for himself that should be explored, or he may become depressed about his leisure time because he no longer can pursue his old recreation activities. Every person has some hidden talents that while they were able to see were either forgotten or lost because of vision. Their hidden talents may lead to new activities that do not require vision.

There are many ways in which a therapeutic recreation program can develop independence in the adventitiously blind or partially sighted person. One is through the use of adult education classes in leisure-time activities. There is a time limit to how long a client is enrolled in any one activity. The structure does not permit a person to become dependent upon the group or the agency. Once the visually impaired adult has learned a skill, he is encouraged to continue this skill in community or commercial recreation services.

One particular case was that of a young woman who wanted to learn to swim and belong to a swimming group. She began in the beginners' class and moved through the intermediate class in two terms. The supervisor of adult education arranged for her to become a member of the Young Women's Hebrew Association. The reports several months later were that she has never had as much enjoyment as she has since becoming a member of the Y.W.H.A.

Classes are held in the evening with one requirement: that the client come on his own or bring a sighted person as his guide. The sighted guide is permitted to take any class that is offered that evening. This adds to the class stimulation, and makes the classes similar to those in the community rather than in a specialized agency for the visually impaired.

The adult classes for the visually impaired offer outlets to them that integrated classes fail to give. The visually impaired person, who is constantly competing with those in the sighted world, finds relief in groups where his disability is not considered a handicap. A number of employed visually impaired persons have often remarked that a change in pace from constantly competing with the sighted is most relaxing. They find that they can water ski without being told it is dangerous, or bowl without rejection because the bowling alley has never had a blind bowler. If recreation is to relax and rejuvenate one socially, physically, emotionally, and intellectually, then there should be a place where this can happen.

Some adult education courses in leisure-time activities may be: armchair travel, discussion group on problems of contemporary America, discussion group on great issues of current interest, human relations, psychology of literature, beginning and advanced languages, creative writing, drama workshop, folk music, beginning and intermediate and advanced bowling, cabaret entertainment (conversation and refreshments—all planned by the students), chess, bridge, physical fitness, self-defense, beginning and intermediate and free swim, yoga exercise, fundamentals of social dancing, film festival, agency orientation through discussions and dialogue on social service, rehabilitation, low vision, Braille I and II, cooking, exploring the city by day, first aid, hairdressing, handwriting, spelling, beginning and intermediate and advanced typing, ceramics I and II, creative crafts, dress design, knitting and sewing.

The curriculum outlines a few of the activities in which the visually impaired persons are interested and participate. The success of the adult program rests upon the leadership of those who conduct the classes. The instructors must allow the visually impaired to do their own work with as little physical assistance as possible. Constant encouragement for them to do for themselves creates greater interest in achievement and a sense of independence. As each participant develops his skills and confidence to perform, he is encouraged to further his interests in the community. Counseling is advisable to explore community resources.

For many it is a new life to find leisure-time activities within the community and with persons other than the visually impaired.

OLDER ADULT RECREATION PROGRAM

Senescence in the visually impaired is the same as with the sighted. The big difference is the loss of vision which may intensify the emotional problems accompanying aging. Many visually impaired suffer from diabetes; they may tend to withdraw from social participation. Low motivation and unstable interest necessitate stimulation. It is therefore important for the older adults to renew contact with their environment or to establish social relationships with others.

The older adults fall into two groups: those who can adjust to an integrated social life and those who desire to associate with others who are visually impaired. The dependent older adult may find it more enjoyable to recreate with others of similar disabilities in a general recreation program. It may be difficult for them to make changes in their lifestyle, and they may require greater attention, particularly in the arts and crafts. Those who are independent may become dependent if the arts and craft groups are predominately dependent. Those who are independent may be affected by those who are dependent who require repetition of instruction, who are slow in following direction, and who have lost auditory reception.

Whenever possible the independent older adult should be separated from the more dependent ones. If recreation for the older adult is to be enjoyable, then an activity that creates frustration should be avoided. Having a predominant number of older adults who are visually impaired in an arts and crafts activity sometimes tends to encourage the independent older adult to become dependent. This tends to dilute the goal set for the visually impaired person who has a potential of functioning in a community center. The independent visually impaired person needs a great deal of encouragement and a taste of successful achievement before he feels ready to leave an all visually impaired group.

A maintenance program for the dependent older adult finds success in entertainment, special events, social parties, singing, bingo, group discussions, dances, lectures, and music. Arts and crafts should be on a level on which the older adults can function and enjoy themselves. Skill and perfection should not be the major goal. Projects in sewing, knitting, tile, weaving, ceramics, and beadwork are a few which they will enjoy.

Those who demonstrate a desire and potential for recreating in a community setting should be encouraged to develop techniques in doing projects by themselves—the use of templates to follow pattern or design, pins to outline design, embossing with clay or cellophane tape or masking tape, or paper designs cut out and placed over the material that can be followed by touch. Any of these devices may be used to cut out material for craft work.

In a rehabilitation setting, activities for the older adult should be patterned on those activities they will find in the community. The transition is easier from a rehabilitation setting program to the community.

FOOTNOTES

[1] John Lear, "Environment and Quality of Life," *Saturday Review*, June 6, 1970, p. 57.

[2] George Dennison, "An Environment to Grow In," *Saturday Review*, October 18, 1969, pp. 74–76.

[3] Ben Patrusky, "Sciene On the Move," *Signature*, November, 1970, 5:16.

[4] Patrusky, p. 16.

[5] Patrusky, p. 16.

[6] Charles K. Brightbill, *Education for Leisure-Centered Living* (Harrisburg, Pa.: Stackpole Books, 1966), pp. 1–228.

[7] Thomas J. Carroll, *Blindness* (Boston, Mass.: Little, Brown and Co., 1961), chaps. 2, 3, and 4.

[8] Lee Meyerson, "Somatopsychology of Physical Disabilities," William M. Cruickshank, ed., *Psychology of Exceptional Children and Youth* (Englewood Cliffs, N.J.: Prentice-Hall, Inc., 1963), p. 8.

[9] Meyerson, p. 8.

[10] Emory L. Cowen, Rita P. Underberg, Ronald T. Verrillo, and Frank G. Benham, *Adjustment to Visual Disability in Adolescents* (New York: American Foundation for the Blind, 1961), p. 21.

[11] Richard Kraus, *Recreation Today* (New York: Appleton-Century-Crofts, 1966), pp. 5–8.

[12] Jay B. Nash, *Philosophy of Recreation and Leisure* (Dubuque, Iowa: Brown Co., Publishers, 1933), pp. 93–96.

[13] Robert A. Scott, *Making Blind Men* (Provo, Utah: Brigham Young University Press, 1966), p. 40.

[14] Scott, pp. 41–42.

[15] Berthold Lowenfeld, "Psychological Problems of Children with Impaired Vision," William M. Cruickshank, ed., *Psychology of Exceptional Children and Youth* (Englewood Cliffs, N.J.: Prentice-Hall, Inc., 1963), pp. 228–229.

[16] Scott, pp. 41–42.

[17] Frank W. Weymouth, "Effect of Age on Visual Acuity," Monroe J. Hirsch and Ralph E. Wick, eds., *Vision of the Aging Patient* (New York: Chilton Co., 1960), pp. 38–41.

[18] Lowenfeld, pp. 231–232.

[19] N.S.P.B. Fact Book, *Estimated Statistics on Blindness and Visual Problems* (New York: The National Society for the Prevention of Blindness, 1966), p. 11.

[20] N.S.P.B. Fact Book, p. 11.

[21] N.S.P.B. Fact Book, *Estimated Total Cases and New Cases of Legal Blindness by States, 1969* (New York: The National Society for the Prevention of Blindness, 1966), Supplementary Chart.

[22] U.S. Public Health Service, *Binocular Visual Acuity of Adults, United States, 1960–1962* (Washington, D.C.: 1964), series 11, No. 3.

[23] N.S.P.B. Fact Book, p. 76.

[24] *Annual Report* (Louisville, Ky.: American Printing House for the Blind, 1965).

[25] N.S.P.B. Fact Book, p. 37.

[26] N.S.P.B. Fact Book, pp. 33–34.

[27] N.S.P.B. Fact Book, pp. 44–45.

[28] N.S.P.B. Fact Book, p. 88.

[29] N.S.P.B. Fact Book.

[30] N.S.P.B. Fact Book, p. 78.

[31] Otto Lowenstein, *The Senses* (Baltimore, Md.: Penguin Books, 1966), pp. 13–15.

[32] Edward Hall, *The Hidden Dimension* (Garden City, New York: Doubleday & Co., 1969), pp. 1–6.

[33] Lowenstein, pp. 32–47.

[34] Hall, pp. 41–42.

[35] Jerome Cohen, "The Effect of Blindness on Children," 13: 1:23–27, January and February, 1966.

[36] Virginia M. Axline, "The Child Who Is Blind," Reprint *Childhood Education*, Association for Childhood Education International, Washington, D.C. 30: 427–430, May 1954.

[37] Evelyn West Ayrault, *You Can Raise Your Handicapped Child* (New York: G. P. Putnam's Sons, 1964), p. 318.

[38] Carroll, p. 10.

[39] Helen Loklin, "Psychological Factors in Case Work with Blind Older Persons," *The New Outlook*, 51:.11:1–8, January, 1957.

[40] Nyla J. Cole and Leonard H. Taboroff, "The Psychology of the Congenitally Blind Child," *American Journal of Othopsychiatry*, 25: 627–643, July, 1955.

[41] James Dreves, "Early Learning and Perception of Space," *American Journal of Psychology*, 68:4: 605–614, December, 1955.

[42] Gabrielle—Catherine Lairy, Problems in the Adjustment of the Visually Impaired Child," *The New Outlook*, 63: 3:33–41, February, 1969.

[43] Cohen, pp. 23–27.

[44] Jeanne R. Kenmore, "The Development Needs of Blind Children," *Exceptional Children*, 4:212–215, November, 1960.

[45] Lowenfeld, pp. 240–243.

[46] Lairy, p. 33.

[47] Irving F. Lukoff and Martin Whiteman, *The Social Sources of Adjustment to Blindness* (New York, Library of Congress Catalog Card Number 73–84034, American Foundation for the Blind), pp. 53–90.

[48] Gordon W. Allport, *The Nature of Prejudice* (Garden City, New York: Doubleday & Co., Inc., 1954), pp. 1–480.

[49] Lairy, p. 36.

[50] Ayrault, pp. 130–134.

[51] Ayrault, pp. 136–151.

[52] Allport, pp. 6–10.

[53] Allport, chaps. 1 and 2.

[54] Allport, pp. 208–209.

[55] Dennison, pp. 74–76.

[56] Charles E. Buell, *Physical Education for Blind Children* (Springfield, Illinois: Charles C Thomas, 1966), pp. 106–121, and 123–139.

BIBLIOGRAPHY

Allport, Gordon W., *The Nature of Prejudice*. Garden City, N.Y.: Doubleday & Co., Inc., 1954.

Annual Report. Louisville, Ky.: American Printing House for the Blind, 1965.

Avedon, Elliott M., and Arje, Frances B., *Social-Recreative Program for the Retarded*. New York: Bureau of Publications, Teachers College, Columbia University, 1964.

Ayrault, Evelyn West, *You Can Raise Your Handicapped Child*. New York: G. P. Putnam's Sons, 1964.

Best, Harry, *Blindness and the Blind in the United States*. New York: Macmillan Co., 1934.

Binocular Visual Acuity of Adults, United States, 1960–1962. Washington, D.C.: U.S. Public Health Service, Series 11, No. 3, 1964.

Blockhall, David Scott, *The House Had Windows*. New York: Ivan Obolensky, Inc., 1922.

Brightbill, Charles K., *Education for Leisure-Centered Living*. Harrisburg, Pa.: Stackpole Books, 1966.

———, *Man and Leisure: A Philosophy of Leisure*. Englewood Cliffs, N.J.: Prentice-Hall, Inc., 1961.

Buell, Charles E., *Physical Education for Blind Children*. Springfield, Ill.: Charles C Thomas, 1966.

Carroll, Thomas J., *Blindness, What It Is, What It Does, and How to Live with It*. Boston: Little, Brown & Co., 1961.

Case, Maurice, *Recreation for Blind Adults*. Springfield, Ill.: Charles C Thomas, 1966.

Cowen, Emory L., Underberg, Rita P., Verrillo, Ronald T., and Benham, Frank G., *Adjustment to Visual Disability in Adolescents*. New York: American Foundation for the Blind, 1961.

Cruickshank, William, *Psychology of Exceptional Children and Youth*. Englewood Cliffs, N.J.: Prentice-Hall, Inc., 1955.

———, and Trippe, Matthew, *Services to Blind Children in New York State*. New York: Syracuse University Press, 1959.

Eaton, Allen H., *Beauty for the Light and Blind*. New York: St. Martin's Press, 1959.

"Eye, Human," *Encyclopedia Britannica*. Chicago: William Brenton Publisher, 1963 ed., Vol. 9, p. 5a, Vol. 3, p. 7, Vol. 20, p. 628c.

Faye, Eleanor E., *The Low Vision Patient: Clinical Experience with Adults and Children*. New York: Grune and Stratton, Inc., 1970.

Ferrell, Gabriel, *Story of Blindness*. Cambridge, Mass.: Harvard University Press, 1956.

Finestone, Samuel, *Aspects of the Travel Adjustment of Blind Persons*. New York: American Foundation for the Blind, 1960.

Garrett, James F., and Levine, Edna S., *Psychological Practices with the Physically Disabled*. New York: Columbia University Press, 1962.

Gowman, Allen G., *The War Blind in American Structure*. New York: American Foundation for the Blind, 1960.

Hall, Edward, *The Hidden Dimension*. Garden City, N.Y.: Doubleday & Co., Inc., 1969.

"Hearing," *Encyclopedia Britannica*. Vol. 11, pp. 296c–297c, Vol. 18, p. 720Bc, Vol. 20, p. 328d.

Hirsch, Monroe J., and Wick, Ralph E., eds., *Vision of the Aging Patient*. New York: Chilton Co., 1960.

Hunt, Sarah, and Cain, Edith, *Games the World Around*. New York: A. S. Barns & Co., 1941.

"Kinesthesis," *Encyclopedia Britannica*. Vol. 3, p. 450b, Vol. 2, p. 322.

Krause, Richard, *Recreation Today: Program Planning and Leadership*. New York: Appleton-Century-Crofts, 1966.

Lowenfeld, Bethold, *The Blind Preschool Child*. New York: American Foundation for the Blind, 1947.

Lowenfeld, Victor, *The Nature of Creative Activity*. London: Paul Ltd., Broadway House, Art Lane, 1939.

Lowenstein, Otto, *The Senses*. Baltimore: Penguin Books, 1966.

Lukoff, Irving Faber, and Whiteman, Martin, *The Social Sources of Adjustment to Blindness*. New York: American Foundation for the Blind.

Merrill, Toni, *Activities for the Aged and Infirm: A Handbook for the Untrained Worker*. Springfield, Ill.: Charles C Thomas, 1967.

Miller, Norman P., and Robinson, Diane M., *The Leisure Age*. Belmont, Calif.: Wadsworth Publishing Co., Inc., 1963.

Nash, Jay B., *Philosophy of Recreation and Leisure*. Dubuque, Iowa: William C. Brown Co., Publishers, 1933.

N.S.P.B. Fact Book, *Estimated Statistics on Blindness and Vision Problems*. New York: The National Society for the Prevention of Blindness, Inc., 1966.

Schneider, Leo, *You and Your Senses*. New York: Harcourt, Brace and World, 1956.

Scott, Robert A., *Making of Blind Men*. New York: Russell Sage Foundation, 1969.

Seamons, Gloria, *Swimming for the Blind*. Provo, Utah: Brigham Young University Press, 1961.

"Smell and Taste," *Encyclopedia Britannica*. Vol. 20, p. 819c, Vol. 16, p. 768d.

Sommers, Vita Stein, *The Influence of Parental Attitude and Social Environment on the Personality Development of Adolescent Blind*. New York: American Foundation for the Blind, Inc., 1944.

Wilson, Gertrude, and Ryland, Gladys, *Social Group Work Practice*. Boston: Houghton Mifflin Co., 1949

10 Recreation and the Economically Deprived

Courtesy Louis Marinoff, New York City Housing Authority

JAMES F. MURPHY

I think it is monstrous, such a state of society as exists in this city. Why, the children, thousands and thousands, have no place to play. . . . It is an offense for them to fly their kites. The children of the rich can go to Central Park, or out into the country in the summer time; but the children of the poor, for them there is no playground in the city but the streets; it is some charity excursion which takes them out for a day, only to return them again to the same sweltering condition. . . . We hold that the value of the land of this city, by reason of the presence of this great population, belongs to us to apply to the welfare of the people. Everyone should be entitled to share in it.[1]

By various accounts there are some 25 to 30 million Americans living below federal poverty standards, with an additional 15 million classified as "near poor." This means that individuals living below the poverty line are expected to subsist on 75 cents a day for food per person in a family of four and on a $1.50 a day for all other essential items.

The deterioration of many of America's cities, where some 20 percent of the urban residents earn less than the amount necessary for a minimum decent standard of living, is compounded when skilled people move out and are replaced by new migrants from the South. The new urban dwellers add to the already poor situation existing in the central cities which consist primarily of low-income families, unemployed people, the aged, and fatherless families. The future potential for a viable and successful recreation program is relatively slim based on current standards of service. The positive correlation between wholesome leisure pursuits with economically deprived people is rather low. The amount of discretionary money and time available to the poor for engagement in community recreation programs is almost nonexistent. A further dilemma to be considered is the high proportion of urban and rural poor slum residents that depend heavily on welfare payments (some 9 million Americans), often with dependent children and no father present.

Poverty in rural America is just as perplexing as the deterioration of the urban scene. In the past, the rural community provided the needed services for farmers and other agrarian people. Technological advancements have served to sharply reduce the manpower needs of agriculture, forestry, fisheries, and mining. From a recreation standpoint, it is important to realize that the larger communities and cities have assumed many of the economic and social functions of the small towns and villages.

The social upheaval that has occurred in America during the last decade has spread among many social institutions. Many deprived people have vented their hostility and frustration against those agencies most closely associated with administering services to them. Community recreation service might be next in line.

The problems of poor people have gained attention in the past few years. The "other America" has been exposed and the poor are no longer hidden under the guise of financial dependence. America is the richest country in the history of the world, and her ability to conquer diseases, build modern transportations systems, develop sophisticated communication techniques, and master delicate and intricate means of technology has transformed the country into the richest country on earth. Unfortunately, there are several millions of Americans who are living in poverty and despair. Poverty and affluence coexist in American life, seemingly in harmony with each other.

NATURE AND EXTENT OF POVERTY

As community recreation service has become more accessible to all groups of people, it has moved further away from neighborhood service to the underprivileged. The poor and various disadvantaged groups are the most in need of community-supported recreation services and have the least human and financial resources available. The degree of deprivation in America is shocking and most discouraging in light of the limited adjustments that have been made by social institutions which have been in a position to ameliorate the conditions of poverty.

Since the turn of the twentieth century, recreation service has steered away from human welfare considerations in the conduct of programs. Poverty is pervasive in America and a closer look at its dimensions will help reveal the ramifications of despair and isolation of one-fifth of the population. To be certain there are important considerations to be understood by the recreation practitioner.

The poor, or for the purposes of the chapter, the economically deprived, are defined as people who are not now maintaining a decent standard of living and whose basic needs exceed their means to satisfy them. The "cycle of poverty" has been well documented and does not need elaboration here. But the problems of poverty and disadvantagement are passed in predictable fashion from parent to child as the cruel legacy of poverty is continued and propagated from generation to generation.

> Poverty breeds poverty. A poor individual or family has a high probability of staying poor. Low incomes carry with them risks of illness; limitations on mobility; limited access to education, information, and training. Poor parents cannot give their children the opportunities for better health and education needed to improve their lot. Lack of motivation, hope, and incentive is more subtle but no less powerful than the lack of financial means.[2]

A description of the poor is revealed in Table 1, "Incidence of Family Poverty, 1966." Poverty takes its heaviest toll upon children and various youth classifications, minority groups, the unemployed, the rural populations, the elderly, and the female family head. Poverty in America has decreased somewhat over the past 25–30 years but there remains an ever-widening gap between the rich and the poor. The continued growth in real income might lead to speculation of the eventual elimination of poverty altogether. However, when poverty is defined relatively, there has not been any decrease since the end of World War II. Unfortunately for the poor, the increase in leisure, the availability of material goods, accessible mass communication in the form of radios, televisions and newspapers, the crowding of people into the cities, poor housing and highly expensive health care further depreciate the condition of the economically deprived.

America's riots of 1966 and 1967 were an unfortunate reminder of urban squalor and revealed the close association of poverty and the feelings of ineptitude and despair that were manifested in the nation's worst civil disorders since the Civil War.

TABLE 1.
INCIDENCE OF FAMILY POVERTY, 1966*

(Numbers in thousands)

Characteristic	All families				With male head				With female head			
		Poor				Poor				Poor		
	Total	Number	Per-cent	Percentage distribution	Total	Number	Per-cent	Percentage distribution	Total	Number	Per-cent	Percentage distribution
Total	48,922	6,086	12.4	100.0	43,751	4,276	9.8	100.0	5,172	1,810	35.0	100.0
Residence												
Nonfarm	46,225	5,598	12.1	92.0	41,199	3,835	9.3	89.7	5,026	1,764	35.1	97.5
Farm	2,697	488	18.1	8.0	2,552	441	17.3	10.3	145	47	32.4	2.6
Race												
White	44,017	4,375	9.9	71.9	40,007	3,264	8.2	76.3	4,010	1,111	27.7	61.4
Nonwhite	4,905	1,711	34.9	28.1	3,744	1,012	27.0	23.7	1,162	699	60.2	38.6
Age of head												
14–24	3,011	510	16.9	8.4	2,761	347	12.6	8.1	250	163	65.2	9.0
25–34	9,560	1,139	11.9	18.7	8,753	668	7.6	15.6	806	472	58.6	26.1
35–44	11,113	1,180	10.6	19.4	10,026	737	7.4	17.2	1,087	444	40.8	24.5
45–54	10,620	919	8.7	15.1	9,503	587	6.2	13.7	1,116	333	29.8	18.4
55–64	7,689	800	10.4	13.1	6,900	635	9.2	14.9	789	166	21.0	9.2
65 and over	6,929	1,538	22.2	25.3	5,807	1,304	22.5	30.5	1,122	234	20.9	12.9
Number of persons in family												
2	16,354	2,271	13.9	37.3	13,978	1,693	12.1	39.6	2,376	578	24.3	31.9
3	10,098	889	8.8	14.6	8,901	532	6.0	12.4	1,197	357	29.8	19.7
4	9,400	793	8.4	13.0	8,687	488	5.6	11.4	712	305	42.8	16.9
5	6,189	649	10.5	10.7	5,805	440	7.6	10.3	382	209	54.7	11.5
6	3,438	501	14.6	8.2	3,230	362	11.2	8.5	209	138	66.0	7.6
7 or more	3,443	984	28.6	16.2	3,146	762	24.2	17.8	296	222	75.0	12.3

Region												
Northeast	12,039	1,037	8.6	17.0	10,650	675	6.3	15.8	1,389	362	26.1	20.0
North Central	13,617	1,259	9.2	20.7	12,400	874	7.0	20.4	1,216	385	31.7	21.3
South	14,978	2,950	19.7	48.5	13,251	2,186	16.5	51.1	1,727	763	44.2	42.2
West	8,288	840	10.1	13.8	7,448	540	7.2	12.6	839	300	35.8	16.6
Type of family												
Male head	43,751	4,276	9.8	70.3	43,751	4,276	9.8	100.0				
Married, wife present	42,553	4,069	9.6	66.9	42,553	4,069	9.6	95.2				
Wife in paid labor force	15,005	743	5.0	12.2	15,005	743	5.0	17.4				
Wife not in paid labor force	27,548	3,326	12.1	54.7	27,548	3,326	12.1	77.8				
Other marital status	1,197	207	17.3	3.4	1,197	207	17.3	4.8				
Female head	5,172	1,810	35.0	29.7					5,172	1,810	35.0	100.0
Employment status and occupation of head												
Employed, March 1967	38,885	3,020	7.8	49.6	36,293	2,376	6.5	55.6	2,593	641	24.7	35.4
Professional and technical workers	5,338	129	2.4	2.1	5,050	107	2.1	2.5	286	22	7.7	1.2
Farmers and farm managers	1,588	315	19.8	5.2	1,572	309	19.7	7.2	16	6	—	.3
Managers, officials, and proprietors (except farm)	5,759	233	4.0	3.8	5,643	216	3.8	5.1	118	17	14.4	.9
Clerical and sales workers	5,146	225	4.4	3.7	4,323	124	2.9	2.9	823	100	12.2	5.5
Craftsmen and foremen	8,050	353	4.4	5.8	8,013	349	4.4	8.2	36	3	—	.2
Operatives	7,696	746	8.4	10.6	7,230	544	7.5	12.7	466	102	21.9	5.6
Service workers	3,011	585	19.4	9.6	2,192	212	9.7	5.0	820	373	45.5	20.6
Private household workers	282	154	54.6	2.5	13	2	—	—	270	152	56.3	8.4
Laborers (except mine)	2,297	533	23.2	8.9	2,270	515	22.7	12.0	28	18	—	1.0
Unemployed	904	248	27.4	4.1	780	180	23.1	4.2	124	68	54.8	3.8
Not in labor force	9,132	2,817	30.8	46.3	6,678	1,718	25.7	40.2	2,454	1,100	44.8	60.8
Number of earners in 1966												
None	4,073	1,978	48.6	32.5	3,017	1,216	40.3	28.4	1,056	762	72.2	42.1
1	20,451	2,620	12.8	43.0	18,163	1,892	10.4	44.2	2,288	729	31.9	40.3
2	17,992	1,112	6.2	18.3	16,608	891	5.4	20.8	1,384	221	16.0	12.2
3 or more	6,405	376	5.9	6.2	5,961	278	4.7	6.5	443	100	22.8	5.5

* Source of material: Mollie Orshansky. "The Shape of Poverty in 1966," *Social Security Bulletin* (March 1968), p. 11.

Some experts have argued that the War on Poverty was inaugurated to divert the civil rights movement into narrower
channels and the same time reduce its potential militancy.
Riots in the ghettos lent plausibility to interpretations that
connected riots with poverty or at least with the poverty-
linked phenomena suffered by blacks.[3]

Poverty is usually associated with hunger. However,
poverty in America may be deceiving to the neophyte who expects to converge on a two-room flat in Bedford Stuyvesant and
find children crawling around the floor gasping for their last
breath in an empty room. This is usually not the case. Of course,
significant numbers of homes are simply atrocious by any decent
standard and many are officially classified as unfit to live in.

In a study of Tunica County, Mississippi, the poorest
county in the poorest state, results revealed eight out of every
ten families have incomes of under $3,000. These figures are
poor by any standards; yet 52 percent own television sets, 46
percent own automobiles, and 37 percent own washing ma-
chines. These families have material possessions but seem to be
suffering from loss of spirit and hope. These possessions may be
relics of an earlier affluence or second-hand goods in disrepair
picked up from a wholesale dealer. Others may have been hand-
me-downs from relatives or friends. National figures demonstrate the relative degree of affluence among families with
incomes under $3,000:

79% own a television set.

51% own both a television set and a telephone.

73% own a washing machine.

19% have a dwelling unit that is not dilapidated and has hot
running water and a toilet and a bath for exclusive use.

14% bought a car last year.[4]

The above figures may be misleading although it seems as
if a high proportion of the families classified as poor have
sufficient material possessions. Herman P. Miller suggests that
material goods, such as ownership of a car or television set, may
actually be one of the contributing reasons for poverty because
they have purchased discretionary items at the expense of a

good diet, medical care, education, or other goods that would yield an increasingly profitable return.[5]

ETIOLOGY OF THE
ECONOMICALLY DEPRIVED

The lower classes are constantly faced with pressures of conformity (standardization of life style), repression and self-control, in addition to the feelings of guilt and competitive anxieties so prevalent in the middle-class. It may be that full participation in a highly mechanized society requires such an adaptation from the lower classes, although new and imaginative methods "must be pioneered in the cultivation of creative leisure for a large segment of the population and a reformulation of the 'productive economically rewarding work ethos' as the American way."[6]

A child who is middle-class and has access to an abundance of material goods is more apt to be successful partly because our society is predominately middle-class. "It could be argued that it is mostly the provinciality and intolerance of the middle-class attitude that condemn the lower-class to a tendency toward failure."[7]

MIDDLE-CLASS VERSUS
LOWER-CLASS VALUES

As can be ascertained from Tables 2, 3, and 4, middle-class values and those of the more financially secure include norms consistent with achievement, rationality, commitment to long-term goals, abstract learning, respect for authority, active manageability of the environment and self-restraint. These and other traits have assisted in the formulation of a very complex and cybernated society which demands a theoretical and behavioral adherence to such values. This tends to reinforce the middle-class way as the correct method for achieving success.

The poor and economically deprived are caught in a web of confusion as their necessary life adjustment to a world of inadequate and discriminatory housing, unstable employment, exploitation, poor health and public sanitation, and insufficient welfare relief causes them generally to assume a more prag-

TABLE 2

EMOTIONAL HEALTH

Child-rearing patterns reported to be more characteristic of families of children who are emotionally healthy compared with relevant patterns reported to be more characteristic of very poor families.

CONDUCIVE	LOW-INCOME
1. Respect for child as individual whose behavior is caused by a multiple of factors. Acceptance of own role in events that occur.	1. Misbehavior regarded as such in terms of concrete pragmatic outcomes; reasons for behavior not considered. Projection of blame on others.
2. Commitment to slow development of child from infancy to maturity; stresses and pressures of each stage accepted by parent because of perceived worth of ultimate goal of raising "happy," successful son or daughter.	2. Lack of goal commitment and of belief in long-range success; a main object for parent & child is to "keep out of trouble"; orientation toward fatalism, impulse gratification, and sense of alienation.
3. Relative sense of competence in handling child's behavior.	3. Sense of impotence in handling children's behavior, as well as in other areas.
4. Discipline chiefly verbal, mild, reasonable, consistent, based on needs of child & family & of society; more emphasis on rewarding good behavior than on punishing bad behavior.	4. Discipline harsh, inconsistent, physical, makes use of ridicule; based on whether child's behavior does or does not annoy parent.
5. Open, free, verbal communication between parent & child; control largely verbal.	5. Limited verbal communication; control largely physical.
6. Democratic rather than autocratic or laissez faire methods of rearing, with both parents in equalitarian but not necessarily interchangeable roles. Companionship between parents & children.	6. Authoritarian rearing methods; mother chief child-care agent; father, when in home, mainly a punitive figure. Little support and acceptance of child as an individual.
7. Parents view selves as generally competent adults, and are generally satisfied with themselves and their situation.	7. Low parental self-esteem, sense of defeat.
8. Intimate, expressive, warm relationship between parent & child, allowing for gradually increasing independence. Sense of continuing responsibility.	8. Large families; more impulsive, narcissistic parent behavior. Orientation to "excitement." Abrupt, early yielding of independence.
9. Presence of father in home and lack of severe marital conflict.	9. Father out of home (under certain circumstances).
10. Free verbal communication about sex, acceptance of child's sex needs, channeling of sex drive through "healthy" psychological defenses, acceptance of slow growth toward impulse control & sex satisfaction in marriage; sex education by both father and mother.	10. Repressive, punitive attitude about sex, sex questioning, & experimentation. Sex viewed as exploitative relationship.

Table 2 (*continued*)

11. Acceptance of child's drive for aggression but channeling it into socially approved outlets.	11. Alternating encouragement & restriction of aggression, primarily related to consequences of aggression for parents.
12. In favor of new experiences; flexible.	12. Distrust of new experiences. Constricted life, rigidity.
13. Happiness of parental marriage.	13. High rates of marital conflict and family breakdown.

Source of material: Catherine S. Chilman, *Growing Up Poor*. Washington, D.C.: U.S. Government Printing Office, 1967, pp. 28–29.

TABLE 3

ACADEMIC ACHIEVEMENT

Child-rearing patterns reported to be more characteristic of families of children who are educationally achieving compared with relevant patterns reported to be more characteristic of very poor families.

CONDUCIVE	LOW-INCOME
1. Infant and child given freedom within consistent limits to explore and experiment.	1. Limited freedom for exploration (partly imposed by crowded and dangerous aspects of environment).
2. Wide range of parent-guided experiences, offering visual, auditory, kinesthetic, and tactile stimulation from early infancy.	2. Constricted lives led by parents: fear and distrust of the unknown.
3. Goal-commitment and belief in long-range success potential.	3. Fatalistic, apathetic attitudes.
4. Gradual training for and value placed on independence.	4. Tendency for abrupt transition to independence: parents tend to "lose control" of children at early age.
5. Educational-occupational success of parents; model as continuing "learners" themselves; high achievement needs of parents.	5. Tendency to educational-occupational failure; reliance on personal versus skill attributes of vocational success.
6. Reliance on objective evidence.	6. Magical, rigid thinking.
7. Much verbal communication, with a flexible, conceptual style and emphasis on both speaking and listening.	7. Little verbal communication, especially of an interactive, conceptual, flexible kind.
8. High value placed on academic achievement.	8. Academic achievement not highly valued.
9. Democratic, rather than authoritarian child-rearing attitudes.	9. Authoritarian child-rearing attitudes.
10. Collaborative attitudes toward the school system.	10. Fear and distrust of the school system.
11. Values placed on abstractions.	11. Pragmatic, concrete values.

Source of material: Chilman, ibid., p. 43.

TABLE 4

SOCIAL ACCEPTABILITY

Behavioral characteristics reported to be more characteristic of socially acceptable school children compared to the relevant child-rearing patterns that are reportedly more characteristic of very poor families.

CONDUCIVE	LOW-INCOME
1. Social skills in dress, manners, speech, games, etc., according to middle-class norms.	1. Little skill in prevalent middle-class behaviors.
2. Sensitivity to feelings and attitudes of others.	2. Slight awareness of subtleties of interpersonal relations.
3. Ability to be flexible & adaptable to group decisions.	3. Tendency to be rigid & nonconforming to middle-class norms.
4. Good impulse control.	4. Poor impulse control.
5. Cheerful, happy, self-assured attitude.	5. Low self-esteem, distrust, tendency to hostile aggression and/or withdrawal.
6. Respect for other children's property rights.	6. Ambivalent attitudes towards property rights.
7. Middle-class (or higher) socioeconomic status.	7. Lower-lower class.
8. Accepting of self and others.	8. Alienation from middle-class; fear, distrust, hostility.
9. Academically successful.	9. Academic failures.
10. Values of neatness and cleanliness.	10. Little value placed on neatness and cleanliness.

Source of material: Chilman, ibid., p. 59.

matic, fatalistic, and alienated view toward life. The distrustful and despairing way of life of the poor is not as readily adaptive to the more goal-committed, involved and verbal style of the middle-class, and this may contribute to high rates of mental breakdowns and emotional instability.

PSYCHOLOGICAL DEPRESSION

The lack of ambition prevalent in depressed areas is engendered from a reaction by the poor to failures and frustrations associated with ghetto life and deprivation. They represent an overwhelming barrier to achievement and hope. This psychological dilemma is a greater burden for many of the economically deprived than that of the extremely competitive, anxious, middle-class drives.

It is hypothesized that emotional depression may be the prevalent life style of many lower-class members and that this depression has its origins in overwhelming anxiety associated with the almost constant powerful frustrations and threats which surround the slum-dweller from infancy to old age.[8]

To some extent it can be generalized that the poor have doubts about the degree of control they exercise over their own destiny, and thus a feeling of anomie and little sense of autonomy exists in depressed areas. The degree to which impoverished people must then claim virtue and satisfaction becomes an immediate ambition with visions of the future an unrealistic and unforseeable goal. There are positive values in mild frustration and research points to the potential ego-strength associated with mild anxiety but the constant and overpowering frustrations of the poor make self-fulfillment an untenable goal.

PSYCHOLOGICAL IMMATURITY

Much of the behavior of the poor is reflected in "anxiety-induced depression" associated with the frustrations and despair of slum life.[9] To the middle-class layman or blue-collar worker this is often viewed as immature. The poor's tendency toward magical thinking, low threshold of tolerance, lack of goal commitment, impulsive activity and physical behavioral styles seems most related to the repression that occurs when people succumb to hopelessness.

The lack of support from the helping services, including recreation service, contributes to the problem of poor people to identify with reasonably attainable goals. Standardization of service in terms of styling it along middle-class value lines has had the net result of by-passing many deprived people who either can't identify with the programs or relate to the methods of service.

HEALTH FACTORS

The quality of health for poor people is devastating. Apathy, lack of goal commitment, and resignation may be due in part to poor nutrition and inadequate medical care. Surveys by the National Opinion Research Center have shown that poorer people are less informed about the symptoms of various diseases and do not readily recognize psychological problems.

Without adequate medicine, a competent physician (or more likely none at all), and family support, it is more easily understood why recreation programs may often have such a low-level priority for the poor. There is really no neighborhood health care for the poor, as most doctors have either moved out of slum neighborhoods in metropolitan communities or migrated to the "nicer" areas of big cities from the poorer, rural areas. Outpatient clinics and emergency rooms in hospitals have been the only source of medical assistance for most poor people. Many deprived Americans don't even receive this meager assistance.

Additionally, there is mounting evidence that malnutrition in early childhood may cause permanent and irremediable mental retardation. An unfortunate circumstance for children of poor families is the fact that they tend to drop out of school which later results in their receiving low-paying jobs and increases the risk of their being poor adults. The elimination of these barriers has become a mystical fantasy for the poor who see an imperfect opportunity structure and can't visualize social services changing their objectives from treating symptoms to that of dealing with the causes of pathos.

NEIGHBORHOOD LIFE—URBAN SCENE

Life in the ghetto has been characterized by some people as being "one step beyond hell." The degree of misery associated with urban slum living has a marked impact on the stability of the ghetto resident. According to Chilman "there is considerable evidence that the urban social life of the very poor may hold little security or pleasure for them, especially in public housing projects or other congested dwelling units in urban areas."[10]

The slum neighborhood generally has less organization and social structure. Even by playing simulation games, such as "Ghetto," the middle-class layman can readily determine that low-income areas have a great number of people who suffer from social pathologies and lack the internal strength and ability to deal with these problems. Of course, these problems are real, not imagined. The poorer areas of cities need assistance and self-help guidance to organize their stricken communities into action. Recreation, as a facet of the community organization process, must become part of the team effort needed to ameliorate social problems besetting poor people.

> If the probability of falling victim to a social pathology is greatly increased if one is brought up in a slum, then the slum is more than a private problem. It is a public and social problem. Private action cannot be expected to cure the social contagions of the slum environment any more than it can deal adequately with contagious diseases. They demand organized action, and organization is what many slums above all lack.[11]

The crowding of people into the cities is resulting in severe strains being placed on social services, already understaffed and overworked. The opportunity for open space and a breath of fresh air in congested inner city areas seems like a fairy tale full of hope but never to become a reality.

The concentration of large numbers of people into relatively little space certainly denies the average citizen elbow room and privacy. To the economically deprived, the lack of space is just one more contributing factor to their imprisonment in poverty. The quality of the recreation environment has lessened the past several years, thus further inhibiting the leisure potential for the nation's poor. To even the most competent, affluent person, an inadequate environment will serve to restrict his participation in it. If an individual lacks motivation and the environment is unfit for participation, he will fail to exercise his physical, emotional, and mental ability to enrich his life. One can easily see that the economically deprived lack basic skills and attitudes to deal effectively in the middle-class oriented society, and any further depreciation of the ecology of the planet will ruin any chances of a leisure renaissance in the ghetto.

> Our increasingly congested cities are already depriving many people of the satisfaction of open space. As cities continue to grow, it will be even more difficult to find a quiet park, an open space, or a secluded beach.[12]

The potential for leisure pursuits is seemingly endless and the low-income resident is probably so tantalized with the constant bombardment of the mass media describing the cultured life of the new leisure-age, that wholesome recreation may become a sadistic form of exclusion for the economically deprived.

Table 5 depicts recreation expenditures in the United States. The amount of money spent on commercial recreation opportunities, including bowling, billiards, skating, swimming,

TABLE 5

ANNUAL CONSUMER SPENDING ON RECREATION IN THE UNITED STATES IN THE LATE 1960's

1. Books, maps, magazines, newspapers, and sheet music	$ 5.6
2. Nondurable toys and sports supplies	3.9
3. Wheel goods, durable toys, sports equipment, pleasure aircraft, and boats	3.4
4. Radio and television receivers, records and musical instruments	7.4
5. Radio and television repair	1.2
6. Camping equipment and supplies	5.0
7. Swimming pools and accessories	1.0
8. Equipment and supplies for home "do-it-yourself" activities	12.0
9. Motion picture houses, gross receipts	1.9
10. Admissions to legitimate theaters and opera, and entertainment of nonprofit institutions	.6
11. Spectator sports admissions	.4
12. Gross receipts, including dues and fees, of clubs and fraternal organizations (luncheon, athletic and social clubs, and school fraternities)	.9
13. Commercial participant amusements, including billiard parlors; bowling alleys; dancing, riding, skating, shooting, and swimming places; amusement devices and parks, etc.	1.6
14. Other purchases and fees, including photography, dogs and other pets, collectors' and other hobbies expenses, camping fees, etc.	2.4
15. Pari-mutuel betting on thoroughbred and trotting horse racing	5.4
16. Domestic pleasure travel	32.0
17. Foreign pleasure travel	5.0
18. Home entertaining	7.0
19. Purchase of alcoholic beverages	14.5
20. Purchase of tobacco and smoking supplies	9.2
21. Hunting and fishing licenses, equipment and related expenses	4.0
22. Lawn and garden supplies and equipment	2.0
Total (Stated in billions of dollars)	$125.9

Source of material: Kraus, Richard, "The Economics of Recreation Today," *Parks and Recreation*, 5:20, June, 1970.

etc., is ordinarily beyond the discretionary means of 30 million poor people who must subsist on less than $3,600 a year for an urban family of four. The plight of the poor is compounded if there are no public tax-supported park and recreation programs in operation to provide constructive and wholesome outlets for leisure expression.

Dr. Richard Kraus states that if this condition persists or if public park and recreation programs have to rely heavily upon fees and charges to support capital improvement and current operating programs, the poor will increasingly be excluded from all but the most minimal and barren recreation facilities.

> The poor are automatically prevented from enjoying most of the forms of private or commercial recreation which are available to the rest of society. The urban family living on less than $3,000 or $3,500 a year does not usually own a car, and vacation travel by other means would be prohibitive. Spectator events, social functions, hobbies, cultural activities, games and sports—participation in all of these is restricted not only by the lack of financial means, but because the poor tend to lack a constructive concept of personal leisure.[13]

Realizing that many commercial recreation opportunities are unavailable to the poor, greater attention should be focused on local, state, and federal government recreation agencies, as well as voluntary social organizations to reach out to the economically deprived in great need of leisure services.

A balance must be achieved in the offering of park and recreation services which will more truly reflect the nation's $126 billion expenditures for leisure pursuits. This figure does not reflect the poorly staffed and equipped inner city playground, broken-down Indian reservation swing and slide set, dilapidated community recreation halls in Appalachia, or the littered park in the barrio. This figure which represents unobligated, enjoyable recreational pursuits, has little meaning in deprived communities where play is still viewed as a frivolous luxury.

> More income, of course, cannot buy happiness, and it is by no means obvious that satisfaction rides along with income. Perhaps the very poor in contemporary America feel most

dissatisfied with their level of income; perhaps not. It may be those who are most dissatisfied have incomes just below the average and see all about them evidence of a generally high standard of living to which they aspire but cannot reach.[14]

Just as there has to be a realization that educational programs are likely to be inadequate if they are not supported by auxillary services, so too will traditional recreation offerings which begin to service the special needs of low-income groups. There needs to be a reciprocal enrichment program in recreation and leisure service in order to cope with the multifaceted problems of economic deprivation. A student who was a member of the author's class in Philosophy of Recreation and Leisure a few years ago, depicted some of the special problems encountered when attempting to provide recreation service in disadvantaged communities.

The white leaders (recreation leaders) cannot relate to the black children. Also, there are not enough black leaders to help the black children. The programs that are set up are not relevant in the black community. The programs are set up for a typical neighborhood; not thought out in terms of their application to ghetto life. The black children of the ghetto cannot relate to this type of program, so they loose interest in participating in the recreation program. When the youth are not involved in the planning and participation of recreation programs there is a tendency for this to lead into a social problem, often called juvenile delinquency.[15]

NEIGHBORHOOD LIFE—RURAL SCENE

Approximately every fourth rural American is poor. Only twenty-nine percent of our population, but forty-one percent of all economically deprived Americans, live in rural areas.

Most of the rural poor are white—11 million of the 14 million. But rural Negroes, Indian Americans, and Mexican Americans have very high poverty rates, and 60 percent of rural nonwhite families are poor. There are about 600,000 Indian Americans, two-thirds of them on reservations or on individual allotments. About 75 percent of all rural Indian families are poverty-stricken, and more than 300,000 rural Mexican Americans are poor.[16]

There are many startling facts about the health of the rural poor and the disease-ridden children and chronic nature of disease among all age groups. Malnutrition is even more widespread. Infant mortality is far higher among rural poor than among the least privileged group in urban areas.

The rate of unemployment nationally fluctuates between 4 and 6 percent but in rural areas the average is about 18 percent. Among the farmworkers, a study undertaken a few years ago revealed that underemployment runs as high as 37 percent. Among Indians living on reservations, the unemployment rate runs as high as 40 to 50 percent. There is a chronic illiteracy rate in rural areas and a sad fact is that more than 3 million rural adults are classified as illiterate.

Many of the poor live under abhorrent conditions. The migrant worker lives in unbelievably poor circumstances with Indian reservations containing similar heavy concentrations of poverty. However, rural poverty occurs in Appalachia, the Southwest, the Upper Great Lakes region, in all sections of our nation. The potential for public assistance and social service is almost unlimited in rural communities because they are so terribly depleted from technological change which has transformed the base of the American economy from the farm into the city. As previously mentioned, the community in rural poverty has all but disappeared as an effective institution.

> The changes in rural America have rendered obsolete many of the political boundaries to villages and counties. Thus these units operate on too small a scale to be practicable. Their tax base has eroded as their more able-bodied wage earners left for jobs elsewhere. In consequence the public services in the typical poor rural community are grossly inadequate in number, magnitude, and quality. Local government is no longer able to cope with local needs.[17]

A balance must be achieved to equate the amount of federal and private money being poured into the urban areas dealing with the poor. A more effective method must be developed to distribute social and economic assistance to the rural poor. This equity in commitment will require that the various anti-poverty programs will have to be directed with equal force to the rural poor as well as to the urban slum dweller. Perhaps some of the problems besetting the cities would be diminished if larger numbers of rural immigrants coming to the metropolitan areas were more properly prepared.

Small rural communities can and have accomplished much in the field of recreation. For years, New Hampshire had a special representative maintained by the National Recreation Association who organized communities to use their own recreation resources and make productive use of them. Communities were able:

> to turn a deserted Grange Hall into a village community center; to develop a ski slope or a lake for their own use; to revive local crafts; to bring young and old together for folk dancing and family camping.[18]

There are some excellent examples of programs which have reached out to all of the people. Kern County, California with a population of over 300,000 and an area of 8,170 square miles (larger than the State of New Jersey), has done an exceptional job of meeting specific needs of local people. There is at least one park in every community with several regional parks scattered throughout the county that provide camping facilities, ski lifts, golf, barbecues, fishing, ball games, children's play, archery, riding, a zoo, midget race track, etc.

The rising number of rural recreation enterprises being established will help the local economy of an area and provide job opportunities so badly needed by the rural poor. They will also help provide some of the badly needed recreation opportunities which are now lacking in many of the depressed rural communities.

The Bureau of Outdoor Recreation has strengthened the recreation potential in rural areas, especially with its financial assistance to impoverished communities that enables recreation facilities to be developed. Like any effective program, plans will probably be difficult to implement unless there is a substantial amount of human initiative engendered to organize the poor into action.

LEISURE CLASSES

The problems associated with widespread leisure have received considerable attention in recent years. Donald N. Michael has predicted the evolution of four leisure classes during the transition period of the application of cybernation (the combined use of automation and computers).[19]

1. *The Unemployed.* will consist of people who are poorly educated, displaced service workers, and well-trained but displaced white-collar workers. For the poorly educated, insecurity and uselessness will be present. There will be a low level of recreation literacy prevalent with the undereducated while the better educated will be making the agonizing shift in style of living required of the unemployed. The effects of leisure on family members of this group will be corrosive and disruptive to their life style.

2. *The Low-Salaried Employees Working Short Hours.* including many people who will drift into this class as a result of being displaced by cybernation. The overall threat of automation will encourage "moonlighting" for low-salaried employees. Severe psychological and social problems may be a possibility if they cannot find more money or have the motivation or the knowledge to search out different activities. If shorter hours are the rule for this group, damaging social problems, including frustrating, ambiguous personal relationships will occur in family life.

3. *The Adequately Paid to High-Salaried Group Working Short Hours.* will have the greatest opportunities for using extra leisure in a cybernated world. This group will represent professional, semi-professional or skilled workers who will command good salaries and possess a high degree of recreation literacy. They will be the most effective group to pass on attitudes and knowledge which will be needed to live in a cybernated world. This group will produce and consume most of its own leisure activities.

4. *High-Salaried Group, Working Long Hours.* with little or no forseeable change in their status. The group is represented mostly by overworked professionals and executives with a seemingly high level of recreation literacy but with no time

available for leisure pursuits. There is no prospect for these individuals to change their present condition from being over-burdened with little or no more leisure available to them.

The low-salaried workers who will be frustrated in not being able to find another job may present the greatest problem for society as differentiated from the unemployed group. According to Michael, our knowledge of how low-income workers become voluntarily interested in adult education is far greater than that of the problem of knowing how to stimulate the interests and change attitudes associated with a large population displaced by cybernation.

We have previously equated work and security as being synonymous and while out-of-work people will be bombarded by advertising glamourizing recreation, further frustrations of not being able to finance commercial pastimes will pose overwhelming emotional problems for the poor.

The prospect of leisure in the future for the economically deprived groups is less glittering than it is for most people. Attempts will have to be made to encourage family stability and acquisition of knowledge suitable for application in a cybernated society. Interpersonal relations among the poor could even cause longer, more damaging effects than the lack of money for the disadvantaged. The added humiliation of second-rate recreation opportunities available in a polluted environment will serve to bore the less affluent. There will have to be pressure to make recreation more visual and applicable on a local basis in disadvantaged areas than is presently characteristic of most centralized, standard park and recreation operations.

PROGRAM PLANNING CONSIDERATIONS

It is agreed by most people engaged in social service that the poor need special assistance with respect to their involvement and participation in leisure-service programs. The disadvantaged require a compensatory approach to their leisure problems. However, the mere addition of people, equipment, and special services do not by themselves constitute compensatory recreation. Recreators must strike at the root and consequences of disadvantagement in order to assure that community recreation service will have a chance of ameliorating deprivation.

The recognition of differences in program offerings as they might affect various ethnic and income groups was perceived at the outset of the recreation movement. The National Recreation Association as early as 1911 in the publication, *The Normal Course in Play*, recognized the different needs and conditions that confronted handicapped, foreign-born, and minority groups. Butler perceived different patterns of leisure expression related to nationality, race, occupation, education, economic status, and standard of living and suggested prior investigation be undertaken by the programmer when planning activities for people of a given neighborhood or community.

> A program which appeals to a cultured, well-to-do community may fail in an industrial town with a high percentage of underprivileged foreign-born. . . . Lighted tennis courts are of limited value in a low-income neighborhood for recreation, so programs must be provided near their homes. On the other hand, in neighborhoods where most families own automobiles, people will drive a considerable distance to take part in a craft, dance, drama, or other group activity.[20]

Butler also stressed the belief that community recreation departments were one of the most powerful agencies for absorbing the various nationality groups into society. He felt that the foreign-born citizens should be encouraged to participate as members of the community as well as participants identifiable with their nationality affiliation, to facilitate ethnic pride.[21]

Early in its history recreation stressed the importance of meeting the special needs of less privileged groups. Much of this concern was built into the initial philosophy of community recreation service but became diffused when it became clear that all people needed recreation.

Some early twentieth-century examples of special efforts employed to serve the disadvantaged are included in the following program description summaries.

1) Cincinnati's Recreation Department was one of the few city recreation departments in the country that inaugurated a special program for transients (similar to migrant workers of today) in an attempt to draw them into wholesome recreation

programs. They began their program in 1933. The early days of the depression brought to the country severe unemployment problems. Special centers conducted programs for the unemployed and their families. The centers were usually kept open longer than normally operated, for the duration of the crisis. Some programs attempted to provide work-oriented vocational skills to the unemployed.

> During the early depression period workshops were established in several cities to provide a place where mechanics, carpenters, and others out of employment could carry on constructive work in their respective fields and also where the unemployed could spend some of their unwanted leisure.[22]

2) Reading, Pennsylvania provided many hours of satisfaction for residents of orphanages and sanitariums. A trained leader, financed by the Junior League, would conduct such programs as storytelling, handicrafts, games, holiday programs, and pageants. The recognition that many children had limited play opportunities and materials caused many departments to establish toy loan centers. Toys were usually lent out for a period of one week to children in nearby neighborhoods. These programs were ordinarily sponsored by a number of community agencies.

3) San Francisco's Recreation Department was one of the first (1941) and most successful recreation agencies to provide service in public housing developments. According to Butler:

> The program was of vital importance to the thousands of newcomers to the city, both white and Negro, many of whom came from the deep South and worked on a three-shift basis, to the Japanese-Americans who returned to their home city from relocation centers, and to the many refugee families liberated in the Philippines.[23]

Unfortunately, programs were generally unavailable to the low-income individual, who worked long hours and had little time for recreation. The unemployed, disadvantaged person had little concern for frivolity when his life orientation was predicated on just surviving. Generally, recreation programs for the economically deprived were either conducted in an institutionalized form—in orphanages, hospitals, correctional facilities—or in the settlement house environment where recreation concerns were part of the total welfare program offerings. Public recreation agencies were not as influential in meeting the special needs of deprived groups after the turn of the century. As recreation became an accepted function of local government, it moved away from the vested interests of individuals living in deprived neighborhoods.

A restoration of the earlier view of socially motivated community recreation service has developed since 1960. The quickening pace of urban life and the anxieties of dealing with day-to-day happenings characteristic of Marshall McLuhan's "electric age," have brought hardships and problems to the economically deprived who are unable to enjoy many of the benefits of automated living. Meeting certain essential health, education, and welfare needs through recreation service is now seen as a realistic approach of reaching millions of low-income and poor Americans.

The anti-poverty push of the federal government in the 1960's brought increased focus on the value and potential of organized recreation service as an effective and needed weapon in the "war on poverty." As Professor Kraus has observed, recreation participation in Community Action Programs (created under the Economic Opportunity Act of 1964) was intended not only to meet the critical recreational and cultural needs of youth and adults but also to stimulate new processes of community organization among the alienated and deprived Americans living in poverty.[24]

Creating pride and initiating badly needed jobs in the economically depressed areas were major goals of anti-poverty programs in the 1960's. The value of stressing self-help skills and extending decision-making into the poorer neighborhoods was seen as an effort to have the economically deprived become more involved in the direction and influence of their own lives. Not all programs succeeded and not every program was clearly defined, but efforts to reach citizens cut off from the mainstream of life were successful to the extent that the deprived began to share in the destiny of the community.

However, the problem of adequate funding in deprived neighborhoods continues in many public recreation programs as the majority of middle-class and upper-class voters tend to defeat bond issues and programs centered in disadvantaged areas, limiting the potential of recreation service in depressed sections of cities. This has proven to be the case in many cities across the country where poorer citizens have been deprived of adequate park and recreation facilities.

> The lowest income parts of the city have an even smaller share of recreation area than they have of personal income, while the higher income sections have relatively generous park and recreation areas. The poorest people, who most need easily accessible parks and playgrounds, often have them least. . . . One of the great myths of the outdoor recreation field is that free public parks are a boon to "poor" people; actually it is the poor who frequently lack them.[25]

The recognition by the recreation profession that there is and will always be a segment of the population at the bottom of the economic ladder is an important prerequisite to be realized, especially if the impoverished are to be allowed to share in America's abundance. According to Harrington, America's middle-class attempted to remove poverty from the realities of twentieth-century living and that to a degree the poor have been invisible and forgotten people isolated from contact with others. Harrington's poignant description of America's poor people is said to have stimulated the Kennedy and Johnson anti-poverty programs. Sadly, poverty was a recognizable problem at the turn of the century, and now it is somewhat of a myth to many affluent Americans, untouched by the ugliness of despair.

> The poor still inhabit the miserable housing in the central area, but they are increasingly isolated from contact with, or sight of, anybody else. Middle-class women coming in from Suburbia on a rare trip may catch the merest glimpse of the other America on the way to an evening at the theater, but their children are segregated in suburbia schools. The business or professional man may drive along the fringes of slums in a car or bus, but it is not an important experience to him. The failures, the unskilled, the disabled, the aged, and the minorities are right there, across the tracks, where they have always been. But hardly anyone else is.[26]

The Baltimore Bureau of Recreation a few years ago took stock of its services and was generally pleased to discover some 60 percent of the city's population was being served through public, private, or voluntary leisure service agencies, with some 15 percent of the city financially independent enough to take care of its own leisure needs. Another 15 percent were unserviceable for a number of reasons, leaving 10 percent of the people without recreation leadership and facilities. Mr. John G. Williams, then Superintendent, recognized that this segment of the population (100,000 people) consisted primarily of minority and low-income youth, "undesirables," and various alienated groups.

In effect, Baltimore realized what the Kerner Commission had reported in 1968, that recreation programs and facilities were lacking in areas where they were most critically needed. Baltimore implemented a program of instant and carryover recreation programs through the use of mobile Fun Wagons, Traveling Playleaders, and portable swimming pools. These programs were set up in areas of the city where recreation was not normally available. Indigenous leaders from these neighborhoods were hired to help staff the programs and efforts were made to build confidence and pride in disadvantaged sectors of the city, cut off from the mainstream of cultural and social participation in society.

The Kerner Commission reported that inadequate recreation facilities and programs were the fifth most important cause of the 1967 summer riots in America. Recreation and education were found to be comparable in intensity of dissatisfaction by ghetto residents. Recreation was found to be an even more significant grievance than the ineffectiveness of the political structure, discriminatory administration of justice, inadequate municipal services, and inadequate welfare programs. Perhaps even more disconcerting was the fact that poor and unsatisfactory recreation facilities were the proximate cause or issue in several of the violent outbreaks of 1967.

However, attempts were begun as early as 1964 to "cool off" the inner city by recreation departments, largely under the auspices of the federal government, but these crash programs were limited to only the summer months. As Kraus mentions, recreation seemed to be the newly found answer to the problems of alienated poor people and the panacea for all of the ills of the slum, once its value was "recognized."

> In city after city, crash programs were mounted which flooded poverty neighborhoods with rapidly expanded sports programs late into the night and on weekends; with "ethnic" dance, music, art, and theater; with portable pools; with mobile science programs and puppet theaters; with mass entertainment by rock and roll bands; vacation day camps; cultural opportunities and remedial education; with last-minute construction and staffing of vest-pocket parks and mobile play units, and a host of other emergency recreation services.[27]

Unfortunately, many of the crash programs ended in August, leaving nine months for the ghetto resident to fend for himself in the crowded, dilapidated, and crime-ridden environment of the slums. By abruptly ending the badly needed recreation outlets and cultural activities, urban slum dwellers were expected to gain a new and positive image of themselves and manifest more socially desirable forms of behavior. Summer crash programs did expose participants to new areas of leisure expression and, to some extent, they served the function of a "threshold" experience which channeled the economically deprived into new forms of involvement in community life. Equally as productive was the hiring of indigenous neighborhood youth and adults as paraprofessionals (sub-professionals) in human service career programs. To many of the new careerists, federally funded crash programs led to expanded opportunities in professional fields including park and recreation service.

NEEDS INDEX

Methods for determining the allocation and extent of need for recreation facilities and programs should be explored more thoroughly in the 1970's. The City of Los Angeles has experimented with and implemented a "needs index" approach to the provision of recreation service in areas of the city with the greatest social need.

Three assumptions made prior to the application of the "recreation needs instrument" were: 1) there are measurable social characteristics and neighborhood recreation resources which indicate comparative need for recreation and youth services by area, communities, or neighborhoods in an urban setting; 2) all citizens have important basic needs for recreation services, but due to different socioeconomic characteristics and interests, they have differing needs for recreation services; and 3) priorities in community-subsidized recreation service should go to those experiencing maximum social pressures from density of population, number of youth, low income, and evidences of social disorganization.[28]

The recognition of variances in neighborhood density and organization, distribution of recreation facilities and leadership, and socioeconomic status of families has assisted the park and recreation department of Los Angeles to assign priority to space acquisition, facility development, and staff assignment in areas of the city in greatest need. All people have a need for recreation, and this is not to say that the poor have a more legitimate claim to the right of leisure expression. One must recognize that the economically deprived person often lacks the basic knowledge, attitude, skills, and habits necessary for voluntary participation in recreation programs. The middle and upper classes are usually more capable of satisfying their leisure desires independently and their interests are ordinarily quite different from the poor.

A comparison between the "resource index" and the "need index," as depicted in Table 6, will yield a "comparative priority of need for recreation services." The instrument was utilized as part of a study of recreation needs in South Central Los Angeles following the 1965 Watts riots. In addition to it being incorporated by the Recreation and Park Department and City Planning Department, the "needs index" is being used by the Los Angeles Recreation and Youth Services Planning Council in its studies.

Part of the need to identify priorities in the administration of community recreation service can be understood by virtue of the accustomed practice of face-to-face leaders in operating recreation programs. Dr. David Gray refers to the present practice of leadership as subscribing to the "chain-link fence" philosophy. The deleterious effect of the philosophy is that it binds the recreation staff to the center or school playground to organize activities, effectively control equipment, develop a safe

TABLE 6

AN INSTRUMENT FOR DETERMINING COMPARATIVE PRIORITY OF NEED
FOR NEIGHBORHOOD RECREATION SERVICES

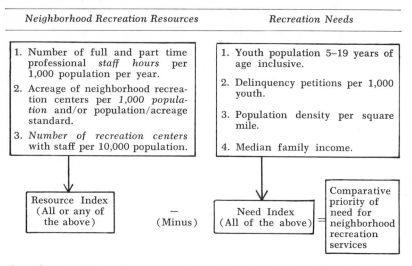

Neighborhood Recreation Resources   *Recreation Needs*

1. Number of full and part time professional *staff hours* per 1,000 population per year.
2. Acreage of neighborhood recreation centers per *1,000 population* and/or population/acreage standard.
3. *Number of recreation centers* with staff per 10,000 population.

1. Youth population 5–19 years of age inclusive.
2. Delinquency petitions per 1,000 youth.
3. Population density per square mile.
4. Median family income.

Resource Index (All or any of the above) — (Minus) Need Index (All of the above) = Comparative priority of need for neighborhood recreation services

Formula used to determine comparative priority of need for neighborhood recreation services

Source of material: Staley, Edwin J., "Determining Neighborhood Recreation Priorities: An Instrument," *Journal of Leisure Research,* 1: 71, Winter, 1969.

facility, and guarantee that all participants comply with the rules and policies of the grounds. In effect, top scholars, researchers, and practitioners are being recruited into education to prepare capable students for positions as facility managers and center custodians.

There is a more recent view held by some educators and practitioners that recreation education should be preparing individuals to play a more active role in the community; to interact with people and assist in the improvement of the community and help tackle some of the social problems besetting American society.

The future will require that a professional recreator have the ability to perceive social ills in community life and assist other community leaders in translating these problems into positive action programs designed to improve the quality or "livability" of the city. The recreation potential of a given neighborhood will increase in proportion to the quality of the health, education, and welfare of a neighborhood. An individual who can cope with his environment or at least has some degree of manageability over his welfare, has a greater chance of being emotionally suited and prepared for learning new skills and acquiring knowledge in a recreation setting.

The ability of a deprived person to function in an urban or rural environment could depend upon the leisure-service professional who will assume the role of a community catalyst. He will serve to stimulate, interpret, organize, advise, teach, and instill a sense of purpose in the lives of disadvantaged people. Recreation is viewed by many of the poor as a rather meaningless and shallow concept when they do not have the degree of preparedness necessary for participation in constructive leisure pursuits.

ORGANIZING RECREATION ACTIVITIES
FOR THE POOR

As previously discussed, the Report of the National Advisory Commission on Civil Disorders confirmed the fact that there were inadequate recreation facilities and organized programs in slum areas. It was further stated that the lack of recreation service provided ghetto residents was a major cause of the nation's riots in 1967. Unfortunately, the Commission did not identify recreation as a form of community service which could improve the status and ameliorate the living conditions of the urban poor.

According to Dr. Sal Prezioso, former President of the National Recreation and Park Association, rioters vent their hostility in a manner which reflects the only leisure activities known to them. The slum environment often provides only destructive forms of leisure and takes the shape of pathological involvement.

> It should be noted that most participants in the recurring inner city civil disorders are adolescents and young adults— the age groups that require more recreational services than any other. The antisocial activities of many of these young people are often extensions of the only organized leisure activities they know—vandalism, gang fights, and crime.[29]

There must be a realization that rural areas also are in need of greater and improved recreation service. Rural areas are fast becoming the forgotten regions of the country and rural inhabitants are just as ignored. Recreation may be the only means of social contact for the rural poor, and in small towns the recreation programs may serve as the only link a deprived person has with constructive leisure. Possibly the only prospect of hope for most of the rural poor is found in the efforts made by the diligent recreator who can help transform dusty, barren acreage into bountiful, wholesome areas for satisfying leisure activities.

Much of the success of the recreation program is found in the amount of organization and planning evident in the conduct of activities. The Office of Economic Opportunity has established guidelines for funding its youth development programs.[30] Among the factors stressed by OEO are:

1. *Youth Involvement.* The most successful programs have been ones in which youth were directly involved in the planning and conduct of the operation. Community Action Agencies will not be funded unless they can guarantee that youth will be actively involved in all phases of the Youth Development Program.

2. *Program Duration.* It is felt that year-round program offerings are essential in order to develop innovative, comprehensive programs that will have real meaning for the participant. Applying agencies must be set up to run their program for a 12-month period. Youth resent programs that are turned on and off, such as summer crash programs which usually only reflect riot fears rather than felt need.

3. *Program Content.* Youth Development Programs must be comprehensive economic opportunity programs. Interestingly, programs that are devoted exclusively to "recreation, camping, cultural enrichment, and other leisure-time activities" are not funded.

The approach to service by OEO is more a design of directly attacking the recurring problems of youth rather than merely providing activities limited to recreation, camping, and other avocational pursuits. This idea must be understood fully when serving low-income groups. There is a level of understanding and appreciation which must be reached before a complete and full acceptance of the values of the recreation experience can entirely be realized by the deprived person.

Efforts to meet the special needs of poor people have multiplied in the last ten to twelve years. However, there are still vast numbers of poor people not being reached by traditionally middle-class oriented public recreation service. The fact that cities have begun to recognize their obligation to provide recreation for the economically deprived has increased the influence and potential of wholesome leisure on the lives of slum dwellers. The National League of Cities conducted a study a few years ago of fifteen selected communities and reached several conclusions applicable to this paper.

1. Location of parks and recreation facilities is a primary factor affecting the success of recreation programs. Consideration must be given to population density and the availability of public transportation in the location of new facilities. . . . Emphasis must be placed on neighborhood facilities.

2. City expenditures for park and recreation purposes have increased substantially in recent years. . . . However, in spite of a virtually unanimous commitment to increase recreation programs and opportunities, cities do not have the financial capability to sustain expanded recreation programs indefinitely.

3. Cities must increasingly look to state and Federal government for the additional financial assistance necessary to sustain the desired level of recreation programs.

4. Optimum utilization of potential recreation resources is not being achieved in most of the nation's cities. . . . To meet the rising demand for recreation, in spite of the declining availability of open space, cities must expand the multiple use of facilities, establish park-school complexes, and employ imaginative designs and new construction techniques.

5. Lack of communication among city, county, and private agencies is a major problem preventing the optimum utilization of existing recreational facilities and programs. In addition, communication between recreation departments and the citizen is frequently inadequate. In the past, recreation officials have felt it sufficient merely to provide recreation opportunities. Today, citizens not only must be informed of the availability of the various programs, but also convinced that participation is worthwhile.

6. Cities must take into consideration the recreation needs of special segments of the population—the aged, the young, the handicapped, the economically and socially deprived—in developing priorities. In most cities surveyed [this corresponds to the Kerner Commission Report], officials readily admitted that the needs of all population groups were not being adequately met.

7. Residents of deprived urban neighborhoods are almost entirely dependent upon public recreation facilities, whereas residents of more affluent neighborhoods have a wide range of recreational alternatives.

8. Residents of urban slum neighborhoods frequently charge that too much effort is directed toward park and recreation facilities for the middle- and upper-income groups, and that recreation planning is being performed by persons having no real knowledge of the needs or desires of the deprived. . . . To be successful, recreation programs must be what the people want, not what the recreation department believes to be best for the people.[31]

EXAMPLES OF SPECIAL PROGRAMMING
FOR THE ECONOMICALLY DEPRIVED

Some of the special efforts that are being utilized to serve economically deprived groups are briefly described in the following program summaries. They represent only a small sampling of the many extensive efforts provided by 1) municipal and private recreation and leisure service; 2) state and federal government service; and 3) voluntary youth serving agencies.

Municipal and Private Recreation
and Leisure Service

The New York City Parks Department has used a 24-hour information tape seven days a week to list city park activities for telephone callers.

A work-study-recreation program in Richmond, Virginia, provides poor youth with a weekly schedule of one day of work in business, one day in community service, two days in special school classes, and one day in recreation.

Cincinnati used the parking lot of an electric firm as a neighborhood playground after 5:30 P.M. weekdays and all day on weekends. The company installed basketball hoops and outside electric outlets for movies and dances, and hired a recreation supervisor to conduct a program.

Los Angeles has instituted an education and competitive sports program for innercity youth. A sample program would consist of competition in arithmetic skills between two teams. The winning team is able to apply bonus points toward its score in a touch football game which follows exercises in educational games.

Washington, D.C., has a 47-member youth advisory council to advise the mayor's office on youth concerns. Council members are paid from $1.60 to $1.87 an hour.

Cincinnati's educational TV station, WCET, sponsors "Focus on Youth," a weekly half-hour show written, produced, directed, and televised by poor youth.

State and Federal Recreation Service Programs

The State of Vermont and the City of New York, with $410,000 in public and private funds, developed programs at several sites in Vermont for 500 Harlem youth and 500 Vermont youth to live, work, learn, and play together.

In 1968, more than a thousand Arkansas poor youth, ages 13–18, were provided a week of free camping at the National Guard's facilities at Camp Robinson near Little Rock.

"Project Co-op" is a Hartford, Connecticut education-employment-recreation program providing disadvantaged youth with an opportunity to work in Model Cities programs, the local CAP agency, Red Cross, and the housing authority. In addition, participants plan their own education and recreation activities, including museum visits, minority culture programs, and arts and crafts projects.

A cooperative program, sponsored by the Boston Recreation Department, Hale Reservation Area, and the U.S. Bureau of Sports, Fisheries and Wildlife provides daily bus travel for poverty youth to the 1,000-acre Hale Reservation for fishing. Special fishing instruction and equipment is provided. Free lunches are given to each participant.

Communities in the metropolitan Washington, D.C. area are invited to participate in "Summer in the Parks," a National Park Service program. Youth participate in such programs as ballet, wood sculpturing, art classes, pottery instruction, and environment games relating to the world of parks and nature. Special activities in parks located throughout Washington's innercity include African Day as well as Spanish and Indian Day, an annual bicycling event, and everyday noontime concerts at downtown parks.

The President's Council on Physical Fitness and Sports sponsors a Summer Youth Sports Program for disadvantaged, innercity youth. The 12- to 18-year-old participants receive a free preliminary medical exam, a daily meal, at least two hours of instruction and competition in sports such as basketball, swimming, track and field, and gymnastics, and instruction in health education and counseling on career and study opportunities.

Voluntary Youth Service Programs

Phoenix Boys' Clubs sponsor a "Jobology" course for youth employed in the Neighborhood Youth Corps.

The Cleveland Central YMCA has worked with a prominent businessman to provide free tours of the city's airport and free flights over the city in a private airplane.

The Reading, Pennsylvania YWCA "Work-recreation" program combines employment and recreation. The program enables youth to work on conservation jobs during the morning, discuss pertinent issues selected by the youth at noon, and participate in recreation activities in the afternoon.

Seattle's Indian Neighborhood House offers a program of Indian art heritage and theater for youth during the summer months.

The Encampment for Citizenship program brings young people from a variety of racial and economic backgrounds to participate in a cultural-educational-recreational project designed to provide leadership opportunities to the assembled youth. The summer camp program holds workshops in black and Mexican-American heritage, Indian American culture, environment, civil rights, and other recreation programs.

SUGGESTIONS FOR PROGRAM
IMPROVEMENT AND DEVELOPMENT

There have been a number of program approaches attempted in an effort to meet the pressing needs of disadvantaged people. Some have been successful while others have failed. The one aspect of the new vogue in recreation programming that seems to have broadened the base of community recreation service is the cultural component now included in the conduct of leisure activities. One administrator views recreation's role as indispensable in two respects: "1) the identification of each culture's grasp for leisure activity and providing for that need; and 2) to expose to all cultures the grace and charm of the different cultures; i.e., promotion of the homogeneous from the heterogeneous cultures."[32]

Many cities have been confronted with the dilemma of reaching the urban poor. The Fresno, California Parks and Recreation Department recognized that the concept of recreation service as presently promoted and utilized by most cities was inadequate and no longer functional. There was a belief that the generally accepted definition of recreation—that it was a voluntary, pleasurable experience engaged in during leisure—was no longer applicable to the present conditions in urban America. According to Mr. Howard Holman, Director of the Department, "recreation must be considered not only an end in itself, but also as a means of achieving other social goals."

The recent additions of detached workers and street club personnel to the staffs of many urban municipal recreation operations is an attempt to serve the disadvantaged youth and "hard-to-reach" youth of the ghetto. The departments have necessarily had to broaden their philosophy of service in order to establish contact and maintain communication with deprived youth who, for a number of reasons, don't frequent the traditional recreation programs.

Mr. Holman, believing that recreation can make a real contribution to the quality of living, has instituted "new" program approaches in an effort to bring attractive, relevant programs to the people.[33]

1. It was concluded that a standardized, city-wide recreation program was irrelevant in many parts of the city. The city has now instituted a decentralized recreation program that serves three geographic areas. Each of the three service areas establishes its own local programs, assignment of local personnel, and hours of operation.

2. It was felt that mutual trust should be established and deepened between the department staff and the public being served. Every person is to be given consideration when requests are made of the department.

3. Fresno has accepted the premise that there are special needs and organization required to serve the disadvantaged and they have established a compensatory recreation program. The amount of money dispensed in disadvantaged areas is frequently greater than the standard applied to the city as a whole.

4. The tendency for playground or community center staff to become custodians of the property or referred to as the "chain link" syndrome, is being eliminated. Leaders are encouraged to carry the recreation program out into the community, beyond the confines of the property.

5. Often departments will make overtures to the public of elaborate programs to be offered and never fulfill these promises. The new philosophy of the department is, "Don't promise it; do it."

6. There has always been a tendency by recreation departments to be highly parochial and provincial in their ideas with very little experimentation encouraged. Fresno has extended the use of various school facilities for programs not previously offered. Experimentation has become a standard operating procedure within the department.

7. The department is recruiting, training, and employing indigenous leaders and encouraging them to continue their education. This often results in the stimulation of neighborhood gatherings, fiestas, and holiday celebrations applicable to the ethnic interest of the area.

8. The challenge of urban recreation in the years ahead will require that recreation become personalized and brought down to the neighborhood level. The alienation and isolation of people living in crowded, congested cities is a phenomenon of the twentieth century. Fresno is accepting the challenge of assuring the citizens that the recreation leaders will become the first-line contact in all neighborhoods of the city. Leaders will

become knowledgeable of community resources and be equipped to field questions and channel them to the proper official or agency.

THE FUTURE

Recreation's role is too vital not to join hands with other community agencies to insure that leisure becomes an anticipated opportunity for people instead of a dreaded experience to be avoided. The recreation experience has potential to be an enlightening opportunity for someone to grow spiritually and physically; make new social acquaintances; and develop new skills and hobbies. However, community recreation service has often become too structured, largely unserviceable to dependent groups, and too unwieldy to be effective at the neighborhood level.

Special efforts must be made to reach citizens who are overwhelmed by the structure of society and are too ill, poor, and alienated to participate and share its benefits. Efforts must be made to develop a sense of community within the rural and urban areas, to de-institutionalize recreation service, and assure that all people will be made to feel like members of the human race.

There is a tendency by recreation departments to offer programs in which the recipients are cooperative, motivated, capable of improvement and even express gratitude to the agency. The ability of all groups to meet the expressed standards of departments is extremely difficult and often ludicrous to economically deprived citizens whose basic needs are usually not satisfied and are unable to identify with the sheltered goals of agencies. The cooperative participants become the models of service and differing people with varied interests are excluded from service.

The feelings of ineptness and inadequacy felt by slum dwellers have been documented. Whether recreation can effect constructive change in the lives of the disadvantaged will be judged in the next decade. Community recreation and leisure service will make a positive impact on ghetto living when the profession realizes it must establish rapport and contact with the poor. To do this, recreation must set up programs which are viable and direct, and serve meaningful functions in the lives of ghetto residents. Rioting becomes an extension of futility and disenchantment with the system that rewards only the affluent, only certain members of society. To the extent that recreation service is able to become a meaningful part of slum life in the city, barrio, and reservation, it will avoid the rock-throwing and firebombs.

FOOTNOTES

[1] Henry George, "The Inalienable Right," *The Playground*, 5: 416, March, 1912.

[2] Hanna H. Meissner, ed., *Poverty in the Affluent Society* (New York: Harper and Row, 1966), pp. 49–50.

[3] Robert E. Will and Harold G. Vatter, eds., *Poverty in Affluence: The Social, Political, and Economic Dimensions of Poverty in the United States* (2nd ed., New York: Harcourt, Brace, and World, Inc., 1970), p. 76.

[4] Herman P. Miller, "Major Elements of a Research Program for the Study of Poverty," *The Concept of Poverty*, Task Force on Economic Growth and Opportunity (Washington, D.C.: Chamber of Commerce of the United States, 1965), p. 122.

[5] Miller, p. 123.

[6] Catherine S. Chilman, *Growing Up Poor* (Washington, D.C.: U.S. Department of HEW, 1967), p. 22.

[7] Chilman, p. 23.

[8] Chilman, p. 31.

[9] Chilman, p. 34.

[10] Chilman, p. 58.

[11] U.S. Department of HEW, *Toward a Social Report* (Washington, D.C.: U.S. Government Printing Office, 1969), p. 91.

[12] U.S. Department of HEW, p. 39.

[13] Richard Kraus, "Recreation for the Rich and Poor: A Contrast," *Quest*, 5:52, Winter, 1965.

[14] U.S. Department of HEW, p. 41.

[15] Shirlon Banks, term paper, "Recreation for the Black Ghetto Child," in course, Philosophy of Recreation and Leisure, San Jose State College, Spring, 1970.

[16] Task Force on Economic Growth and Opportunity, *Rural Poverty and Regional Progress in Urban Society* (Washington, D.C.: Chamber of Commerce of the United States, 1969), p. 19.

[17] Will and Vatter, p. 71.

[18] Lee G. Burchinal, ed., *Rural Youth in Crisis: Facts, Myths and Social Change* (Washington, D.C.: U.S. Department of HEW, 1965), p. 302.

[19] Donald N. Michael, *Cybernation: The Silent Conquest* (Santa Barbara: Center for the Study of Democratic Institutions, 1962), pp. 29–33.

[20] George D. Butler, *Introduction to Community Recreation* (New York: McGraw-Hill Book Company, 1940), p. 223.

[21] Butler, p. 328.

[22] Butler, p. 318.

[23] George D. Butler, *Pioneers in Public Recreation* (Minneapolis: Burgess Publishing Company, 1965), p. 150.

[24] Richard Kraus, *Recreation Today: Program Planning and Leadership* (New York: Appleton-Century-Crofts, 1966), pp. 13–14.

[25] Marion Clawson and Jack L. Knetsch, *Economics of Outdoor Recreation* (Baltimore: The Johns Hopkins Press, 1966), p. 151.

[26] Michael Harrington, *The Other America: Poverty in the United States* (Baltimore: Penguin Books, Inc., 1962), p. 12.

[27] Richard Kraus, "Providing for Recreation and Aesthetic Enjoyment," *Governing the City* (New York: Frederick A. Praeger, Publishers, 1969), p. 99.

[28] Edwin J. Staley, "Determining Neighborhood Recreation Priorities: An Instrument," *Journal of Leisure Research*, 1:69, Winter, 1969.

[29] Sal Prezioso, *Youth and Leisure* (New York: New York State Division for Youth, 1969), p. 14.

[30] A comprehensive list of guidelines related to program planning and administration of recreation and leisure services for the disadvantaged is found in the text, *Recreation and Leisure Services for the Disadvantaged: Guidelines to Program Development and Related Readings*, Lea and Febiger, 1970, by John A. Nesbitt, Paul D. Brown, and James F. Murphy.

[31] Department of Urban Studies, *Recreation in the Nation's Cities: Problems and Approaches* (Washington, D.C.: National Leagues of Cities, 1968), pp. 1–2.

[32] W. Jack Perez, "The Decentralization of Recreation," *California Park and Recreation*, 11:25, December, 1969.

[33] Howard Holman, "Urban Recreation Today," *California Park and Recreation*, 12:7–8, April, 1970.

11   Recreation
and
Racial Minorities

Photo by Tania D'Avignon

IRA J. HUTCHISON, JR.

INTRODUCTION

The overall problem of providing adequate service to minority group populations reached a peak for the recreation profession with the onset of social unrest and disorder in most of the nation's cities in the 1960's. Valid studies and surveys now support the long-standing contentions of minority group citizens that they have never received a rightful share of public and private recreation resources and services.

The frequently cited Kerner Commission,[1] for example, in reporting its findings regarding the 1967 riots stated: "Grievances concerning municipal recreation programs were found in a large majority of the 20 cities and appeared to be one of the most serious complaints in almost half. Inadequate recreational facilities in the ghetto and the lack of organized programs were common complaints."

In a 1967 study, *Public Recreation and the Negro: A Study of Participation and Administrative Practices,*[2] conducted by Richard Kraus, under the sponsorship of the Center for Urban Education, the following was noted: While all programs purport to serve both races equally, and to provide comparable facilities, in most cases Negro neighborhoods possessed the oldest, most limited, and rundown recreation facilities in the communities studied.

Recreation administrators candidly admit that inequities have and continue to exist, but point to long-standing fiscal restrictions, binding social practices and customs, and related factors that are beyond their control and authority, as prime causative factors. Although both the Kraus and the Kerner Commission reports refer specifically to an aggrieved black population, it is not too farfetched to assume that most other minority groups are equally ignored by the recreation service system. The caliber of public recreation services for the Puerto Rican living in New York's East Harlem is likely to parallel that of the barren recreation services provided blacks in New York's Harlem. The same can be said for blacks, Chicanos, and Indians in the Los Angeles and San Francisco ghettos.

Following the riots, in a burst of concentrated efforts, the public and private human service sectors attempted to improve services to minority group citizens. However, the results leave much to be desired. In spite of massive input of tax dollars, professional application, and public receptivity to social change, most minority groups continue to be deprived of their rights to optimum recreation services.

A History of Regression

To fully comprehend the difficiencies in the recreation program for minority group citizens, the origin and evolution of the recreation profession should be explored. Contrary to popular impression, the present problems are not unique or unprecedented. A large proportion of urban slum residents of yesterday belonged to minority groups and suffered many of the same socioeconomic indignities lamented today. The most obvious differences are: 1) slums are now referred to as "ghettos" and "barrios," and 2) the descendents of the Irish, Polish, and Jewish minority groups that populated these areas have decentralized to the greener pastures of midtown or suburbia, abandoning the slums to migrations of black and Spanish-speaking groups. The recorded history of the recreation and park profession spells out quite succinctly the responsive role that public recreation played in respect to resolving the social problems that plagued the big cities in the 1800's.

The concern of early recreators with the slum environment and its debilitating effects on children led to the formation of the Playground Association of America.[3] An article entitled "An Organization is Born," published in 1965 in the monograph *Recreation: Pertinent Readings*,[4] described the slums of the early 1900's as follows: "City children were playing in the streets in those days, in vacant lots, railroad yards, on construction projects, or wherever they could find an open space." Attention to the recreation needs of minority groups, and the quality of their environment in the 1800's, is the prime raison d'etre for the existence of recreation as an area of specialized human services today.

The leadership of the Playground Association pledged the limited resources of their fledgling organization to the task of providing programs and facilities to the slum dweller. In 1909, the Playground Association's first paid Secretary, Howard Braucher, accepted his appointment on the provision that the organization would become the spearhead of a "nationwide movement to bring broad recreation opportunities to all people regardless of age, sex, and religious faiths."[5] So, in reality, the roots of the profession are buried deep in a foundation of auspicious and relevant efforts calculated to improve the social and physical well being of citizens who were being overlooked by the normal flow of public services.

The Price of Success

Those familiar with the auspicious beginnings of the recreation profession should be puzzled by its current inadequacies in providing services to minority groups. To what factors or circumstances can this deterioration of professional concerns and activities be attributed? In the opinion of many, the successes that the early recreation professionals achieved in serving urban slum needs actually precipitated the disappearance of an identifiable specialized human service or minority group thrust in the recreation movement.

In essence, it could be said that at its highest point of success, the recreation profession unwittingly allowed the prime focus of its mission to shift from the delivery of specialized human services to professional development and facility management. Unfortunately, it appears that the provision of services to people became a means to broader goals, purposes, and professional status, rather than remaining a vital and satisfying end unto itself.

As nearly as can be determined, the whole of the organization's special attention to the recreation needs of minority group members during the period 1906–1942 was vested in the creation and maintenance of a Bureau of Colored Work.[6] The contributions of the Bureau to the cause of recreation services for minority groups have been debated in many quarters with almost as many different conclusions reached as there have been arguments. The fact remains, however, that until the late 1960's the Bureau represented the last identifiable national effort on the part of the organization and the field to recognize and serve the needs of a minority group. Attempts to meet these special needs consisted of individual efforts on the part of "enlightened" local recreation administrators. Despite the discontent evidenced by the riots of the 1960's, most minority group citizens, regardless of social and economic status and capability, are still forced to cope with a common base of overt discriminatory policies, programs, and leadership at the hands of public and private recreation systems.

MINORITIES: A DEMOGRAPHIC PERSPECTIVE

An in-depth and applicable understanding of those factors that influence the attitudes and behavior of minority groups is crucial to the optimum development and management of the public service sector, particularly in its recreation systems. The direct and indirect relationships that exist between the citizen and the systems of this sector are characterized by a constancy, dependency, and proximity that are not recognizable in the functioning of other institutions.

It has become increasingly obvious that the most awesome and debilitating aspects of delivering adequate services to minorities—especially non-white—are manifested in the large, complex, urban city. Public sector specialists, specifically those working in the urban recreation service system, should have a fundamental, integrated awareness and understanding of the nature of the minority group population, the urban socioeconomic climate, the broad public service sector, the recreation service system, as well as pertinent facts of social and cultural processes—all as they relate to the environment, the needs and the desires of minorities.

The Minority Population

The American Heritage Dictionary of the English Language defines minorities as being "a racial, religious, political, national, or other group regarded as different from the larger group of which it is a part."[7] *The Webster's Seventh New Collegiate Dictionary* also includes "a part of a population differing from others in some characteristics and often subjected to differential treatment"[8] in the definition of minorities presented. Although the terms "minority" or "minority group" are frequently used in the political or religious contexts, the terms, until most recently, commonly referred to an individual's racial or ethnic background. Since the early 1900's, however, most so-called minority groups of Caucasian extraction have achieved a nonthreatening level of assimilation into mainstream America. The use of the term "minority group" in today's sociological, political, and economic circles is used to refer almost exclusively to the nonwhite population of the country. It is in this nonwhite minority group framework that the matter of differential delivery of urban recreation services has and will continue to be the most conspicuous.

The Nonwhite Minority Population

In the United States, black Americans comprise the largest nonwhite minority group, with a 1966 black population of 21.5 million.[9] Blacks constitute the largest nonwhite minority of most major urban cities, as well.

Other nonwhite minority groups are found in lesser numbers in urban cities, and in specific geographic areas in the country, their numbers are substantial: Puerto Ricans and other people of Spanish culture in the Eastern and Northeastern regions; the Spanish-speaking groups of Mexican descent in the Southwest and West Coast regions; the American Indian groups in the Southwest and Western regions; and the Oriental groups in the West Coast and Northwest regions. The problems and needs of these groups, although severe in many other socioeconomic respects, have yet to reach crisis proportions in respect to recreation services. Many believe that it is the leisure and recreational experiences that remain available through well-preserved intragroup cultural and religious activities that minimize the expectations and demands of these groups for a larger share of public recreation services. Therefore, it appears as though the nonwhite minority groups of the big urban cities are most affected by the inequities of the public service sector and its recreation service systems.

The Socioeconomic Climate

The socioeconomic climate refers to the collective or singular state of major social, economic, and related demographic factors in a particular community. It is the prevailing socioeconomic climate that primarily influences the quality of life or lifestyle of those who reside in that community. For example, in an urban setting high population density spawns housing

and health problems; a fragile economy perpetuates unemployment, out-migration, and inferior public services; discrimination
and segregation stimulates ethnic population shifts, substandard
educational services, and limited political privileges.

Of primary concern, is the heterogeneous community with
a diverse socioeconomic climate that affects its members in
diametrically opposed ways. For example, regardless of economic conditions, it can mean increased employment for some
individuals or groups (majority) and severe unemployment for
others (minorities). In another instance, housing problems
created by density of population can generate new and improved
housing conditions for one group (majorities), and doom another
to a chaotic and unhealthy day-to-day existence (minorities).
When socioeconomic conditions worsen, the urban minority
groups are the most severely penalized.

The Public Service Sector

The urban public service sector is made up of public agencies
and systems designated or designed by the government to provide
the public with those services and resources that are rightfully
the responsibility of the government. In practically all instances,
the public service sector and its systems have public monies
at their disposal to organize the manpower, facilities, and expertise needed to fulfill their public service obligations. The public service sector functions to serve such human needs as
health, welfare, transportation, etc. Ideally, the public service
sector is expected both to protect the citizen from the negative
aspects of the socioeconomic climate and to facilitate exposure
and acquisition of socioeconomic benefits. The public recreation
service system is a legitimate component of the urban public
service sector.

MINORITIES: A SOCIAL PERSPECTIVE

The patterns of social organization existing within organized
communities determine how and to what extent essential cultural patterns are created, incubated, and manifested to the
necessary point of impact and influence. Even the most primi-

tive tribe has its social arrangements to ensure the survival of its cultural traits, habits, and artifacts.

In most societal structures, it is these social arrangements and concomitant requirements that induce conformity and discourage deviation from the prescribed cultural norm. These same arrangements prescribe means for transmitting the desired cultural patterns of the economic, political, and spiritual institutions.

The public service sector, as a socioeconomic and political institution, is required to conform to such social arrangements. But it also has the privilege to utilize its particular talents and resources to improve these social arrangements for the greater benefit of the community. As a part of the public service sector, the public recreation system can exercise this requirement or responsibility more effectively in some areas than others.

Social Security

Individuals depend upon the public service sector to mollify those anxieties and needs that emerge as they strive to conform to society's requirements. As these requirements change, the public service sector and its operable systems, such as public recreation, must be relevantly responsive.

Social Welfare

The public service sector, particularly its urban recreation system, is the primary remedial resource when conformity to the existing social arrangements places the individual at a social, political, economic, or cultural disadvantage. The urban recreation system can facilitate the use of existing vehicles for conformity and, when necessary, can originate acceptable means for satisfactorily meeting established requirements.

Social Service

Society's organized efforts to attend to the individual's vital needs and desires, such as health, education, and leisure, are channeled through the public service sector, particularly its urban systems. These systems must develop tools and techniques to serve the broadest spread of ethnic and minority groups. In addition, the corresponding economic and cultural needs and desires of these groups must be served.

Social Disease

Social disease (in this instance excluding completely any reference to pathological physiology) refers exclusively to the unfavorable economic, political, religious, and sociological conditions under which the mass of a given society exists. The public service sector is responsible for developing and implementing those methods that support healthy and productive attitudes and behavior, modifying or replacing those that place undue sanctions, responsibilities, and punishments on individuals or groups.

Social Advocacy; Social Studies

The public service sector, through advocacy of programs that benefit the social welfare, social security, and social service, and that obliterate social disease, functions to reinforce the positive aspects of broad-based societal attitudes, as well as to introduce change when necessary. In order to fulfill these functions, the public service sector has a critical responsibility to continually explore, study, and demonstrate rationales for its advocacy of social innovation. These efforts are particularly critical in meeting the sociocultural needs, including recreation, of ethnic and nonwhite minority groups.

MINORITIES: A CULTURAL PERSPECTIVE

The following three definitions of culture are set forth in the seventh edition of *Webster's Collegiate Dictionary:*

- "the act of developing the intellectual and moral faculties especially by education"
- "enlightenment and excellence of taste acquired by intellectual and aesthetic training"
- "a particular stage of advancement in civilization"; "the characteristic features of such a stage or state"; "behavior typical of a group or class."

In many ways these definitions can be considered the what, why, and how in the relationship of "culture" to human society. Viewed collectively, they could easily serve the public service sector and its systems as a broad, open-ended framework within which purposes and objectives for serving the cultural needs of minority groups could be constructed. Again, viewed collectively, these definitions not only suggest the prime processes that are involved in human cultural development, but suggest corresponding societal tools and resources that are appropriate and effective for the task.

Indirectly, the Webster definitions reinforce the idea that in a societal structure, the responsibility for developing and perpetuating "culture" within some meaningful dimensions is a responsibility of the individual and his peer group, plus the social, political, and economic institutions represented in the societal structure.

There are, however, two other facts worth noting if we view the Webster's definitions of "culture" in tandem with the public service sector as it operates today. First, these definitions implicitly assume the existence of a homogeneous society within which there is a minimum degree of deviation from a common sense of institutional responsibilities and individual habits, behavior, and attitude. It is this implicit assumption that requires those guided by the Webster definitions, or others in a similar vein, to apply them within a flexible and open-ended framework. For these definitions ignore the relationship between the development and pursuit of culture, and the unique intellectual, biological characteristics, and aesthetic interpretation that is represented in a society whose membership is comprised of various ethnic or minority groups. For example, if it is the urban recreation system that is attempting to apply these definitions, it should be recognized that in an ethnically heterogeneous society, cultural needs rarely, if ever, manifest themselves in a totally integrated pattern. In serving the cultural needs of our modern society, it would be wise to make sure that any consideration of the essential nature of the task, objectives, and human processes set forth in the Webster definitions occurs in practical relationship to the cultural uniqueness associated with the ethnic or minority groups being served.

Secondly, Webster and other similar definitive sources, while duly noting the arts, music, religion, literature, and other forms and vehicles for creating, sustaining, and transmitting culture, fail to stress the extent to which a given societal sub-group might choose to shape its use of these forms and vehicles to satisfy unique and indigenous cultural needs.

Perhaps it is assumed that the successful and common-place manner in which this society has managed to accommo-date divergent cultural forms and vehicles within its structure is responsible for this omission, i.e., Catholic and Protestant reli-gions, classic and blue grass music; musical comedy and soap operas, etc. However, whatever the rationale, the public service sector and its systems cannot ignore this factor as responsibili-ties are defined in respect to minorities. What is needed is a double-edged conceptual baseline that simultaneously gives at-tention to the divergencies in the values and uses of particular cultural forms and vehicles by minorities or ethnic groups and the cultural conformity demanded by the dominant society.

The logical assumption should be that the divergent use of prescribed cultural forms and vehicles by ethnic and minority groups represents an effort to adjust to the dominant culture, rather than a rejection of that culture. Ethnic and minority groups form important and necessary subcultures within the framework of the larger society. For example, the blues of the black American, musically speaking, does not signify a cultur-ally independent music form. It represents, in terms of service needs and personal satisfaction, the unique interpretation that an ethnic or minority group has made to shape an approved cul-tural form to its own needs.

The public service sector, particularly the recreation sys-tem, should concentrate its allocation of resources and services in meeting the specialized cultural needs of each minority or ethnic group.

MINORITIES: HISTORICAL PERSPECTIVES

The history of American social thought and tradition conspicu-ously reveals a continuing effort in this country to weld a con-glomerate of ethnic or minority groups into a single harmonious and productive sociocultural entity. An examination of this his-tory should lead to a better understanding of the problems that the public service sector and its systems are currently experiencing as they strive to cope with the sociocultural needs and desires that exist in and among minorities, particularly non-white groups.

The Foreign-Born Immigrant

Social engineers in the 1800's were at first convinced that a process could be developed that would lead to the total integration of the arriving European and other foreign-born immigrants into the sociocultural mainstream of the United States. However, these engineers came to recognize that the ideal of complete sociocultural assimilation was unrealistic. Eventually, they compromised and considered assimilation successful if and when the sociocultural attitudes and practices unique to specific immigrant ethnic groups no longer conflicted with the established social, cultural, and economic structure of the dominant society.

As this compromise of theory and reality began to manifest itself in actual practice, the various immigrant groups were faced with a major problem; namely, how could they best fulfill their own social and cultural obligations without simultaneously being deprived of vitally needed social and economic services. Ultimately, immigrant ethnic or minority groups were forced to compromise. On the one hand, they deemed it fitting and proper for their members to adopt and practice the attitudes, customs, and habits of the dominant society that would enhance their chances for socioeconomic survival or improvement. On the other hand, immigrant ethnic groups decided that it was their primary responsibility, with or without the support of the public service sector, to perpetuate and protect the sanctity and practice of those indigenous customs and traditions important to the group. In turn, the public service system accepted an increased responsibility for serving the basic socioeconomic needs of the destitute immigrant minority groups that chose to affiliate with the cultural organization of their adopted home.

This division of labor now forms the cornerstone of present systems for planning and delivering services to minority and ethnic groups. In recent years, the demands and expectations of minority and ethnic groups for the public service sector to recognize and consider their social and cultural needs have decreased. As a result, the public service sector has been privileged until recently to serve an essentially common consortium of social and cultural needs as it saw fit.

The public service sector faces new and different challenges in attempting to meet the needs of American blacks and Indians, as well as newly arrived Spanish-speaking populations.

The Public Service Sector
and the American Black

Effective as the public service sector and its systems might have been in accommodating the sociocultural needs and expectations of immigrant ethnics and minorities, it has historically experienced great difficulty in effectively accommodating American blacks within the framework of its delivery system.

The punitive and circuitous route by which blacks eventually achieved a recognizable slot within the socioeconomic order of this country has to be a prime causative factor. Suffice it to say that there is not, nor will there ever be, a research instrument with the capability to accurately assess the moral, spiritual, and psychological damages inflicted upon American blacks by virtue of the social and political whims and ideology of succeeding generations of American "citizens." Distasteful as it may seem, only by objectively recognizing this fact, and exploring the causative circumstances, can the public service sector and its systems be guided to recognize and more effectively attend to the needs of the American black population. The sum total of the problem can be attributed to a number of factors unique to the United States and its black population respectively.

Slavery

At the height of slavery, 85 percent of the slave population was native to West Africa.[10] Contrary to the case of the immigrant, very few, if any, slaves volunteered to come to America, and, in the case of first-generation slaves, few remained of their own free will. Taking into consideration that the first-generation slave population was cut off completely from its native African culture, was forced into a totally alien culture, and was totally deprived of economic opportunities and resources available to subsequent generations of slaves to facilitate adaptation to the foreign culture, it is not too difficult to understand why the economic, social, and cultural heritage of the American black rests on its present fragile and constantly shifting base.

The black cultural heritage was further damaged by the white majority's severe sanctions against the slaves practicing their African culture. This effectively eliminated, in rather short order, most chances for the perpetuation of a deep-rooted genuine African sociocultural base in this country although some surface rudiments did survive.

The attitude of Americans towards later white immigrant groups was far more positive, and Americans took pride in their ability to welcome, accept, and "Americanize" these divergent groups. The slaves enjoyed no such beneficent acceptance. In fact, slave owners and the public in general found it difficult to recognize the African slave as a human being.

Thus, the opportunities for the slave to become acculturated to his new environment remained nonexistent for a considerable period of time. Divorced effectively from any indigenous frame of sociocultural reference, and denied any reasonable opportunity to acquire and benefit from the social and cultural resources in his new environment, the slave was left to his own ingenuity and limited resources to survive socially and culturally. Two factors were primarily responsible for the limited success enjoyed by slaves in this respect.

First, since the African slave was perceived to be a nonhuman entity, restrictions placed upon his activities were more to maximize productivity rather than to control his social and cultural posture. Thus, those activities of the slave outside of the worksphere were considered nonthreatening and were disdainfully tolerated. It is under these circumstances that the African slave was able to salvage rudiments of his heritage in music, dance, and religion. Given this opportunity, the slave then added to these rudiments new layers of social and cultural significance shaped by his existence in his new environment. Succeeding generations continued to build upon this base, and it is in this manner that music, dance, and religion came to be the significant aspects of the sociocultural structure of black America that they are today.

Secondly, in spite of the fact that he was not considered human, the slave was permitted to move freely within the sociocultural structure. LeRoi Jones, in his book, *Blues People,* quoted

Frederick Olmstead as reporting in 1863 ". . . I am struck with the close co-habitation and association of black and white —Negro women are carrying black and white babies together in their arms; black and white children are playing together (not going to school together); black and white faces constantly thrust together out of doors to see the train go by."[11]

The result of this contact between slave and master was neither intended nor expected. The impoverished state of the slaves' social and cultural bank created a tailormade target for the acculturation process. It was inevitable that the social, economic, and cultural aspirations of the slaves would be influenced and shaped by that of the dominant society.

Again, quoting from the book, *Blues People*, ". . . the American-born slave had only the all-encompassing mores of his white master. Africa had become a foreign land and none of the American-born slaves could ever hope to see it."[12]

Theoretically, it could be hypothesized that were it not for the two sociological accidents or oversights on the part of the dominant society that have just been described, the slave, had he retained that status, would eventually have justified being called an animal.

Emancipation and Reconstruction

The opportunity to retain and modify his heritage of music, dance, and religion to his own sociocultural advantage, and the stimulus and image provided through contact with the dominant society, gave the slave both the tools and impetus to begin forging an "Americanized" social and cultural structure. The results of these efforts constituted the basic ingredients of the sociocultural heritage the American slave carried into his new role as an American "citizen" and a duly eligible public service sector constituent.

The period of reconstruction offered little in the way of resources and opportunities to build upon this heritage. The meager store of political and economic resources and capabilities possessed by the slave, in combination with the even more emphatic denial of access to the rights and privileges of the dominant society, left the black neophyte "citizen" little and, sometimes, worse off than before his emancipation.

Emancipation was basically a component of a larger politi-

cal exercise calculated to aid and perpetuate the labor, industrial, and agricultural interest of the dominant society. Most of
those who strongly supported the freeing of the slaves did so
within this economic framework or on a highly moral and spiritual plane, much the same as many today view the mistreatment
of animals. There is little evidence that the most devoted aboli-
tionist groups or individuals included any applicable concern
for the economic, social, and cultural plight of the slave in their
grand efforts to bring about "freedom" for the slaves. It goes
without saying that the negrophobe of the North or South was
not the least inclined toward any effort that could be construed
as recognizing or developing the black as a social or economic
equal. Wendell Phillips, one of the few enlightened abolition-
ists, emphasized the sterile conditions created for the emanci-
pated slave when he said, "That proclamation frees the slave
but ignores the Negro."[13]

Any expectations that the freed slaves would at the same
time gain full citizenship, educational privileges, and greater
access to the economic resources were short-lived. Wendell
Phillips, again on the mark in his assessment of the situation,
said in a speech two years after the emancipation proclamation,
". . . the Negro still endured every characteristic of slavery except the legal fact of permanent bondage. Race subordination,
'the great principle of the South,' still survived."[14]

No doubt this assessment includes the fact that the total
responsibility for economic, social, and cultural development
continued to be the sole responsibility of the slaves themselves.
How the uneducated, socioeconomically disenfranchised, habit-
ually dependent mass of black "citizens" managed to survive in
a hostile society, and yet continue to build constructively upon
their economic, social and cultural base, is a wonder of contemporary history.

The many diverse conscious and unconscious strategies
used by the American black, and any supporters picked up along
the way, are still being historically recorded. Those blacks who
chose to stay in the South did so in full awareness that a
struggle was ahead to maintain the status quo in social, economic, and cultural self-determination as well as to develop a
reasonable relationship with the sociocultural system of the
dominant society.

Those who chose the migratory path to the North, particularly the urban city, found a no less hostile environment. Their need for sociocultural self-expression as well as a sympathetic public service secor willing to serve their sociocultural interests did not diminish appreciably.

Summary

In the succeeding years since slavery, emancipation, and reconstruction, the American black has continued to be deprived in relation to his sociocultural needs and values.

In contradistinction, the immigrant ethnic or racial minority group has parleyed the sociological compromise executed in the 1800's to an increasingly profitable and comfortable relationship within the dominant society. The fruits of the labors of immigrants in the marketplace of the dominant society has provided their progeny with the necessary resources to successfully perpetuate and protect their legacy of social and cultural artifacts in spite of a niggardly public service sector. Today, the Jewish Community Center, the Knights of Columbus Halls, and facilities operated by such groups as the Catholic Youth Organization stand as mute testimony to the success of this compromise.

It would seem then that the key to maintaining a public sector compatible with the sociocultural needs of the majority, as well as the minority, is twofold. One, the minority group is willing to adapt the sociocultural system of the majority group and, two, the majority group is, at the same time, willing to grant the minority group access to the social, but particularly the economic resources and assets it controls. It is in this roundabout pattern of socioeconomic interaction that the public service sector arrived at what it believes to be an effective role in respect to ethnic or minority groups.

One last look at history reveals a plausible explanation for the failure of this role in respect to the sociocultural needs of the nonwhite minorities. Only one-half of the key has functioned. Access to the social and economic resources of the majority society is still difficult and often unsuccessful. The black minority, lacking sociocultural self-determination, has remained perpetually destitute and dependent upon the majority society for support and assistance. That the public service sector is unaware of this state of affairs is obvious.

In retrospect, it can be assumed that the public service sector's failure to serve is a problem peculiar to nonwhite minority or ethnic groups. The status of the relationship between the public service system and the Indian, Puerto Rican, Chicano, and other Spanish-speaking peoples lends strength to this observation.

A passing statement made by a Virginia statesman: "I never thought that (minorities) have any other *right* than that of freely, peaceably, and legally converting themselves into a *majority* whenever they can"[15]—has had no meaning for nonwhite groups.

MINORITIES: CONTEMPORARY PERSPECTIVES

Pre-Riot Era

The public service sector and its systems, including recreation, were well aware of the history of deprivation that characterized the social, economic, and cultural conditions imposed upon the nonwhite minorities. In fact, the public recreation system remains among the more notable perpetuators of the sanctions and penalties imposed upon citizens belonging to nonwhite minority groups. James Murphy, writing in *Recreation and Leisure Service for the Disadvantaged*, quoted the following from the publication *Minorities in American Society:* "In Southern cities, Negroes were generally excluded from public parks, and only a few cities had parks for Negroes. Except in a few instances where a special section of a public playground was set aside for them, the colored people were not permitted to use public playgrounds. At one time, a fairly common sign in Southern parks was "Negroes, Soldiers and Dogs keep out."[16]

Blacks and their offspring migrating south to north did not find the situation to be much better. Again, according to James Murphy, "The recreation movement was founded on ideals of service to the underprivileged and disadvantaged people of large cities; it was ironic that twenty years after the recognized beginning of organized recreation, blacks were still unable to utilize public park and recreation facilities throughout much of America. . . ."[17]

Over the years, and through alternating periods of national prosperity and depressions, the public service sector and its systems continued to serve nonwhite minority groups in an easily recognizable pattern. On the one hand, while efforts were made to maintain a satisfactory level of services in the environment of the majority group, there were conspicuous gaps in the delivery of basic services to the urban nonwhite minorities. This pattern in effect represented a two-pronged process that was, to say the least, chronically counterproductive. The inadequate or deficient public recreation programs referred to in the Report of the National Advisory Commission on Civil Disorders and the Kraus study are distinct and readily identifiable examples of this process.

It is no wonder, then, that credible human service specialists began to predict with increasing frequency that minorities could be expected to react violently to the social and economic conditions that were being forced upon them. Unfortunately, the truth of these predictions was borne out in the nationwide civil disturbances of the 1960's.

Post-Riot Era

Most nonwhite minority group persons refer to the period immediately following the riots as the era of the "plantation system." From the standpoint of the attitudes and practices of public and private human service practitioners during this time, it could also be described as the era of "pragmatic omnipotence." In either case, the meaning and implications are most similar and equally pronounced. Essentially, this was an era where the bulk of public service sector programming was based on a premise that it was an inherent responsibility of the "haves" not only to decide to what extent the expressed needs, desires, and grievances of the "have nots" were legitimate, but also to prescribe follow-up patterns for their distribution and use. Evidently, it was calculated that the long-standing privilege of open and free access to the prime goods and services to satisfy their own needs and desires endowed the "haves" with the wisdom and perceptiveness to perform this all-powerful function for the "have-nots."

An array of human service specialists fanned across the country to implement a national plan of action that would supposedly remold nonwhite minority group environments and lifestyles in the image of existing majority group communities. The era of pragmatic omnipotence was in full swing.

At the beginning of this era, optimism for achievement was high in both the public service sector and the nonwhite minority community. The level of response and interaction in program and service development was encouraging, and harmony reigned in the camps of both. Some rather unique socioeconomic factors were responsible for this early success.

First was the apparent accord between the public service sector suppliers and the nonwhite minority group recipients as to the urgency and scope of the needs that required satisfaction. Temporarily numbed and humbled by the impact of the campaign mounted in their behalf, nonwhite minorities tended to accept without question the advice and counsel of the public service sector in respect to their needs and aspirations. For all practical purposes, nonwhite minority groups were silent and consenting partners in the planning and decision-making that took place in the public service sector during this era.

Secondly, the seemingly unlimited amount of available dollars made it possible to extend the range, expand the variety, and increase the speed with which local public service programs could be implemented in the nonwhite minority community. This in turn perpetrated a happy illusion that the supply of available public goods and services were, or soon would be, equal to the demands of nonwhite minority citizens. As a result, the impatience and frustration of this group with the public service sector were reduced to a less threatening level.

In the initial stages of this era there was a decided shortage of human service professionals and specialists working in the nonwhite minority communities. As a result, these communities for a time had to consistently draw upon the expertise of the public service sector for these kinds of services. Faced with the reality of their deficiencies, the nonwhite minority group leadership had little or no choice but to support and work within the framework of expertise maintained by the public service sector.

It is highly probable that neither the public service sector nor the nonwhite minority group leadership realized the extent to which these factors influenced the manner in which programs and services were being organized, administered, and received. In the flush of apparent success, the public service specialist was convinced that it was his knowledge and experience that made it possible. With their more pertinent needs receiving priority attention, the nonwhite minority community was not inclined to find fault with the processes by which this task was being accomplished. This set of circumstances lent undeserved credibility to the pragmatic omnipotent approach to public service distribution, which in turn minimized the critical importance of including sociocultural variances among those criteria used to determine the design of public service policy and programs.

However, the much-heralded triumphs and successes of this era proved to be short lived. As it turned out, the same socioeconomic factors that inadvertently bolstered the pragmatic omnipotent approach served to show its weaknesses and inadequacies. Once again, breeches have begun occurring with increasing frequency in the accord between the systems of the public service sector and minorities.

MINORITIES: IMPLICATIONS FOR RECREATION SERVICES

As previously acknowledged, the recreation system as a part of the public service sector has begun to exhibit an increased ability to program more effectively and consistently in deference to minorities.

The road to this limited success has not been without trials, tribulations, successes, and failures. Examining the past and present sphere of service delivery, there appears to be a cumulative lack of knowledge and attention to the unique influence that factors such as the socioeconomic climate, the functioning of the public service sector, functioning of the recreation service system, and relevant social and cultural factors all have on the welfare of minorities in this society.

Aside from the demands and urgings still arising from minority group communities, there are some critical implicators for even more stringent measures to realign or restructure the recreation system to better serve minorities.

Population Growth Rate

The National Advisory Commission on Civil Rights reported that in 1966 the number of blacks living in metropolitan cities was up to 14.6 million, with over one-third of this number concentrated in the twelve largest U. S. population centers. This figure has risen since 1966.[18]

When the present and projected growth of the nonwhite urban population in major urban centers is considered in conjunction with related socioeconomic factors such as urban population density, limited or nonexistent open space, and the dwindling tax base, the implications for readjusting priorities and increasing program flexibility in the urban-based public recreation system are obvious. Open or green space in minority group communities remains a premium commodity. If business and industry continue to favor locating in the suburban countryside, the public tax dollars available to finance metropolitan services will continue to drop. In effect, public recreation administrators are faced with the prospect that the task of developing an improved caliber of services for an ever-increasing urban minority group population will have to be accomplished within a comparatively rigid framework of resources. On this basis, innovation, experimentation, and resourcefulness with respect to facility development, program organization, fiscal management, and manpower development will be crucial requirements for successful social service.

Problems in Service Delivery

Citizens, violently venting their dissatisfaction with the system, spurred policy makers in the public and private sectors to pledge and contribute massive quantities of resources for application to the needs of urban cities. It was declared in no uncertain terms that the quality and quantity of public services would be raised to levels of effectiveness that would satisfactorily meet the social, economic, and health needs of practically every citizen.

In the midst of this purge of public conscience through material support, the public recreation service system gained

access to previously unavailable resources. For most urban public recreation departments, the "War on Poverty" came to mean
available federal and state dollars for large-scale construction
of swimming pools, community centers, parks, camping facilities, multipurpose arenas, and a variety of portable facilities
and equipment. Nonwhite minority groups in urban cities were
by design the prime recipients of these new services. However,
with the tightening of the national economy, plus multiple
shifts in the nation's priorities, the growth of public service
capabilities in general and public recreation operations specifically, began to lag. Nevertheless, many public recreation
servants considered pre-1960's gaps and abuses in service as history, and felt that a new era of responsive and equitable distribution of recreation services had been launched.

Now it has become obvious to alert recreation administrators and the nonwhite minority group users of their services,
that this judgment was only partially accurate. It was recognized that the increase in the number of permanent and portable facilities and equipment located in nonwhite minority
group communities represented basically a quantitive level of
success. Too late many realized that the decision-making
processes that resulted in the selection and location of facilities
and equipment lacked the critical qualitative evaluative input
that is acquired through positive interaction and involvement
with the intended users of the services. In too many instances,
urban recreation administrators discovered too late that a
particular facility, attractive and functional as it was, failed
to match the needs or expectations of the intended non-white
minority group consumers. As a result, facilities and equipment expected to serve hundreds of citizens were used by a
comparatively few or not used at all. Under other circumstances, facilities and equipment became prime targets of vandalism or were used for a variety of illegal activities. Perhaps
the scope of the task originally facing the operators of the public recreation system has been visibly lessened, but at the same
time, to the bulk of the nonwhite minority group population as
well as to many practitioners, the gaps and the abuses remain
evident.

Judging from all evident socioeconomic indicators, the public recreation system as a whole will not reach or regain in
the foreseeable future the level of fiscal and attitudinal public

support received in the post-riot years of the 1960's. Excepting the fabled "hot summer" funding, recreation administrators will have to meet the needs and demands of nonwhite minority group members within the traditional framework of public or municipal resources.

The possible downturn in the nation's economy and shifting of public social priorities can deal a fatal blow to whatever chance exists to eliminate the gaps and abuses in recreation services to nonwhite minority groups. Already the pace of facility construction in the communities inhabited by this group is slowing and, in some instances, has ground to a halt.

To avoid what in truth would be a catastrophe, public recreation administrators must profit from the experiences of the past and abandon the premise that the indiscriminate delivery of facilities and equipment is the optimum and most productive means of serving the nonwhite minority group community. New emphasis must be placed on developing a framework of professional leadership, program organization, inter-agency planning, service delivery, and citizen participation that adheres to quality and at the same time is rigidly appropriate to nonwhite minority group needs and desires.

Attitudes and Expectations

No one, least of all the recreation administrator, can afford to interpret the absence or reduction of overt civil disturbance in nonwhite minority group communities as a sign of satisfaction with the present level of service delivery. Utilizing organizational and decision-making vehicles established through various federal and state supported community-based programs, citizens in these communities remain concerned and intent on acquiring their just portion of recreation programs and services.

The degree to which the public service administrator communicates responsively with the nonwhite minority group members or their representatives strongly influences the manner in which attitudes and expectations are collectively expressed. It is to this end that the recreation administrator must expand and reinforce his relationship with the nonwhite minority group community. If indeed attitudes and expectations are to be understood and properly addressed, no resource for valid and comprehensive input should be overlooked. From both the lay and professional standpoint, a proportionate involvement of nonwhite minority group members must be involved in the planning and decision-making.

The minority group population, rich or poor, is no less aware of the value and need for recreation services. In most instances, their attitudes and expectations in this regard differ from those of the majority group to an insignificant degree. Thus it can be expected that there will be a significant reaction to inequitable allocation of public monies and insensitive responses to their expressed needs and desires.

Summary

A regressive pattern in the evolution of the recreation profession's concepts and practices has undoubtedly contributed to the limited capacity of recreation practitioners to respond effectively to the needs and demands of minority group members for recreation services. State, county, and municipal recreation departments will have to quickly discover ways and means to overcome the crippling communication gap that has developed over the years. The awareness and sensitivity needed to close this gap do not have to remain out of reach.

To the credit of the leadership of the profession, solid remedial efforts have been launched to improve the delivery of services to minority groups. These efforts include actions calculated to achieve the necessary reorientation of professional philosophy and conceptual principles and guidelines. In addition, priorities for resource allocation and program and service delivery emphases are being scrutinized and, where possible and necessary, reordered in favor of minority group problems and needs.

Large numbers of practicing recreators in the urban community setting are being positively influenced and stimulated by a combination of factors that include 1) the concentrated concern and actions of the professional leadership, 2) a shift in public policy and attitudes from apathy to concern and response, and 3) the insistent demands of minority group constituents at the local level.

In retrospect, the recreation profession should never have lost sight of minority group needs, and throughout its evolution should always have been as responsive as it currently is.

For the present, it should be recognized by theorists and practitioners alike that as long as the recreation system shares the public tax dollar it has the serious responsibility to develop a permanent but flexible capability to serve the needs and desires of all citizens including minority group members. There is a further responsibility to develop a communications network to transmit knowledge about social, environmental, and economic factors that influence citizens'—including minority groups—demands, needs, expectations, and aspirations. This network could be developed through the vehicles of local, state, and national professional organizations.

The establishment and operation of such a network can be a prime deterrent to further deterioration of the framework of public recreation service and, in fact, could significantly increase the existing level of program delivery to minority groups. Methods and means for achieving this objective must be the priority of all foreseeable generations of professional recreators.

FOOTNOTES

[1] "Kerner Commission Report: Grievances," chapter in *Recreation and Leisure Service for the Disadvantaged*, J. A. Nesbitt, Ed.D., P. D. Brown, Ed.D., and James F. Murphy, eds.(Philadelphia: Lea & Febiger, 1970), p. 43.

[2] Richard G. Kraus, *Public Recreation and the Negro: A Study of Participation and Administrative Practices*. A publication of the Center for Urban Education (New York, 1968), p. 34.

[3] Arthur Williams, "An Organization Is Born," in the chapter "Notes on History and Theory" in Jay B. Nash *Recreation: Pertinent Readings—Guideposts to the Future* (Dubuque, Lowa: Wm. C. Brown Co., 1965), p. 18.

[4] Arthur Williams, p. 18.

[5] Arthur Williams, p. 19.

[6] Arthur Williams, pp. 62–63.

[7] *The American Heritage Dictionary of the English Language*, William Morris, ed. (New York: American Heritage Publishing Co., Inc. and Houghton Mifflin Co., 1969), p. 836.

[8] *Webster's Seventh New Collegiate Dictionary*, based on Web-

ster's Third New International Dictionary (Springfield, Mass.: G. & C. Merriam Co. 1965), p. 540.

[9] Tom Wicker, in the Introduction, *Report of the National Advisory Commission on Civil Disorders* (New York: Bantam, Inc., 1968), p. viii.

[10] LeRoi Jones, *Blues People* (New York: William Morrow and Co., 1963), Introduction, p. x.

[11] LeRoi Jones, p. 15.

[12] LeRoi Jones, p. 15.

[13] Richard Hofstader, *The American Political Tradition* (New York: Vintage Books, 1948), p. 154.

[14] Richard Hofstader, pp. 156–157.

[15] Richard Hofstader, p. 91.

[16] "Kerner Commission Report: Grievances," *Recreation and Leisure Service for the Disadvantaged*, J. A. Nesbitt, Ed.D., P. D. Brown, Ed.D., and James F. Murphy, eds. (Philadelphia: Lea & Febiger, 1970), p. 116.

[17] "Kerner Commission Report," p. 116.

[18] *Report of the National Advisory Commission on Civil Disorders*, p. viii.

BIBLIOGRAPHY

Cleaver, Eldridge, *Soul on Ice*. New York: McGraw-Hill, Inc., 1968.

Cruse, Harold, *The Crisis of the Negro Intellectual*. New York: William Morrow & Company, Inc., 1967

Downs, Anthony, "Alternative Futures for the American Ghetto," *Daedalus, Journal of the American Academy of Arts and Sciences*. Boston: American Academy of Arts and Sciences, Fall, 1968.

Goldman, Eric F., *Rendezvous With Destiny*. New York: Vintage Books, 1952.

Guggenheimer, Elinor C., *Planning for Parks and Recreation Needs in Urban Areas*. New York: Twayne Publishers, Inc., 1969.

Hofstadter, Richard, *The American Political Tradition*. New York: Vintage Books, 1948.

Huizinga, J., *Homo Ludens: A Study of the Play-Element in Culture*. Boston: The Beacon Press, 1950.

Jones, LeRoi, *Blues People*. New York: William Morrow and Company, 1963.

Kraus, Richard G., *Public Recreation and the Negro: A Study of Participation and Administrative Practices*. New York: Center for Urban Education, 1968.

Lindsay, John V., *The City*. New York: W. W. Norton & Company, Inc., 1969.

Morris, William, ed., *The American Heritage Dictionary of the English Language*. New York: American Heritage Publishing Co., Inc., and Houghton Mifflin Co., 1969.

Nesbitt, J. A., Brown, P., and Murphy J., eds. "Kerner Commission Report: Grievances," *Recreation and Leisure Service for the Disadvantaged*. Philadelphia: Lea & Febiger, 1970.

Shapiro, Harry L. (edited only, contributors upon request) *Man, Culture, and Society*. New York: Oxford University Press, 1960.

Tucker, Sterling, *Why the Ghetto Must Go*. Public Affairs Pamphlet No. 423, New York: Public Affairs Committee, 1968.

Webster's Seventh New Collegiate Dictionary, based on Webster's Third New International Dictionary. Springfield, Mass.: G. & C. Merriam Co. 1965.

Wicker, Tom, in the Introduction, *Report of the National Advisory Commission on Civil Disorders*. New York: Bantam, Inc. 1968.

Williams, Arthur, "An Organization Is Born," in the chapter "Notes on History and Theory", in Jay B. Nash *Recreation: Pertinent Readings—Guideposts to the Future*. Dubuque, Iowa: Wm. C. Brown Co., 1965.

12 Recreation and the Problems of Youth

Photo by Tania D'Avignon

DONALD A. PELEGRINO

YOUTH AND LEISURE TODAY

Adolescents are a special population with many special problems in our society. Adults should be aware that today's youth face many problems and situations that did not exist in the youth of the older generation.

It has been said too often that youth now have more money, more equipment, more opportunities, more commercial outlets, more recreation centers, and more programs to satisfy their leisure needs than ever before. It sounds great but the nagging thought remains, how well are those needs really being met? Let's discuss some of the problems youth actually are facing today, and what recreation is doing to help find some solutions to these problems.

To do this we must realize that we are talking about a vast field: comprised of a greater number of youth than ever before, with more varied needs, and subject to more varied pressures than ever before. Broadly speaking, this group ranges from those who have everything, think they've seen it all, experienced it all, are bored and uninterested; to those who feel that nothing belongs to them, who actually have no money and no "know-how," and are alternately belligerent and apathetic.

PHYSIOLOGICAL NEEDS OF ADOLESCENTS

A major concern in the study of adolescents is: what are the biological characteristics of this age group? An in-depth search into psychology, physiology, and anthropology could be considered here. However, we will take a down-to-earth approach, believing this to be most practical in presenting concepts that can be understood by youths and adults—particularly adults who work with youth.

Children and adolescents grow and mature at different rates. This individualism is reflected in differences in: sex, body development, heredity, and in exceptional youth. Each has implications for the recreator as he approaches programming for the young.

Sex Differences

Well before a child becomes a teenager, he usually has learned the physiological differences between boys and girls. What the teenager wants to know about sex may not be about its physiological aspects, but rather its social and moral implications.

During adolescence, girls generally mature physically earlier than boys. While adolescent females are more interested in physical appearance, social relationships, and feminine activities, the males are often more interested in objective reality, science, engineering, sports, and other masculine concerns.

As he matures, the young male adolescent becomes interested in relating to girls. He starts thinking about dating and starts planning his future with an idea of getting married one day. During these years, adolescents have dating problems, many of which involve questions of sexual behavior. Some of these problems arise because many times adults, either through ignorance or embarrassment, fail to give boys and girls adequate information about sex. Children so uninformed frequently turn for information to their peers or older brothers and sisters, coming away with distorted impressions about sex and their bodies.

Often young people want birth control information, which parents fail to provide in the mistaken belief that such knowledge will promote sexual activity. In other cases, parents themselves lack knowledge about contraception. Too many parents fail to understand the importance of giving their offspring necessary sex knowledge.

Body Development

Painfully embarrassing uncoordination is a common symptom of adolescence. This uncoordination is caused by the extensive physical changes that take place during the teen years. For example, muscle growth is most rapid during adolescence when the individual begins to "fill out" and approaches adult height and proportions. During this time, the body may not be ready to handle the growth phenomenon. The youth may become uncoordinated; however, this condition only lasts for a few years.

Proper exercise is essential during this period, for it helps build muscle tone and also keeps the body in shape. The female, during early adolescence, goes through dramatic physiological change and begins menstruation.

Hereditary Traits

Heredity is a complex phenomenon. Its implications for personal growth and development are not fully understood, for no one knows how much of our being is shaped by our environment and how much is due to our genes. The following quotes set some of these matters in perspective.

> Bodily and temperamental traits combine in such a multitude of ways that it is difficult to classify any individual with a single formula. The deepest aspects of individuality are biochemical, metabolic, and physiological.[1]

> Growth is a unifying concept which resolves the dualism of heredity and environment. Environmental factors support, inflect, and modify, but they do not generate the basic progressions of infant-child growth development. These progressions are largely determined by genetic constitution.[2]

> The dimensions of personality which are most influenced by heredity are such traits as our physical characteristics, motor skills, intelligence, sensory acuity, and other fundamental abilities and capacities.[3]

Any society is likely to place a high value on a certain combination of inherited physical characteristics; other individual characteristics may be distasteful to the society, and persons having such characteristics may react to a society's discrimination by rejecting that society. Often this rejection takes the form of juvenile delinquency and, eventually, adult criminal behavior. Both heredity and environment interacting, have played a part here. Experience points to the observation that the environment, and what is within the environment, can account for many of the problems that occur in society.

Exceptional Youth

Mental deviation, often caused by hereditary traits, sometimes results in individual and/or social problems. What does the genius do to fulfill his needs? What are the many barriers a retarded youth must face? To both gifted and retarded adolescents, these concerns are so critical that many times frustrations result because solutions are not available. Gifted adolescents represent a human resource in growth potential which needs to be discovered, encouraged, and conserved. The bright young person's environment plays a major role in developing his behavioral pattern. The retarded adolescent also represents a vast reservoir of human resources, but needs to be nurtured differently.

Many times exceptional youth are denied the attention they need in our mass educational system. Some of these individuals have very high ability potential; others very low or limited potential. The adolescent who has abilities in music or athletic skills is usually given opportunity to practice and improve. Whereas, the intellectually gifted, as well as the limited ones, often are regarded as "problem children." Today, with massive education programs in the colleges, with the space age, with the fight against pollution and other social ills, intellectually talented young people have the opportunity to fulfill themselves through mental involvement. Intellectually limited youth, however, frequently have few sources for involvement and help.

PSYCHOLOGICAL ASPECTS

The psychological condition of adolescents, largely determined by specific environmental factors, determines how well teenagers function and solve their problems. Much emphasis has been placed on discovering those conditions that lead to a youth's psychological "maladjustment." These conditions, for our purposes, will be grouped under the following headings: 1) psychological problems in identifying with the "adult establishment"; 2) family and home situational problems arising from the blocked needs and drives of special populations; 3) psychology of the school dropout; 4) the psychological makeup of the community and the neighborhood; and 5) conclusion.

The problems of special groups seem to be due to rapid and sudden changes in the physiological, intellectual, and social development of these youth. This transitional period seems to be the most traumatic period in adolescent development. Youth's physical changes are quite dramatic and seem to have certain psychological effects upon attitude. Exceptional youth find themselves growing out of their childhood fantasies, and are suddenly faced with confusing ideas about life that are too intellectually demanding of them. Parents, school, and society force these young people to think and act "more like adults."

Identifying with the Adult Establishment

Contrary to the popular impression about youth, *Newsweek* recently stated that "the teenage population, instead of riding roughshod over helpless adults, is actually being segregated, shunned, manipulated, discriminated against and forced into a deluxe teenage ghetto where tastes and mores of a distinct subculture flourish only for lack of meaningful integration into a stable adult society."[4] It seems that there is a basic flow in society towards a general mistrust between the adult world and youth. Many young people have become quite disturbed over the discrepancies between what they are told about the world and what they see and experience. These youth, therefore, logically conceive that "if they (adults) taught me a lie, then they must be liars.' " Consequently, this type of reaction exhibits the feelings of these youth toward the "adult establishment." They view adults as being "self-interested, egocentric people who can't trust anyone." Too many adults have seemingly taken every available opportunity to show suspicion and disbelief toward any actions of this younger generation. The important thing to remember is that the attitudes of adults toward youth depend not so much upon whether the adult establishment accepts these individuals as it does upon the basic understanding of their needs. Youth's problems in relating to adult society and attitudes can be partly attributed to abnormal family and home situations.

Home and Family

Studies show that the most vital factors influencing character development are found in the home and in the parent-child relationship.[5] The home environment should provide for the physical, psychological, and social needs of the teenager; the home may either have positive or negative effects upon the youth's development. A home which is characterized by family unity in work, play, and decision-making is more likely to have favorable effects upon the character of the adolescent involved. In contrast, where young people grow up in homes complicated with parental dissension, suspicion, and inconsideration for members of the family, great difficulty is experienced in establishing adequate character behavior patterns. As a result of such unfavorable conditions at home, youth usually resort to deviant and delinquent behavior as an escape. Consistency in family functioning is essential for emotional stability of youth. If his parents disagree, a young person is torn or forced to choose between two loves. As a result, his behavior becomes inconsistent and unpredictable.

In establishing an adequate emotional climate within the family unit, each member must be respected as a unique individual. Studies evidence that when a high degree of parental role differentiation or inconsistency exists in middle-class American society, it contributes to emotional and social maladjustment among adolescents.[6] Unfortunately, this factor of parental role differentiation is more predominate in the lower-class than in the middle-class family; in lower-class families the problem is further complicated. For example, when there is no father, or where the mother is forced to work all day, or a divorce causes a separation in the family, the youth of these families are more likely to become involved in truancy, stealing, and other delinquent behavior. It can be seen that the home plays a very vital part in the psychological development of todays' youth.

Parents are probably the most influential factor affecting the character of development of the youth. They can either aid or hinder the youth's development and maturity. For example, a very dominating, autocratic parent may insist upon strict conformity to demands at all times, limiting the need for independence. A parent, by restricting an adolescent's life and preventing healthy friction in life experiences, often leaves the adolescent unprepared for conflicts and frustrations in his school and play environment. Conversely, an understanding, democratic parent offers not only security but also opportunity for independance and responsibilities that an individual needs.

There is a much more trusting attitude in the democratic parent-child relationship.

Parents' values are often very important in youth development. In today's conglomerate society, we often see parents who are irresponsible, too materialistic, overconforming, too content, overly passive, and too money conscious. They seem to have no real answers to the problems bothering their young people. As a result, at times many parents feel inadequate when their teenagers come home for advice and guidance. Since parents often cannot give their own child solid practical solutions to his problems, they resort to giving very vague and uncertain support.

Another factor which could discourage a favorable home environment is low socioeconomic status, although this is not always the case. A "poor" home is not necessarily a "bad home." However, poverty youth may be affected by poor living conditions, lack of an inadequate diet, and a family attitude of discontent and bitterness arising from such conditions. Such youth are more likely to engage in "unacceptable" behavior.

Both extremes, the affluent home where overprotection leads to overpermissiveness, and the poverty home with abnormal environment conditions, seem to have significance in cases of abnormal psychological development of youth.

Drives and Needs

All teenagers, whether from affluent or disadvantaged environments, have certain dynamic inner drives and needs that influence their thoughts, emotions, attitudes, and behavior patterns. The teenager's adjustment to his life frustrations is largely determined by the satisfaction of these needs and drives. These drives may force a young person into behavior which goes counter to what he could ever afford without feeling guilty about it afterwards. Fritz Redl and David Wineman in *The Aggressive Child,* state that "under certain group psychological conditions, behavior can be afforded as being tax-free from guilt feelings which otherwise could not."[7]

Some of the basic drives and needs that affect the behavior of the "disadvantaged" youth are ones associated with the need for recognition, independence, success, superiority, conformity, and excitement.

Recognition

Most teenagers want to be known; they want attention. They are constantly seeking identification and approval of their acts from an environment that does not readily give such approval and recognition to its members. When a youth engages in an activity, he usually wants others to share it with him so he can observe their reactions. Usually, within the environment where these youth interact, there is no feeling of satisfaction that should accompany the success of achievement. In these communities there are no adults available to give these youth the intensified pleasure of identity and recognition that they deserve. They, therefore, become frustrated. A good example of this concept can be seen in the school behavior of these youth. When a youth fails to receive an adequate amount of recognition and approval for his efforts, he will eventually find other ways, usually deviant, to attract the attention of the teacher and the other students. Since his peer group ranks high in his social priorities, he will usually find some "delinquent" means to gain the approval of his classmates if the opportunities for more acceptable achievement are limited or blocked.

It can be seen then that problems of recognition could be resolved if adults would take the time to give appropriate praise and recognition for acts that are performed well. Just take the time to recognize the good attributes—they are there.

Independence

Many parents and adults deny youth the power of free choice. They make most of their decisions for their young people and make them accept them. Often adults, through tactful manipulation, choose their childrens' friends, their clothes, and their immediate lifestyle. They ultimately decide whether their child will go to college and, often, what he will study when he gets there. Parents sometimes "steer" their youth toward possible mates of whom the parents approve. While youth should have the privilege to disagree with such decisions, they are usually denied this right. Adults having such attitudes will surely generate conflict, emotional disturbance, and even outright rebellion. It can be generally agreed that though youths need some controls and guidance, more than that, they need understanding of their needs and desires, especially the need to function independently.

Success

Many young people, due to environmental conditions, have not had the chance to really experience success. Various studies have proven that the success factor serves as a motivating force in the lives of most people. It is also an important link in the personal development of young people. The normal youth who has experienced the satisfaction that goes with successful achievement is likely to be stimulated to pursue other activities that interest him. Conversely, the youth who has not experienced the satisfaction from successful accomplishment probably will not be motivated toward other interests. Opportunity to succeed within their immediate surroundings must be afforded young people in order that they may advance in their development. A recreation program with a variety of opportunities for involvement and one built upon the expressed needs and planning of youth themselves can assure some of these developmental successes.

Superiority and Conformity

All youth wish to excel at something. Throughout the "disadvantaged" youth's life he craves to excel in one activity in which others have only average ability. Whether this activity happens to be street fighting or swiping merchandise from the liquor store, it is something for which he can take pride. Of main importance to him is how much better he is able to perform in a specific skill as compared to the skills of others in his peer group. We all know what the urge is like to be "No. 1" in something. If the right conditions for being superior in an activity are not available to the youth, he is forced to satisfy this urge by some other means, usually deviant.

The desire for conformity can be seen vividly during the teenage period. In dress, language, social habits and other social mores, youth desire to conform to others, especially in their peer group. Today's teenager very much wants to be "in"; whether it be the "hippie" lifestyle or the traditional university look, he wants to be in the "groove." Probably the two most obvious mannerisms are dress and language. If bell-bottoms are the current style, then wearing them is the "right" thing to do. If some other type of clothing is "out," then it becomes "un-hip" to be seen in that dress.

Many adults will testify to the fact that today's youth communicate through a particular type of language. Young people are etymologists: they invent and develop words, a few examples being "heavy," "up tight," "split," and "groovy."

Excitement

The need for exciting activity seems to be one of the most important psychological needs of all youth. Curiosity to discover something new is normal for all teenagers. However, the teenager in the disadvantaged area does not always have the same numerous "acceptable" opportunities to express this urge as does his more affluent counterpart. During this adolescent period, many outside factors, such as popular magazines and other forms of mass media, influence youth to discover new things and investigate them.

If the teenager, hampered by his environment, is unable to experiment with the new and different, he may feel compelled to change either his immediate surroundings or himself. He may pop pills, drop out of school, or become destructive or delinquent because of boredom, or he may become listless because of the lack of new and vicarious experiences. This need for thrill-seeking adventure may take a variety of forms. It may be driving 100 m.p.h. down some old abandoned farm road or siphoning gas from the city police cars. Whatever such ventures entail, they appear exciting and challenging to these young people.

The need for new exciting experiences is also referred to in the terms "behavioral exploration." Because of the lack of experiences within an individual's environment (neighborhood), he may find it necessary to use the method of "trial and error." These youth are interested in trying out a particular activity to "see what it is like." Delinquent acts often begin as behavioral explorations and the need to be involved in an activity that is alluring because it is unfamiliar. Parents and teachers must accept the fact that youth will find experiences in one way or another. Therefore, the logical thing to do is to provide the right opportunities for such experiences.

School—The Drop Out

The school, just as the home, has the responsibility to help a young person achieve those behavior patterns which will aid him in making adequate adjustments in today's society. Unfortunately, the present education practices, particularly in the disadvantaged areas, are far from perfect and require continuous revision and improvement in order to meet the needs and abilities of an educational system's clientele. Teenagers in these schools are fully aware that there is something wrong with their schools: constant pressure for grades, mediocre teachers, uninspiring curriculum, and an unawareness of their own responsibility to themselves and their environment. These facts are especially apparent in the ghetto school. However our main emphasis at this point of the discussion relates to the problem of youth dropping out of school.

A primary reason for many teenagers leaving school is lack of interest. This may mean a number of things depending upon the individual. It may mean that the disadvantaged teenager is discouraged about his progress in school. He may dislike a particular subject or teacher in school, or possibly the entire school atmosphere is not concurrent with his feelings or attitudes. Many of these youth leave school because of low marks which they take as a personal threat rather than as a challenge to improve themselves. Many of these youth fear tests because they are afraid that such examinations will be personally belittling. As a result of these feelings many young people begin to feel inferior in their class and often resort to taking out their feelings on their teachers, which seems only to compound their problems.

School dropouts often come from homes where there is little or no encouragement. Sometimes teenagers drop out of school to help supplement the family income or to aid relatives. In a study conducted by the Maryland State Department of Education over half of the dropouts were from homes where the father was either not trained or was currently unemployed. Young people from disadvantaged areas have many problems to overcome. Usually their parents do not have a complete education, and they are without educational resources such as books or even intelligent discussion. Because of financial limits, there is little chance for these youth to leave their homes for new experiences. And the financial burden of a college education is usually out of the question.

The teenager's greatest difficulty is finding out who he is and what he can do. If he views himself in an inferior capacity, then his self-identity suffers greatly. He can easily get confused and quit school. Then he is lost as a student and, too often, as a person.

Community and Neighborhood Influences

Studies indicate that just as community characteristics are related to delinquent behavior, many problems of a more distinctly psychological kind vary with the environment. This is fairly easy to comprehend, since it is known that many mental disorders are nothing more than unsuccessful attempts to adjust to the demands of the environment. The environment of the disadvantaged is usually quite complex, disorganized, and more threatening to the individual than may be true in the normal middle-class community environment. The general conclusion is that there is a distinct relationship between community organization and certain psychological disorders. However, this is not to say that the psychological makeup of the community is merely a reflection of the physical and social makeup of that community. This is evident in cities of similar makeup, but which have varying rates of delinquency and crime. The traditions, standards, cultures, and moral structures of the community have greater influence than do the external appearances—a reality we are becoming more and more aware of today.

It becomes quite apparent that certain psychological characteristics of a community become "communized" and emerge as the lifestyle of that community. They are a conglomerate of sharing of common experiences, attitudes, values, mores, difficulties, conflicts, and interests. Through these conditions the community, and especially the neighborhood, assumes a sort of psychological character. This character is developed within the community and "absorbs" the teenager into identifying with that environment. Therefore, he is forced to function according to the attitudes, interests, desires, and feelings of that community.

It can be determined, then, that community psychology plays a very important role in the development of a youth's personality. For instance, if a neighborhood adopts an apathetic attitude toward delinquency, crime, and other deviant acts, the chances are that these patterns will flourish among its young people. The reverse is also true.

It would appear that certain cultural factors within the community also would have an apparent effect upon the personality development of the teenager. If, for instance, there are no well-equipped schools, libraries, theaters, and recreational facilities in the immediate area, then the development of attitudes, values, interests, and use of leisure time will be greatly affected.

Conclusion

It appears that youth from special populations often become the youth nobody wants. Furthermore, it is evident that, even though we may know the reasons why they have become antisocial in their behavior, once they reach that point they are practically impossible to live with. It seems, by and large, that their homes, their schools, their communities and neighborhoods are all unable to accept or put up with what these teenagers have become.

The reasons why these youth are not tolerated by their communities may vary. Some of these young people may resort to delinquent acts or open displays of aggression. Others may hide behind a compliance which lasts only as long as they want it to, and still others withdraw completely from their surroundings and any relationships that go on around them—an indicator of mental illness. No matter what the causes of these psychologically oriented problems are, the youth of special populations become an unsolvable problem for communities in which they live. The ultimate result is a vast amount of human waste. In communities all throughout the United States there are literally thousands of such youth. They are the youth that nobody wants.[8]

SOCIALIZATION OF YOUTH

The child has three social worlds which are of about equal importance to him: the world of family; the world of the school; and the world of the neighborhood. The adolescent's peer group becomes his dominant social world. He not only spends proportionately more time with the peer group, but its influence becomes the strongest social force in his life.

For the adolescent this relationship results in a confusion between old and new values and a clash between the desire to be identified with the peer group and his parents' demands that he continue to regard the family as the major force in his social world. Choosing to follow his peer group could lead to constant friction in the home and, unless his status in the peer group is very secure, he may have a feeling of not belonging anywhere.

Our society encourages its youth to be irresponsible concerning money, and teaches the teenager to do business with the adult world. Business encourages fads in clothes, records, rock groups, stars, slang, hair styles, cars, magazines, books, and cosmetics for both male and female. As adults, we contribute to many of the problems of youth.

Youth and Sex

Confusion regarding the role of sex in social relationships is traumatic for many young people. Though there are females who engage in sexual relationships to seek popularity, most girls regard sex as an expression of love because most have been told by their parents and society that sexual intercourse is only engaged in when two individuals are in love or married. Consequently, when a male says or shows her through sexual manipulations that he desires her, she may think he desires her as an individual rather than merely desiring to make love to her body. The female may rationalize the strong sexual urges she feels towards the male and consider them to be love rather than sexual frustration. Since society says she must only feel this way when she is in love or married, in order for her not to feel guilty, she must be in love, and the young man must love her. This type of relationship usually leaves the female with a great deal of guilt and depression when the relationship is over. This is a very dramatic and emotional time in a young woman's life, and everything seems to be a life-and-death type of emotion. The age span of sixteen to eighteen years is a most dangerous time if the young woman becomes pregnant from such a relationship and finds out the male involved has little or no feeling toward her and is unwilling to marry. The female will usually become extremely irrational and think of the worst possibilities: 1) her parents will kill her; 2) she'd rather die than have her parents know; 3) no one will ever love her again; 4) how can she ever face her friends; 5) who would ever marry her after she had a baby; and 6) her life is ruined—so why not kill herself if she can't afford an abortion.

The female who engages in sexual relationships to seek popularity usually feels she is unattractive, undesirable, intellectually inadequate, and has a horrible personality. Her parents may reinforce these thoughts of inadequacy by constantly asking why she does not go out like other girls her age. She, therefore, may decide that the only way she will get asked out twice by a boy is to succumb to his sexual advances on the first date. Therefore, she thinks she will become a desirable date and will please her parents and appear to be popular to her own peers.

Dating

Today, it is not unusual for a teen to start dating at the age of thirteen or fourteen. The first dates are usually "doubles." This relieves the awkwardness and lack of communication that often accompanies a single date which is due to a lack of dating experience. To the teenager and to some parents early dating is a sign of an "all-around healthy personality." When speaking of dating one must consider the aspects of going steady. The idea of "steadies" eliminates the problem of being left without a partner for social affairs. Teens also feel that "dutch treat" relieves financial burden from the boy.

Steady dating has become more permissive, allowing the partners more independence. Each partner does not want to "hold down" the other. This mutual attitude is possibly a continuing test of the relationship.

The "In Group"

Another security that young people enjoy is the "in group." Among the disadvantaged this need is greater because they lack other resources for recreational activities. An in group may consist of a dozen or fewer teens. Usually this group has many things in common such as level of living, income, tastes, and types of interest. To teens it is more important to be accepted by an in group than it is by a club which anyone may join. Recreation program planners had best take note of this!

Commercial Recreation

Commercial recreation has played an important part in the teen's social life. Girls usually will not attend any event unless they know that boys will also be there. The teen fairs that occur during Christmas and Easter vacation draw teens by the thousand. Popular resorts such as Palm Springs and Big Bear Lake are also great teen havens. Teen clubs, band concerts and battles, popular singing stars, car races, beach activities, Disneyland, etc., all bring the teens together for social interaction. Both girls and boys will attend many activities not for the pleasure of going, but for the pleasure of meeting a "guy" or a "chick." Thus, although commercial recreation has much to offer both sexes of the teen set, the motivating force for teen involvement is not always the recreation activity, per se, but rather the social opportunities that one expects to accompany such an activity.

Juvenile Delinquency

Delinquency in any society is related in fundamental ways to other characteristics of that society. Our society is based on set patterns and an order which prizes material success. Delinquency often emerges from situations where communities and families fail to provide conditions, services, and experiences that enable young people to participate competently in American life.

Three problems need to be kept in mind as we discuss substantive issues in delinquency. First, vagueness of the concept of delinquency is important. Many of our difficulties at all stages of prevention, adjudication, and correction are rooted in the tremendous variety of acts that may at different times and places be defined as delinquent. Secondly, some authorities limit their usage of the concept of the delinquent to those who have engaged in actual legal infractions, while others conceive delinquency as being synonymous with youth. The third problem is posed by the division between programs for the prevention of delinquency and those for the correction and rehabilitation of delinquents. The correctional program only operates after the fact.

In the prevention of delinquency, programs supported by the President's Committee fall into three chief areas. First, opportunities for learning a basic skill and for employment opportunities should be provided. Work skills and employment are basic elements in social competency and integration into the community. Secondly, the educational services should fit needs of youth in deprived or slum areas. All should be given a chance to learn. Thirdly, community organization programs should be developed as a means of increasing the competence of community members to deal with their own problems. The key to this program is motivation and opportunity. It should give the potential delinquent a chance to become an active part of society, and to say, "I did achieve" or "I reached my goal."

Often the young person who gets into trouble comes from a background in which the parents are so absorbed in their own affairs or so overcome by the pressures of survival that they are unaware of what their children are doing. The reason why many juveniles and youth are "turned off" by society is that today's youth want to be recognized, but are denied this by an adult society which is preoccupied with its own concerns and feelings. Now, how do you expect youth to respect adults if adults don't respect youth? To seek their security, youth turn to their peers for drugs, drinking, and sex. They want instant gratification and recognition. Their symbols of freedom and righteousness are Beatles, beards, beads, long hair, LSD, acid, grass, bennies, etc.

Many people feel that our youth are not growing up in an America that is "One nation under God with liberty and justice for all," but an America of alienation of black and white, rich and poor, war and peace, slums and affluence. Our youth want to grow up in a nation that is indivisible, under God, with liberty and justice for all. But to create and sustain this modern America, youth must have the help of parents, teachers, and civic leaders who will enlist the energies and idealism of youth to work with them—not against them.

Alcohol and Drugs

There are many reasons why adolescents drink and use drugs. A young person may secretly long to hit back at parents for some real or fancied neglect, restriction, or overprotection. A young person may want to prove to himself, his peers, and his parents that "I am an adult." Teenagers may drink or use drugs to cover up the feelings of inadequacy and doubt about their own worth or about their ability to love other people. Young people experiment with drugs or drink to experience thrills, to replace dullness and boredom with moments of exhilaration and danger. Many others indulge themselves in order to find solace for their fears, doubts, and the growing realization that life ahead may be tough, threatening, and disappointing. Another reason for such indulgence may be a desire to escape from responsibility and tension.

Sex Morals

Because young people are concerned over their future and the need for security, they have developed a major interest in improving the quality of living by satisfying relations between the sexes. In the past, sex behavior was regulated by religious teachings that stressed the values of continence and fidelity and the threat of punishment for sexual sin. There was the concern of detection, disease, and pregnancy. Today, sexual behavior is often regulated by the desire to share a meaningful relationship—to be honest and to trust.

SOME THOUGHTS
AND POSSIBLE SOLUTIONS

The field of recreation has a definite commitment to young people, in fact, its history has been one of youth concern and programming. Today, however, recreation programs are often ineffective since young people balk at entering such traditional activities as "Teen Clubs," "Boy's Clubs," "Girls Clubs," etc. Teenagers reject organized recreation's traditional programs partly because they are no longer stimulated by them, partly because they prefer coeducational recreation, and partly because they are looking for meaningful experiences which they feel cannot be gained from these efforts.

One of the most effective techniques for working with young people is to become aware of the group, or groups, in the recreation settings and to become aware of the particular needs of those groups. An alert recreation director will discover for himself who the leaders of the group are, who the discipline problems are and why. Then the leader must find a way to become accepted by the group—to be sure that they like and trust him. To do this, the recreation director must be sincere in his relationships with these young people—he must be honest with them and never betray a confidence. It is also important that he be aware of the constantly changing needs of the group. What is vitally important today may have no relevance at all tomorrow.

The best recreation program for young people takes into consideration natural peer groups and finds ways to work with them. When each individual can interact with others in social development, the recreation experience is beneficial. A teen is in the process of becoming an adult and needs to establish identity as an adult, as well as security and peer acceptance.

If feasible, a teen center or drop-in spot should be furnished for youth. If this is not possible, then definite time slots should be allotted for teen activities. Adult supervision or counsel should be available for special needs at all times.

Whenever possible teens should be allowed to experiment in self-discipline. It may or may not work, but the experience for young people is valuable. Adult counseling should always be available for guidance and security.

In order to effectively work with young people, one must be aware of the changes that occur constantly. Fads, needs, activities, music, dancing, etc., are like the winds that come and go. However, when adults have a cordial interest in the leisure-time activities of young people, the roaming at loose ends and the association with indifferent people is reduced.

We also should be aware that young people today are playing for meaningful stakes. They don't like the traditional forms of ambition, and we should not be surprised if they prefer to work with the Peace Corps rather than aspire to a "soft life" in suburbia. Recreation places should be settings with which these teens can identify. Often a dingy coffee house is a popular place to go because young people can have dialogue there. The fancy recreation center with its structured program may not have any appeal for many young people.

Adults working with young people must employ patience and knowledge to be effective. And they must be sincere. They must be good listeners and not talkers. They must provide a realistic vision of the future and allow ample opportunity for intelligent decision-making and choices by young people.

It is important to let the teens plan and run their own programs as much as possible. They are vitally interested in and will support that which they feel is their own effort. They also soon lose interest in a program in which they have had no hand or word in planning.

The role of recreation for young people should include: meeting developmental needs with physical activities; encouraging co-recreational relationships; offering a variety of means for creative, social, aesthetic, and cultural experiences; and encouraging mature attitudes within each individual toward himself, the group, the family and the community. If this is done, there should be a much greater likelihood for success in serving this segment of society.

FOOTNOTES

[1] Arnold Lucus Gesell, Frances L. Ilg, Bates Ames, *Youth: The Years from Ten to Sixteen* (New York: Harpers, 4th edition, 1956), p. 26.

[2] Gesell, p. 27.

[3] Floyd Leon Ruch, *Psychology and Life* (Glenview, Ill.: Scott Foresman, 4th edition, n.d.), p. 51.

[4] ———, *Newsweek* (March 21, 1966), No. 12, p. 67.

[5] Sheldon and Eleanor Gleuck, *Family Environment and Delinquency* (Boston: Houghton Mifflin, 1962).

[6] Phillip E. Slater, "Parental Role Differentiation," *American Journal of Sociology*, Volume 67, 1961, pp. 296–311.

[7] Fritz Redl and David Wineman, *The Aggressive Child* (New York: Free Press, n. d.), p. 149.

[8] Fritz Redl and David Wineman, p. 22.

BIBLIOGRAPHY

Anaheim Parks and Recreation Department, "Teenage Interest Survey." Anaheim, California: Anaheim Parks and Recreation Department, 1967.

Blanchard, William H. "The Rebellion of Rousseau," *Los Angeles Times*, October 1, 1967, p. G-3.

Boys' Clubs of America, *Needs and Interests of Adolescent Boys' Club Members*. New York: Boys' Clubs of America, 1960.

Brown, Michael, *The Politics and Anti-Politics of the Young*. Beverly Hills, California: Glencoe Press, 1969.

Carter, Genevieve, "Social Trends and Social Planning," *Recreation*, LVIII (October, 1965), pp. 378–380.

Cox, Claire, *The Upbeat Generation*. Englewood Cliffs, N.J.: Prentice-Hall, 1962.

Department of Community Services and Youth Commission of Los Angeles County, "East Los Angeles Youth Speak Out." Conference Report, Los Angeles: Department of Community Services and Youth Commission of Los Angeles County, May 20, 1967. (Mimeographed)

Federation of Community Coordinating Councils, *Youth in Upheaval: Can Our 1965 Approaches Meet Their Future Need?* Proceedings of Delinquency Prevention. Los Angeles: Federation of Community Coordinating Councils, 1965.

Fox, Jack P., *Youth Quake*. New York: Cowles Educational Books, Inc., 1967.

Friedenberg, Edgar Z., *Coming of Ages in America: Growth and Acquiescence*. New York: Random House, 1965.

———, *The Vanishing Adolescent*. New York: Dell Publishing Company, Inc., 1959.

Hurlock, Elizabeth B., *Adolescent Development*. New York: McGraw-Hill, 1955.

Hopkins, Jerry, *The Hippie Papers*. New York: Signet Books, 1968.

International Council on Health, Physical Education and Recreation, *Leisure Time Activities of Youth in America*. A working paper prepared for the International Conference on Youth. Washington: International Council on Health, Physical Education, and Recreation, 1964.

Konopka, Gisela, *The Adolescent Girls in Conflict*. Englewood Cliffs, N.J.: Prentice-Hall, 1966.

Los Angeles Chamber of Commerce, *The Dynamics of the Youth Explosion—A Look Ahead*. 1967.

Los Angeles Department of Parks and Recreation. "Objectives and Goals," (n.d.)

Meeker, Marchia, *Estimating Age Distribution of the Population of Los Angeles County by Health Districts 1965 and 1970*. Los Angeles: Department of Mental Health, 1966.

———, "Meet the Restless Generation," *Changing Times*, XXI (June, 1967), pp. 6–11.

Olds, Edward B., *Study Material on the Youth Survey of Spare Time*. Washington, D.C.: Health and Welfare Council of the National Capital Area, 1960.

Pine, Gerald J., "The Affluent Delinquent," *Phi Delta Kappa*, XLVIII (December, 1966), pp. 138–143.

Schinckel, Richard, "Why Young People Are Seeking New Values," *Redbook,* CXXVII (May, 1966), p. 73.

Shivers, J. S., "Special Recreation Needs of Teenagers," *Parks and Recreation*, II (August, 1967), pp. 20–21, p. 47.

Siegel, Jules, "Surf, Wheels and Free Souls; in California," *Saturday Evening Post*, CCXXXIX (November 19, 1966), pp. 32–37.

Simmons, J. L., Winograd, Barry, *It's Happening*. Santa Barbara, Calif.: Marc-Laird Publications, 1968.

Survey Research Center, Institute for Social Research, University of Michigan, *Adolescent Girls: A National Study of Girls Between Eleven and Eighteen Years of Age*. Ann Arbor: University of Michigan, 1956.

———, *A Study of Adolescent Boys*. New Brunswick, N.J.: National Council Boy Scouts of America, 1955.

———, *A Study of Boys Becoming Adolescents*. New Brunswick, N.J.: National Council Boy Scouts of America, 1960.

"T.A.M. A Lost Word," *Esquire*, LXIV (July, 1965), pp. 30–39.

"Teen Time," *Esquire*, LXIV (July, 1965), pp. 30–39.

The President's Commission on Law Enforcement and Administration of Justice, *The Challenge of Crime in a Free Society*. Washington, D.C.: United States Printing Office, 1967.

"The Teen Agers," *Newsweek*, LXVII (March 21, 1966), pp. 57–72.

"We Are Not Interested," *America*, LXV (August 6, 1966), p. 129.

YMCA of San Francisco, *A Proposal to Discover, Develop, and Demonstrate Ways of Which a Metropolitan Area Can Provide Greater Place, Responsibility, Challenge, and Status for Youth in America*. San Francisco: The YMCA of San Francisco, 1963.

Zimmermann, Gereon, "The Open Generation: We Want Self Identity Before It Is Too Late," *Look*, XXX (September 20, 1966), pp. 105–108.

13 Recreation
and
the Aging

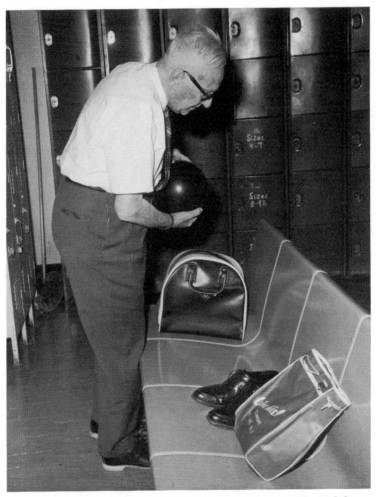

D'Arlene Studio, Courtesy The Lighthouse

PETER J. VERHOVEN

The number of Americans 65 years of age or over exceeds by a million the total population of our 20 smallest states. This means that almost one out of every ten persons in the United States has already celebrated his or her 65th birthday.

Not all of these 20 million persons are aged. Society has too often disregarded the differential processes, such as biological, sociological, and psychological change within the individual, and conveniently stereotyped the older person as aged when chronologically he has reached the age of 65. However, gerontologists agree that chronological age is a wholly unworthy criterion to apply to the aging process. Aging is a continuous process, becoming more accelerated in the middle years of life.

Recreation services for the aging, for the most part, have failed to go beyond the stereotypes of our culture. Many persons working with the aging individual in a recreation service system still view this person as sick, friendless, handicapped by chronic disease, and unable to make his own decisions. Programs for this age group have too often been relegated to a second-rate status, fragmented, and isolated.

Regardless of the setting, it is important to consider the essential, unique, and individual characteristics of persons in later maturity. This is indispensable to the provision of meaningful and successful recreation services. Some older persons do fit the above descriptions but it is the diversities and not the regularities in the aging process which are most impressive. These diversities and their significance to recreation program planning will be explored further, but first let us look at this special population statistically and demographically to disclose the heterogenous composition of aging persons.

DEMOGRAPHIC BACKGROUND

Since the turn of the century the nation's population has tripled to its present 200 million figure. During that same period of time the elderly portion of the population has grown seven times as large, from 3 million to the current 20 million figure. This represents almost 10 percent of the total population. Population experts are predicting that by the year 2000, about 30 million persons will be over 65 years old.

A significant point in planning recreation services for the aging is that the aging population is getting older. Almost 37 percent of these persons are over 75. While the total aged population is anticipated to have a 50 percent increase, the population 85 and older may nearly double over the years 1960 to 1985.[1]

Women dominate the statistics of aging. They outnumber men by a ratio of 135 to 100.[2] Since women are expected to continue to outlive men in this age category, there will be a preponderance of widows in the older population, especially at the higher ages. There are currently almost four times as many widows as widowers.[3] This fact alone has a significant relationship to the nature, type, and delivery of recreation services.

LIVING ARRANGEMENTS

Nearly 80 percent of all older Americans live in households of their own. Only 18 percent of that number live alone. The vast majority of them share their living arrangements with a spouse, relative, or friend.

A very small number of aged persons, only 4 percent, reside in institutions such as nursing homes, hospitals, homes for the aged, or mental institutions.[4] This leaves an overwhelming majority of our aged population who live with varying degrees of self-sufficiency, yet independently, in the community. A third of the nation's aged live in the deteriorating cores of the big cities.[5]

Income

From an income perspective, the elderly must be considered deprived. In 1968, approximately one-fourth of all older persons were living in households with incomes below the poverty line for that type and size of family. Almost 30 percent of the older families had incomes of less than $3,000 in 1968; more than 40 percent of the older people living alone or with nonrelatives had incomes of less than $1,500.[6]

Education

The educational level of older adults is increasing but is still far below that of the population as a whole. Of the 20 million elderly, half never went beyond elementary school; nearly 17 percent are illiterate or functionally illiterate.[7]

Health

Nearly three-fourths of persons aged 65 to 74 have one or more chronic conditions. Over 80 percent of persons over the age of 75 possess such chronic conditions.[8] Among the leading chronic diseases of elderly persons are heart disease, arthritis, diabetes, and activity-limiting visual impairments. It is important to note, however, that half the older persons with a chronic condition report no limitation of activity of any kind.[9]

Labor Force Participation

Since the turn of the century, the percentage of older persons in the labor force has plummeted. In 1900, almost two-thirds of 65+ men were in the labor market; now only about a quarter are.[10] This reduction can be directly attributed to our highly technological society and its accent on youth. The existing trend toward reduced employment of the elderly is not likely to reverse itself. In fact, increased retirement benefits such as social security and pensions may increase the percentage of retired elderly in the years ahead.

Obviously, many of the stereotypes of old age have been proven invalid by the material presented above. These characteristics have a direct or, at least, tangential effect on that population's leisure needs and the provision of adequate recreation service programs for them. In summary, the population of older citizens in this country is large. A modal description of this age group depicts them as being a majority of "older" persons, predominantly female, retired from the labor market with barely subsistence incomes and living in the community. They are a relatively uneducated group with a propensity to chronic illness. Of course, this description pertains to only one segment of the older population as hundreds of thousands are healthy, economically sufficient and able to care for themselves. Perhaps the one most common denominator of this population is their overabundance of time which, because it is not shared with work, becomes almost synonymous with leisure.

LEISURE AND THE AGING

Leisure, as a block of time, represents a significant portion of life to the person in later maturity. Indeed, for some elderly individuals nearly their entire existence is predicated on leisure.

Society in general is today more accepting of leisure as an important and basic component of life. Thus, leisure is viewed as a goal in itself and not merely as a means to the goal of work. However, the elderly segment of the population, those persons born during the latter decades of the 19th Century and first decade of the 20th Century, are less accepting of this concept.

Today's older citizen has his roots in a culture which still manifests a great distrust and skepticism of leisure. This person has been conditioned to a philosophy in which work is all-important, and all material successes and achievements have been directly correlated with work. He is imbued with the puritan ethic which holds that life without work is meaningless. Leisure pursuits represent the epitomy of uselessness to which society has relegated him. Whether the older citizen has been forced out of the mainstream of society as a result of a disabling chronic disease, or through a process of mandatory or self-imposed retirement, he suddenly has great amounts of leisure thrust upon him. Thus, the things which were once afforded through a work experience: recognition, status, prestige, self-expression, and friendship, must now be derived from leisure.[11]

Too often, leisure has proven a poor substitute to replace work as a cultural value. Under these circumstances, leisure is unable to reduce the problem of finding new identity and role. This lack of occupational identity is culturally characteristic of the old, and leisure only supports the position of the old as non-meaningful, nonfunctional or, at best, superannuated.[12] Recreation programs for this age group can provide a chance to realize acceptable roles. New meanings for recreation need to be given whereby persons can use their leisure to contribute significantly to their community and to other individuals, still maintaining a high degree of respectability and dignity although their contributions may not be made through financially remunerative work.

Practitioners working in a recreational setting with older people have a problem of convincing them that leisure activities have more meaning and value than just a "fun" motive. In this context, golf has therapeutic overtones; bridge may sharpen the wits and provide an additional avenue to social contacts; rolling bandages is a service to others; and the sale of a hobby-craft item is acceptable, for it shows society that an older person is still a somebody.[13] Whether the setting for the provision of recreation services to aging persons is a nursing home or a public-supported senior citizens club in the community, the objective must go beyond a program of "childlike" activities offered solely with a diversionary motive in mind.

The ideal goal of recreation service as part of the rehabilitation process in nursing homes, institutions, homes for the aged, and extended care facilities is to provide the basis for a patient's return to the community, or if this is not possible, to at least improve that individual's physical, emotional, and mental health. Similarly, the goal of recreation services to the non-institutionalized aged person should be not to have him become disengaged from society but to make every opportunity available to him to remain useful.

The Connecticut State Department of Health has formulated a number of objectives which are worthy of mention. Although these were written for the nursing home patient in recreation service, they nonetheless have equal significance as positive and developmental objectives of recreation programs for the entire aged population, regardless of the setting.

1. To offset empty hours, monotony and boredom. To help the patient adjust to his illness.
2. To afford personal enjoyment and satisfaction. To improve morale.
3. To develop a feeling of usefulness and belonging, which strengthens a patient's confidence in himself.
4. To relieve tensions arising from mental, emotional and physical strains.

5. To add incentive, to renew and refresh physical strength.
6. To develop skills, talents, and abilities.
7. To stimulate desirable social relationships and promote sociability with fellow patients and staff.
8. To develop awareness.
9. To enrich attitudes, interests, and experiences.
10. To encourage creative, inventive, and expressional efforts.
11. To enable the patient to explore vocational and cultural pursuits.[14]

Each objective may be viewed analogously to a series of rungs on a ladder. The maximum potential of a recreation experience in offsetting the effects of retirement or at parrying the consequences of reduced income or chronic illness will not be met unless the top rungs of the ladder are reached.

Prerequisite to the provision of leisure services which will reach any or all of the aforementioned objectives is a fuller understanding of the aging person as an individual. While the previous demographic analysis was helpful in reaching that end, it did not provide the substantive information on the biological and medical conditions and psychological and sociological factors involved in the aging process.

BIOLOGICAL AND MEDICAL CONSIDERATIONS

Biological change in old age can be conceptualized in terms of loss of the organism's capacity to maintain homeostasis. Characteristically, the older person requires a longer time to readjust to a state of normal functioning. Consequently, it is more difficult for an aged person to maintain a resistance to infectious disease.

With regard to physical exercise, motor performance declines and it takes the older person a longer time to have his pulse rate return to normal. This condition may prohibit sudden bursts of energy and require that adaptations in strenuous physical activities be made. Similarly, age-related changes in vision, hearing, stamina, and memory may affect the aging person's uses of leisure and should be taken into consideration when programs consisting of recreation activities are being provided.

PSYCHOLOGICAL FACTORS

Adjustment to old age or retirement can be aided considerably by the older person becoming psychologically prepared for it. This psychological preparedness is a direct reflection of an individual's personality. A further aid involves the attitude and individual perception of what constitutes a worthwhile role. One extensive study of personality reveals at least three clearcut types of aging persons and their association with high life satisfaction:

1. The "mature" type includes individuals who accept the facts of aging, adjust well to losses, are realistic about their past and present lives, and face death with relative equanimity.
2. The "armored" type includes persons who cling to middle-class behavior patterns, deny aging, keep as busy as ever, and manage to get along very well.
3. The "rocking chair" type, which is growing as society becomes more leisure-oriented, includes persons who accept passivity, sit and rock without feeling guilty about it.[15]

How leisure activity is defined by the older person is important. "In much the same manner as the person preparing for an occupation attempts to determine the worth of the activity on which his identity will be based, the aging retired person established the worth of his avocational activity to legitimize a base for a new social identity—that is, to justify a career of leisure."[16]

The high life-satisfaction type aged person is likely to adapt readily to extensive hours of free time and enjoy the satisfaction inherent in recreation activities. He is able to bridge the gap between the work-oriented existence of the past and the leisure-oriented existence of the present and immediate future. He represents, however, a small minority of the aging population. The majority of the aging are less able to acclimatize as easily and acceptingly to their new leisure lifestyle. Their roots have been too deeply planted in a culture which placed an undue emphasis on work. This type individual is unwilling and unable to accept the social loss of occupational identity and likewise unable to develop in himself a rationale which, to him, legitimizes leisure activity. He perceives participation in groups created for him such as senior centers as another way of society reinforcing a disengaged subculture of aging.

Medical Sociologist, Stephen J. Miller suggests that the way to alleviate this psychological state is by introducing aspects of work into leisure.

> The retired leisure participant is in the unique position not only of having to find an activity in which to participate but, once having found such an activity, if he wishes to reduce his social loss, also of establishing a meaningful rationale for participating in that activity at all. The current compatibility of work and leisure offers the older person an opportunity to change his social situation—that is, to establish the cultural value of his leisure which will act as the basis for a social identity. He may do so by introducing, in much the same fashion as leisure has been introduced into work, aspects of work into his leisure. . . .

> The attitude regarding meaningful leisure participation and the elements of a rationale are expressed in the following comments of the wife of an aging leisure participant: "Hobbies are eccentric when you never make anything (useful) out of them or get anything (monetary) out of them.[17]

The satisfying and constructive use of leisure is a key factor in the morale and self-image of aging persons. After having dropped or at least substantially reduced the work role, it becomes exceedingly difficult for them to find interesting and rewarding uses of their leisure. This factor poses a real challenge to the person involved in providing recreation services to the aging but it is a challenge which must be met if a contribution is to be made to the continuation of a useful and meaningful existence during later maturity. This is not to imply that all people seek to participate in organized recreation services provided for them. Indeed, the individual who is psychologically adjusted may choose not to become an active participant in a recreation activity. This individual, due to prior life patterns, has the ability to seek out meaningful experiences on his own. It is the person who lacks this capacity or has no prior knowledge that a program exists who should be of concern to the recreation practitioner serving the aging.

A point worth repeating is that every aging person is different from every other aging person. Individuality carries over into leisure. How older people use their time is influenced by health, personality traits, and cultural background. In this light, it is important that practitioners keep in mind the individual and his freedom to choose how he wants to pursue his leisure.

There have been many studies on how aging persons use their leisure. The most often mentioned leisure activities of the aging included: reading, watching television, visiting, working around the yard, and going pleasure driving. These activities are strikingly similar to the types of leisure activities participated in by people of other age groups. To continue to perpetuate stereotyped activities and label them "senior citizen" activities is a gross injustice. The uses of leisure in old age can and should be creative, educational, and stimulating. Recreation activities can be a source for further personality development. Therefore, recreation service systems should offer a wide variety of educational, cultural, recreational, and community service activities from which the person in later maturity may choose.

SOCIOLOGICAL FACTORS

Retirement for the aging person now comes earlier than ever before. With increased longevity the present average of 14 years of retirement living is the equivalent of all the free hours available throughout the entire working life. As life expectancy is extended, the demand for leisure services among the aging can be expected to increase substantially. There is less assurance, however, as to where these leisure services will be sought. Several sociological factors seem to influence this. Cultural background, family relationships, income, and adjustment to retirement are but a few of the more important ones.

A much higher percentage of older men and women at the higher social class levels are active in clubs and lodges, community and church, work and travel than is found at the lower social class levels.[21]

This social-class consciousness, coupled with income, may be part of the reason Williams[22] reported only about 10 percent of the total aged population active in organized recreation service programs, and Miller[23] noted that only eight percent of a national sample studied indicated any interest in or participation in organized senior citizen's programs.

A more recent national survey involving 1002 senior centers contains more specific information on the number and type of older participants attending these facilities. The results of that survey reveal, among other things, that only 33 percent of the estimated target population, which was defined as the number of older persons in the community divided by the number of centers, were members. Estimates are that 19 percent are minority group members; 32 percent are poor; 55 percent are socially isolated, 29 percent are male, and 11 percent are disabled.[24]

Most older people spend their leisure and find satisfaction in family relationships. This is contrary to a prevailing belief that family ties are less sustained in the later years. If the older person's leisure participation pattern is centered more around the home and immediate living environment, then this factor may suggest a reversal of the common practice of erecting centers for older people to come to and participate in recreation experiences. H. Douglas Sessoms writes:

> It may be that the home and neighborhood environments contain the majority of resources needed for satisfaction and adjustment and that older people are inclined to want to draw upon those resources, thereby rejecting the recreator's ideal of the highly active participant in organized programs.[25]

Another sociological factor is that of adjustment to retirement. Retirement in a work-oriented society creates problems in status and role. These role and status factors, along with social class, influence leisure activities.

Practitioners' concepts of how leisure should be occupied may be in conflict with what the older person can and wants to do. Much of the present programming for aging persons represents a return to a childlike structure of recreation activities because we too often label old people as childish.

Appropriate recreation service programs can provide an an-
tidote to cultural exclusion and replace the status and role lost
by retirement from an occupational activity.

It is important to understand that biological, psychological,
and sociological aspects of the aging process are indispensable
to determining the leisure behavior of older persons and in
making provisions for recreation service programs for them.
When these three factors are brought into play one gets a
better understanding of the problems and potentials of leisure
services for the aging. It is convenient, therefore, to divide the
aging process into three separate, yet not distinct, categories.
These are: post-retirement, the transitional period, and the
later years.

POST-RETIREMENT

The major dilemma faced by persons upon retirement is the
increase of free time and the decrease in income. Persons
whose lives have focused entirely on work-related activities
and contacts often feel they have been cut off from society
when their occupational role ends with retirement; feelings
of insecurity may result when they venture into new and different types of involvements. They may be unable to cope with
large amounts of leisure and, becoming despondent and dis-
interested with life, fall ill and become permanently institutionalized. These persons are in the minority. Other portions of
the older population may seek answers to their post-retirement
problems by participating in community-sponsored recreation
programs or find solitude in retirement communities. Still
others in this population have learned early to accept large
amounts of leisure and have adequately prepared for it by
developing individual interests to their satisfaction.

TRANSITIONAL PERIOD

A marked physical decline, which frequently limits participation in vigorous physical activities, takes place between the
ages of 75 and 85. Often traumatically affected by the death
of a spouse or close friend, the individual may turn his atten-

tion inward. Social contacts dwindle. His health may become erratic and ultimately cause more serious physical problems. Many persons enter sheltered living situations such as homes for the aged during this period. Recreation services which are modified in relation to the older person's declining physical condition can result in continued involvement and emotional stability.

THE LATER YEARS

The period beyond 85 years old is most often characterized by chronic disability and a deterioration of mental and intellectual powers. Considerable recreation program modifications are necessary to allow for the participant's decline. Treatment-oriented facilities often utilize recreation activities for remedial purposes to prevent further disability in the individual.

It is suggested that perhaps a fourth period in the aging process will emerge. Indeed, it may already have begun to do so. This is the period of pre-retirement in which an education for leisure living would be at the core and could make the transition from work-dominant to leisure-dominant existence smoother. Kaplan, for one, feels that perhaps the answer lies in "inching" toward retirement and suggests a gradual retirement scheme wherein employees are not retired in one fell swoop but a few months per year at a time.[26]

SETTINGS FOR RECREATION SERVICES FOR THE AGING

Service to the aging person is a dynamic ongoing process directed at maintaining or re-establishing him at as complete a level of physical-psycho-social-vocational functioning as possible. Spurred on by recent national movements of formalizing service efforts to the elderly, a multiplicity of agencies have been developed. Recreation services are provided as an ongoing portion of the programs of most of these agencies whose primary ascribed functions usually include the following: rehabilitation, counseling, custodial care, nursing care, housing, education, and recreation.

The information that follows, although in no way exhaustive, contains the majority of settings in which recreation services to older citizens are provided. They are divided into two major categories, Community Oriented, and Institutionally Oriented.

Community Oriented Programs. Here are found publicly or governmentally sponsored programs of recreation and park departments and public welfare departments. Additionally, United Fund agencies, church groups, and retirement communities are illustrations of public programs sponsored by private agencies.

Institutionally Oriented Programs. Among this group are programs found in homes for the aging, hospitals, nursing homes, and extended-care facilities.

Recreation and Park Department Programs

Public programs for older people sponsored by recreation and park departments most generally contain membership groups of elderly individuals, although these older persons are usually not excluded from participating in any portion of the department's program.

The most prevalent activities provided by these programs include card-playing, arts and crafts, dancing, social gatherings, tour programs, and informal discussions on a variety of topics. Because most of the program offerings require physical health and fitness, and since many facilities are not readily accessible without transportation, few older citizens with major impairments participate.

Some local public agencies have expanded traditional senior citizen recreation concepts to include special therapeutic activities for the physically disabled; limited counseling programs; and even employment services such as the "Over-60 Employment Service" of the Arlington County, Virginia, Recreation and Park Department.

Public Welfare Sponsored Programs

The major goal of public welfare programs for older people is to help the elderly person maintain himself in the community rather than seek institutionalization. Unlike the older partici-

394   RECREATION AND THE AGING

pants in park and recreation department sponsored programs, the majority of older adults who frequent these agencies' programs are the less able, older aged persons. Recreation programs usually focus on social interaction but many provide lectures on age-related topics such as health, nutrition, and culture. Casework and referral services are other components of these programs.

Public Programs of Private Agencies

The philosophy of these programs is based on the belief that many older persons haven't the economic resources to pursue their recreation and social needs and, consequently, are often isolated from the community.

Programs of these agencies most often provide avenues for peer group relationships and socialization through social recreation activities. Some programs' activity offerings are quite limited while others are far reaching and provide a diversification of services which include art, music, courses in language, discussion groups, volunteer service, counseling, and even nutritionally balanced meals once a day. A few programs have made a concerted effort to reach out to physically or emotionally disabled older persons by providing transportation, meals at a nominal cost, and rest and first-aid facilities.

Churches have rapidly developed older citizen clubs and offer a wide variety of free time activities. Counseling, casework and referral services may also be provided.

Retirement Communities

The recent development of age-segregated retirement communities in this country may indicate that the older population is becoming more accepting of leisure. Older persons who reside in these communities represent a rather homogeneous group of more affluent and higher educated individuals who, contrary to the majority of the elderly population, have found self-gratification in nonoccupational roles.

In a recent study of four planned retirement communities in Arizona, Bultena and Wood tested the proposition that activities of retirement community residents are consistent with their personal orientations toward leisure.

Continuity was found in the pre- and post-retirement activity levels of the retirees, the prominent pattern being for migrants to disengage from formal groups in their home town and to engage in the social life of the retirement community through increased participation in leisure activities. The migrants were oriented toward a leisure life-style in retirement and were attracted to these age-graded communities partly because of the opportunities available for an active social life in old age.

The data suggest that most retirement community residents prefer to pursue consummatory-oriented roles rather than to engage in instrumental activities. The retirement community provides both the facilities and psychological atmosphere for the type of life they are seeking. Retirement in their home communities, on the other hand, might have exposed them to social norms which affirm the value of work and the importance of older persons remaining in productive roles.

Concentration of these retirees in separate communities appeared to serve three functions in facilitating their adaptation to the retirement role: (1) age peers with compatible leisure orientations provide a reference group which legitimizes leisure behavior; (2) age-density permits the development of specialized recreational programs for this age group; and (3) the age-grading and status-grading in these communities produces a relatively homogeneous population which enhances the likelihood of residents developing viable friendships.[27]

Almost all of the community-oriented programs mentioned above conduct a majority of their activities in a community-based center facility. Regardless of sponsorship, there appear to be a number of common characteristics to all such programs. They provide recreation, education, and social interaction with older persons, and information and referral services. They also share several common problems such as inadequate staff, facilities, and finances, the inability to locate and service individuals with isolating physical or emotional disabilities, and they find it difficult to attract greater numbers of older persons due to transportation-related problems.

One way of potentially overcoming these apparent difficulties may be to effectuate a consolidation of resources much in the same manner as schools, hospitals, and rehabilitation services have consolidated. Information dissemination, protective services, outreach programs, referral to appropriate agencies, and advocacy for the older person in the community, might best be handled through a central service center. In turn, several dispersed activity centers could be established in closer proximity to where the older person is known to engage in leisure pursuits, namely, in his immediate neighborhood. The major functions of these dispersed centers would be recreation, education, and social needs planned and operated primarily by older persons themselves, with consultative assistance being provided.

Institutionally-Oriented Programs

Nursing homes, hospitals, homes for the aged, and extended care facilities provide a protective environment for older persons unable to fully care for themselves due to some degree of physical or emotional disability. Recreation services can play an important and vital role toward the patient's return to a community situation by improving his physical, emotional, and mental health.

These facilities provide shelter for the aging person as well as routine nursing and medical care.

But, the question is, do these kinds of service give a person any incentive to try to rein a measure of independence? The downhill road from partial ambulation to becoming totally bed-bound is mapped out for any aging person who does not receive care that is rehabilitation-oriented. Along the way, he gives up, sinks into apathy and increased dependence, and rapidly loses those mental and physical capacities which might have been salvaged had he been stimulated to do as much as possible for himself.[28]

Recreation activities have the potential to provide rehabilitation. Recent Amendments to the Older American's Act have recognized recreation's important contributions in this area and currently require that nursing homes and homes for the aged have patient activity programs in order to continue to receive benefits from Medicare and Medicaid. Many of these activity programs have been limited in scope and effectiveness due to an all too prevalent adherence to traditionalistic, child-like activities.

Only through experimentation will the true rehabilitation benefits of recreation activities be exploited. Practitioners should, therefore, not arbitrarily preclude some activity as impossible because they have placed self-imposed limitations upon patients. More emphasis should be placed on understanding the patient as an individual and planning should be done for and with him. Obviously some patients may require simplified and adapted activity in a group situation, but this could be managed with each patient working or participating at his own level.

A reevaluation of functions and services is required to provide a maximum number of older citizens with a meaningful variety of leisure activities. Social activities are but one medium among a myriad of experiences in which the older citizen can find self-satisfaction and possibly regain the status and recognition he was once afforded by a work experience. The provision of volunteer services by older citizens to others, noneconomically remunerating work experiences, and continuing adult education are examples of satisfying leisure pursuits not otherwise purely classified as recreation activities which should gain the attention of practitioners who provide recreation service to elderly persons. Examples of these types of programs, some sponsored by recreation service system agencies, others offered by a variety of other local, state, and federal agencies are worthy of mention.

PURPOSEFUL PROGRAMS

Much of the impetus in the way of new and innovative programs has been provided by the Federal government, primarily to aid in the employment of the elderly. These programs have a two-fold objective in that they not only provide a source of income but also an opportunity for meaningful activity for the older person.

Foster Grandparents

Men and women over the age of 60, whose incomes are below the poverty index, are given the opportunity to provide care and affection to children deprived of the love of a concerned adult. The program is administered by the Administration on Aging.

Home Health Aides

Under this national demonstration program, jointly sponsored by the Office of Economic Opportunity, Administration on Aging, and the Public Health Service, older persons are given the opportunity to serve other older people on a one-to-one basis in nursing homes and other longterm care facilities by performing a variety of tasks. Conceivably, with a minimum of training, recreation services could become part of the repertoire of tasks which might be performed by these individuals.

VISTA (Volunteers in Service to America)

Several hundred persons over the age of 60 are working for VISTA, the domestic version of the Peace Corps. They are given the opportunity to contribute a year of service in rural slums, in migrant work camps, and on Indian reservations. The potential of having older persons serving as recreation leaders should be exploited to its fullest capacity.

Operation Green Thumb

Older low-income people are being hired to beautify highways in the rural sections of several states under this program directed by the Office of Economic Opportunity.

Head Start

Older persons may volunteer or apply to become tutors and classroom aides in this program designed to enrich the background of preschool children. The program operates through the Community Action agencies of the Office of Economic Opportunity.

Community Action Programs

Components of the Office of Economic Opportunity's Community Action Program may be designed for older people. These programs enable communities to attack their local poverty problems in a positive and coordinated manner. At least one community which has taken advantage of this program in the context of recreation services for the aging is Cincinnati, Ohio.[29] The Therapeutic Recreation project served to train and employ people of low income in providing much needed therapeutic recreation to elderly patients in sheltered care institutions in the Greater Cincinnati Area. The program was jointly sponsored by the YMCA, College of Mt. St. Joseph, and the Jewish Community Center. Within a 22-month period the project staff of 76 (71 percent of whom were over 69) had served over 1,050 persons in eighteen shelter care facilities.

Private employment programs for older persons have also begun to flourish in a number of communities. In some instances they have been designed to provide middle-aged persons with a second career, but others of them are specifically designed for older retired adults.

Sheltered Workshops

Originally, sheltered workshops were established for rehabilitating the physically handicapped, but most recently they have been found useful to offer nonhandicapped older people an opportunity to work under conditions commensurate with their capacities and abilities. These types of experiences, if exploited in a recreation context, could prove exceedingly beneficial and self-satisfying to the older person. This type of leisure experience may serve a two-fold purpose as well. For example, crafts could be made and the products marketed or given to a special education program for mentally retarded children.

Volunteer Service Programs

Volunteer service is a source of great satisfaction to older people. Volunteer work serves a double purpose; it restores to older people some values earlier inherent in an occupation, and it makes available an abundance of their talents and skills to supplement the often inadequate staffs of community agencies. Examples of successful volunteer service can be found in such programs as the Veterans Administration Voluntary Service, Service Corps of Retired Executives, American National Red Cross, Senior Service Corps, and the International Executive Service Corps.

Home Care Programs

The objective of these programs is to provide a complete spectrum of services required to care for the chronically ill in the home. Usually these programs are under the direction of a physician and involve a multidisciplinary team including nurses, dietitians, medical social workers, and physiotherapists. It is not out of the question to consider that therapeutic recreation service personnel could be added to the ranks of this medically oriented team.

Friendly Visitors

These are programs that recruit volunteers to visit isolated, disabled, and friendless older people in their homes or in nursing facilities. The implications for recreation personnel are obvious.

Volunteer Services

Often called Senior Service Corps, Senior Service Bureau, or Senior Volunteers, these groups of older persons have been organized to provide a variety of volunteer assistance. Some of the more tangible benefits of such programs would be: to provide meaningful roles to older people; to bring needed services to a variety of agencies; to provide a vehicle for the older person to remain active in the mainstream of community life; to provide the retired worker recognition and status; and to enable the older person to grow and learn through new experiences.

Adult Education Programs

Adult education programs for older persons are of relatively recent origin. Many of the present generation of aged lack basic elementary educations and, therefore, may become more isolated from today's highly education-oriented society. A number and variety of agencies recognizing this fact have begun to initiate programs of basic education for elderly persons.

Public schools, community councils, and senior citizen clubs provide a broad range of educational courses which deal primarily with health, nutrition, family life, economics, and other age-related problems. A few states, notably New York, even include a special Division on Aging in their state department of education. Other notable examples of adult education for the elderly can be found in the pre-retirement programs offered by labor unions and industry.

Colleges and universities are becoming increasingly involved in programming for aging persons. From courses on the Sociology of Aging and Social Gerontology, these institutions have moved toward establishing entire curriculums to prepare students to work in several settings with older people. In addition to programs *about* aging persons are a few examples of programs *for* these individuals. The most notable in this category is the Herman L. Donovan Fellowship for Senior Citizens of the University of Kentucky. This program, coordinated by that institution's Council on Aging, is based on the hypothesis that high morale in retirement is achieved by becoming engaged intellectually, socially, and physically, in meaningful experiences.

In the words of the director of the program, Dr. Earl Kauffman, "intellectual engagement comes from attending classes and studying; social engagement from free association with students of all ages, as well as their own peers in the Donovan Club; physical engagement comes from hiking to and from classes, climbing stairs, and, occasionally, enrolling in courses in physical education." This program has come to be known as Educare. It has no restrictions as to geography, previous educational background, or test scores. Tuition fees are waived for Donovan Scholars.

More colleges and universities, especially the community colleges, would do well to explore the possibility of starting programs in Educare. This represents potentially another leisure pursuit with a significant contribution toward making old age a meaningful, productive, and wholly self-satisfying period of life.

PRINCIPLES TO PLANNING

In recent years, greater attention has been placed on learning more about the process of aging. Although much still needs to

be understood, considerable strides have been made in providing increased services to the elderly population. We see new
ways in which the income of the aged is being protected
through pension plans and social security. More attention has
been placed on providing safe and healthy housing for them.
Health services and programs have been greatly expanded.
Another revolution in health services is in the growth of the
rehabilitation concept in both physical and mental health.

There has also been an increased movement toward finding new ways to making life more meaningful for the aging
population. It is in this area that recreation and leisure services have contributed much. Yet, the maximum potentials of
recreation services have not nearly been exploited to their fullest potential. Herein lies the challenge to planners of recreation
services to the aging. From what we now know and understand
about the leisure behavior and recreation interests and needs
of older people several general planning principles might be
offered:

1. More emphasis should be placed on pre-retirement
counseling for the aging. In addition to the more traditional
adult education types of subjects such as health, diet, family,
and economics, which deal mainly with subsistence and suste-
nance topics, should be added topics on an education for leisure
centered living.

2. The older person should be more actively involved in
planning his own types of recreation programs. One interesting
finding of a national study on senior centers was that those
centers with larger budgets and more professionally qualified
staff tended to have fewer participants. On the contrary, those
centers which relied on the senior citizen members themselves
to plan the program attracted large numbers of elderly members.[30]

3. More leisure services should be provided to older persons near their homes and immediate neighborhoods. Several
practical ways of implementing this idea would include the
development of a series of satellite activity centers within easy
access to a large number of elderly community residents. Attention should also be drawn to providing leisure services on
a home visitation basis similar to existing home health visitation
programs. Additionally, more emphasis might be placed on

providing meaningful information on home and family recreation experiences.

4. Recreation activities for older persons should be less prone to the provision of diversionary childlike experiences. Greater attention should be given to permitting work types of experiences in a leisure context. The use of older persons in providing volunteer services should be encouraged and expanded considerably. In a recreation setting, an older person could achieve a dual satisfaction by volunteering to instruct in a given program activity. First, he could gain respect and status from those he is teaching, and secondly, he could gain the enjoyment and personal satisfaction inherent in the activity itself.

5. Greater emphasis must be placed on leisure services reaching that portion of the elderly population who are economically deprived, isolated, or ill and handicapped and reside in the community. Among those items which should be considered are reduced fees for specialized activities and lower transportation fares to recreation related areas and facilities.

6. A more concerted effort must be undertaken by persons working in recreation service for the aging to team their efforts with other community service personnel such as physicians, social workers, planners and architects. Likewise, a more interdisciplinary approach to institutionalized aged must be effectuated with nurses, psychologists, psychiatrists, occupational therapists, and physical therapists.

7. Efforts should be made to greatly minimize or all together reduce the possibility of aging persons becoming embarrassed by participating in recreation activities. Such situations might occur when an individual is unable to continue participating due to the physical exertion of an activity, a time restraint when the performance of the activity is to be completed, or it may be purely a matter of insufficient funds to purchase materials necessary to complete a project.

8. Aging persons should be afforded a greater opportunity to participate in programs with other age groups. Rather than the now common practice of offering age-segregated activities, there should be substituted a more valid criterion, namely, a common interest in the activity. In this same vein, groups of aging persons themselves should not be segregated solely be-

cause of a handicapping condition. Whether this is intentional or not, it is obviously necessitated at times due to the architectural barriers of the building in which an activity is being offered.

9. Professional recreators working with the elderly should assume fewer direct leadership roles and function more nearly in the capacity of resource consultants. In this manner, programs and services would tend to be more nearly planned *with* the older person and not just *for* him.

THE FUTURE

As we move full force into the decade of the Seventies a number of questions must be posed by all who provide recreation services to the aging. Are there positive, contributing roles that can be made available to older people? Will society recognize leisure-oriented roles as expectations of society? Will society enable older people to share in the rising health, social, educational, and recreational opportunities available? The answer to each of these questions must necessarily be an unequivocal *yes*.

The recreation professional must assume the role of social engineer and change agent. In so doing, he will witness a future in which retirement may become the major "career" of most older men and women; education will change its emphasis from one of preparing for occupational competency to one of fostering unlimited creativity; and above all, leisure will become more revered than work. This is the challenge for those who provide recreation services to the aging.

FOOTNOTES

[1] Public Health Service, *Working with Older People,* p. 38.

[2] Administration on Aging, "Older Americans Speak to the Nation," *Aging,* May, 1970, p. 8.

[3] Administration on Aging, p. 8.

[4] Administration on Aging, p. 8.

[5] *Time,* "The Old in the Country of the Young," August 3, 1970, p. 50.

[6] Administration on Aging, p. 10.

[7] Administration on Aging, p. 10.

[8] Elliott M. Avedon, "Aging, Apprehension, and Antipathy," *Recreation Issues and Perspectives,* p. 114.

[9] Public Health Service, p. 42.

[10] Administration on Aging, p. 9.

[11] Jerome Kaplan, "Satisfying Use of Time," p. 143, in *Selected Readings in Aging,* Gerontological Society, Inc., 1967.

[12] Stephen J. Miller, "The Dilemma of Leisure for the Aging," *Recreation Issues and Perspectives,* p. 85.

[13] Jerome Kaplan, "Functions and Objectives of a Senior Citizen's Center," *Geriatrics,* 17:771–777, November, 1962.

[14] L. Hooper, D. G. Mullen, and I. J. Kennedy, *Recreational Service in Connecticut Nursing Homes and Homes for the Aged,* pp. 2–3.

[15] Public Health Service, pp. 6–7.

[16] Stephen J. Miller, pp. 90–91.

[17] Stephen J. Miller, pp. 87–88.

[18] Sebastian De Grazia, *Of Time, Work, and Leisure,* p. 441.

[19] Robert W. Kleemeier, *Aging and Leisure,* 1961.

[20] Jacquelyne Jackson, *Triangularity: Model Neighborhoods, Recreation, Senior Citizens,* unpublished paper given at Region III Model Cities Workshop, October, 1969, p. 10.

[21] E. M. Duval, "Aging Families," *Family Development* (Philadelphia: J. B. Lippincott Co., 1962), pp. 435–475.

[22] Arthur Williams, *Recreation for Senior Citizens,* p. 18.

[23] Stephen J. Miller, "The Social Dilemma of the Aging Leisure Participant," *Older People and Their Social World,* Rowe and Peterson, editors, p. 84.

[24] Nancy N. Anderson, *Senior Centers: Information From a National Survey,* p. 42.

[25] H. Douglas Sessoms, "Aging: Its Implications for the Recreation Movement," *Aging: Its Physiological, Recreational and Health Implications.*

[26] Max Kaplan, *Leisure in America: A Social Inquiry,* p. 46.

[27] Gordon Bultena, and Vivian Wood, "Leisure Orientation and Recreational Activities of Retirement Community Residents," *Journal of Leisure Research,* 2: 3–16, 1, Winter, 1970.

[28] Elliott M. Avedon, p. 116.

[29] Mary E. Bashaw, "Cincinnati's Community Action Therapeutic Recreation Project for the Aged," *Therapeutic Recreation Journal,* 2: 16–19, 3, 1968.

[30] Nancy N. Anderson, p. 45.

BIBLIOGRAPHY

Administration on Aging, "Older Americans Speak to the Nation," *Aging,* May, 1970, 15 pp.

Anderson, Nancy N., *Senior Centers: Information From a National Survey.* American Rehabilitation Foundation, Minneapolis, Minnesota, 1969, 52 pp.

Avedon, Elliott M., "Aging Apprehension, and Antipathy," in *Recreation Issues and Perspectives,* pp. 114–119, edited by Herbert Brantley and H. Douglas Sessoms (Columbia, S.C.: Wing Publications, Inc., 1969).

Bashaw, Mary E., "Cincinnati's Community Action Therapeutic Recreation Project for the Aged," *Therapeutic Recreation Journal,* 2: 16–19, 3, 1968.

Brantley, Herbert, and Sessoms, H. Douglas, *Recreation Issues and Perspectives* (Columbia, S.C.: Wing Publications, Inc., 1969), 173 pp.

Bultena, Gordon, and Wood, Vivian, "Leisure Orientation and Recreational Activities of Retirement Community Residents," *Journal of Leisure Research,* 2: 3–16, 1, Winter, 1970.

De Grazia, Sebastian, *Of Time, Work, and Leisure* (New York: Doubleday and Company, Inc., 1962), 548 pp.

Duvall, E. M., "Aging Families," pp. 435–475 in *Family Development* (Philadelphia: J. B. Lippincott Co., 1962).

Hooper, Langdon, Mullen, Dorothy G., and Kennedy, Irene J., *Recreational Service in Connecticut Nursing Homes and Homes for the Aged* (Hartford, Conn.: Connecticut State Department of Health, 1968), 55 pp.

Jackson, Jacquelyne, *Triangularity: Model Neighborhoods, Recreation, Senior Citizens* (Unpublished paper given at Region III Model Cities Workshop, October, 1969).

Kaplan, Jerome, "Functions and Objectives of a Senior Citizen's Center," *Geriatrics,* 17: 771–777, November, 1962.

Kaplan, Max, *Leisure in America: A Social Inquiry* (New York: John Wiley and Sons, Inc., 1960), 350 pp.

Kleemeier, Robert W., ed. *Aging and Leisure* (New York: Oxford University Press, Inc., 1961), 447 pp.

Lowy, Louis, *Training Manual for Human Service Technicians Working with Older Persons*, Part II (Unpublished manual supported by a grant from the Administration on Aging, 1968), 241 pp.

Miller, Stephen J., "The Dilemma of Leisure for the Aging" in *Recreation Issues and Perspectives*, pp. 83–96, edited by Herbert Brantley and H. Douglas Sessoms (Columbia, S.C.: Wing Publications Inc., 1969).

Projects Division of Gerontological Society, *Selected Readings in Aging:* Parts I and II (St. Louis, Mo.: Gerontological Society, Inc., 1967).

Public Health Service, *Working with Older People*, Vol. II (Washington, D.C.: U.S. Government Printing Office, 1970), 51 pp.

Sessoms, H. Douglas, "Aging: Its Implications for the Recreation Movement," *Aging: Its Physiological, Recreational and Health Implications* (Lafayette, Ind.: Purdue University, October, 1969).

Shelton, Rudolph H., "Recreation for the Handicapped and Aging: The Need in Westchester County, New York," *Therapeutic Recreation Journal*, 2: 9–13, 3, 1968.

Stein, Thomas A., "The Need and Approach to Recreation Services with Older Persons," *Therapeutic Recreation Journal*, 2: 3–10, 2, 1968.

Time, "The Old in the Country of the Young," August 3, 1970, pp. 49–54.

Williams, Arthur, *Recreation in the Senior Years* (New York: Association Press, 1962), 252 pp.

14   Epilogue
and a
Design for Action

H. DOUGLAS SESSOMS

THOMAS A. STEIN

OBJECTIVES AND PHILOSOPHY:
A RESTATEMENT

It is possible that the reader, even though initially attuned to the objectives of this book and the philosophy of the authors (as stated in the first section), can lose sight of these goals. Therefore, before attempting to bring together suggestions which have interpopulation application and to offer a procedure for activating a program, a brief restatement of purpose might be helpful.

To begin, a set of basic assumptions have been made:

1. The overwhelming majority of people in most special populations are found in the community rather than in highly segregated institutions.
2. Activity is a universal need and is universally sought or desired by all people no matter what their advantages or disadvantages, abilities or disabilities, might be. Recreation is a form of activity and, therefore, universally sought.
3. Recreational opportunities can be an important facet of life, i.e., in the growth, development, health, and general well-being of each person.
4. Special populations, in general, have not been the recipients of service from community recreation agencies. In instances where opportunities are afforded, they are too often sporadic or fall woefully short of satisfying the leisure needs of many persons in these minority groups.
5. Recreation programming should be designed so that each individual who has the potential, no matter what his station in life may be, has the opportunity to move into regular, non-sheltered, integrated activities. Community programs should include aspects which could allow a person to develop the needed social and activity skills and experiences to become an effective member of a chosen recreation group.
6. Every present and future recreation professional, as well as other influential community leaders, should be sensitive to the existence and needs of special populations and have a commitment to include such individuals within the framework of general community recreation planning and services.
7. Recreators who have the training and ability to provide competent leadership to a general citizenry can be effective

in serving people from special populations. However, it is essential that these leaders have an orientation to any special or unique differences and problems of such people and be endowed with a set of attitudes which minimize or are void of stigmatizing, biased feelings.

In no way is it being suggested that recreation professionals dilute or withdraw their services to the general population in deference to special groups. All that is desired and expected is a broadening of the base of service to include, rather than exclude, people who have been disenfranchised of their community recreation rights. However, it may be necessary to exercise greater than usual effort in reaching out to the disadvantaged to encourage their use of our services—to go beyond our traditional means of attracting participants. It should be remembered that many of these persons have been excluded or ignored all of their lives. They have "learned" to expect little and, unfortunately, such "learning" has been continuously reinforced. Consequently, recreators are obligated, it seems, to do more than merely state "all persons are welcome." An active seeking out of these citizens is needed.

Once an individual is located, encouragement should be in specific terms. He, as well as the families of some children and adults, should be informed of the program of activities available for various levels of skill development: from beginner to expert; from simple to complex. Although many will be able to enter an on-going activity without disadvantage to others or themselves, others will probably require a sheltered beginning where necessary social and activity skill development can occur.

SEQUENTIAL PLANNING

Some of our authors, when discussing specific populations (i.e., the mentally ill and the physically disabled), recommended the need for a transitional plan to move individuals from an institutional or protective setting to an integrated, nonsheltered community setting through the process of a sequential schema. In effect, they suggested that the participant would enter a regular recreation situation by way of a series of stages. As soon as he has the social and activity skill competencies to move to the next plateau, he would be given the opportunity to do so. Such a developmental progression is, of course, not new. The entire concept of formal education, personnel development in business and industry, and, in fact, nearly everything we do requiring knowledge and skill is based on such a structure. Certainly, we can all recognize that proficiency improvement in recreation skills is, or should be, one of our principle program objectives. At the same time it is important to actively encourage social skill development and in the same manner of sequential development. For example, to select a single black youngster, whose life experience has been almost totally limited to other blacks, and place him into an activity with an all-white group without preparing both him and the group for the transition, or to place a previously oversheltered severely disabled adult in a group of ablebodied persons might be begging for failure. These "block-busting" methods have been tried, often with traumatic results. Some discerning readers might attempt to refute this argument by pondering a Jackie Robinson or other individual who was able to move directly into a nonsheltered situation without going through planned transitional stages. Yet, in nearly every case where this has occurred, it is probable that prior experiences provided a kind of preparation; Robinson's college experiences, athletic and otherwise, were not in a totally segregated environment.

If it can be accepted that a more gradual assimilation is needed for many people in special populations, then we must also admit that there are some persons for whom a particular stage will be terminal or who may always require some degree of sheltering, i.e., the individual who is profoundly mentally retarded, or one who is so physically incapacitated as to require constant care and assistance. However, such persons represent an extremely small percentage of any special population. The fear is that recreation administrators, planners, and policy makers may visualize the sheltered, segregated program as being the final stage of progression for *all* members of a group. Such shortsightedness must be avoided because of the far-reaching implications for the individual. If a person is to become an effective, contributing member of a community—and surely we can all see the advantages of that—and if he is to live a meaningful, satisfying community existence, he must be able to interact successfully with all types of people, not only those in his particular special population.

One other consideration should be mentioned. The authors contend that interaction between people in heterogeneous or mixed groups is potentially beneficial to everyone—not only the disadvantaged. What better way is there to breakdown and even eliminate misunderstanding, misconception, bias, and prejudice than within the integrated play environment? Here is one "arena" where differences, when they exist, can be contained and even subordinated to individual personalities and abilities—where the similarities between people can become the dominant factor in social relations and an appreciation of an individual's uniqueness developed.

COMMON PROGRAMMING TRENDS

Each contributing author was requested to develop his materials according to a predetermined format. Basically, he was asked to discuss the factors that made the group special, that is, the conditions which prohibit the individuals from fully participating in community recreation services, the historical conditions underlying the disability, and the methods society has chosen to employ with each population. Also, attention was to be given to the historical development of recreation services for each disability. Finally, suggestions were made by each author as to how recreation services might be further developed to meet the needs of their respective concerned groups. Little or no attention was given to the identification of activities which could be participated in by the various disability groups; nor were suggestions for the modifications of activities presented for any of the groups.

This is a text on programming for special groups, not a compilation of activities for the disadvantaged. There are scores of excellent recreational activity texts available. There are works which suggest modification of activities in order to meet the needs of the blind, the physically handicapped and the like, but what is missing in the literature is a discussion of the factors that should be taken into consideration when programming for special populations. That became the intent of this work.

In reviewing the contributions of each chapter, we were struck by the commonality of the threads which were woven by each author. Each cited that there were few activities which, with limited modifications and adaptations, could not be entered into by the disadvantaged. In other words, the recreational needs and potentials of the special populations are essentially the same as those of the general population. Secondly, and common to all of the chapters, was the request to make available recreation opportunities for the handicapped populations, for if programs are available to them, they will be available to all. Finally, most authors agreed that need for special information about the disadvantaged is secondary to a full understanding of the importance of recreation services and the recreational behaviors of all our citizens. The specialty aspect relates only to an understanding of the forces which may require adaptations when dealing with each special population group and the many groups in a community which have specific interest and commitment to the disadvantaged population segments.

As stated previously, few community recreation departments will employ recreation specialists to work with each of the disadvantaged groups. More likely, a department will employ one specialist prepared in therapeutic recreation to work with all of the special populations in the community. His primary task will be to coordinate services and to work with the various groups and organizations developing programs for the disadvantaged. His training will enable him to relate to therapeutic recreation specialists who work in an institutional setting, to communicate with medical and special education personnel who have a language related to disability etiology, and to interpret the recreation needs and abilities of the special populations to the other participants in the community recreation service. Recreators prepared to work with special groups are program oriented. This factor more than any other sets them apart from the preparation of other recreation specialists who tend to be activity and administratively oriented. If the department is unable to employ such a person, it is hoped that this text plus participation in various institutes and workshops would adequately prepare any recreator to assume this role.

Programming is the heart of the recreation service. Through it, recreation departments demonstrate the meaning and validity of the recreation experience. If the program for special populations lacks depth and fails to meet the needs of these clients, chances are the recreation program in general is failing to meet the needs of the people it proposes to serve. Programs for special populations must be founded on the same sound principles of recreation programming used for nondisadvantaged groups.

Among the basic program principles are:

1. Opportunities for recreation experiences must be varied and within the experience range of the participants.
2. Recreation opportunities must be consistent with the lifestyles, i.e., social background, educational attainment and interests, of the people served.
3. Recreation programs should offer both learning experiences for the development of skills, which may be used in leisure moments, as well as structured events and facilities which may be engaged in under supervision or at one's own volition.
4. Recreation programs are modified and influenced by a variety of social and physical forces—a full understanding of the role played by these is essential to the successful conducting of recreation experiences.
5. The recreation experience is more than momentary participation; it embraces the anticipation and memory of the event as well as the event itself.
6. A recreation program should be based upon the expressed interest of the people it serves as well as the knowledge and skills and philosophy of the recreation specialist. A blending of the two is desired.
7. Recreation programs are an extension of the philosophy of recreation services and require sound financing, adequate facilities, and proper leadership if program objectives are to be achieved.
8. Recreation programs should be evaluated in terms of the stated objectives of both the agency and the participants.

Programs are influenced by a number of factors. Primary among them are the climatic conditions, the seasonal aspects, the recreation experiences of the groups, the leadership and facilities available, sociological and psychological backgrounds of the participants, and the resources of the agency and community. The latter two are more frequently emphasized when considering programs for special populations. The first of these two was fully discussed by each author. The element of community resource evaluation and a program of community action is now proposed. Its importance is essential to the successful development of community recreation services for the disadvantaged and disabled populations.

A PLAN FOR ACTION

Let us assume, for purposes of this discussion, that the reader will either be serving as a community recreation generalist with a program responsibility for special groups or will be a therapeutic recreation specialist working in the community. If he is to translate a sensitivity for special populations into community action, it will require careful and systematic planning. Therefore, it may be useful to comment on the ways or means of gathering essential information upon which to base his planning efforts. First he will need to know some relevant facts about the specific population he intends to serve. He also needs to have some awareness of who and what his resources are, how to make use of them, and how to dovetail the recreation services of his agency with those of other public, private, commercial, and voluntary health agencies and institutions for the ultimate benefit of the potential participant.

In this section it is our intent to offer some suggestions that may be helpful in approaching the problems of data-gathering and of implementing a plan of followthrough to achieve a satisfactory result. It should be understood that these proposals are far from exhaustive or all-inclusive. Perhaps they could be better considered as a point of departure for community study for there are many methods and procedures for accumulating and assimilating pertinent information.* Also, we can expect that each community has some uniqueness that may require the use of alternative approaches. Resources— agency, leadership, financial, etc.—will vary from community

* One excellent resource that the reader would find profitable is: Roland L. Warren, *Studying Your Community* (New York: The Free Press). This book presents a useful methodology as well as a wide variety of questions that should be answered as they relate to a variety of social concerns—including recreation services.

to community. Population size, density, and other demographic considerations will also vary. Therefore, the following format is quite general and, as noted above, should be tailored to each situation and to each specific population under study.

Demographic Background

Although it may be feasible to begin some program development for some groups without gaining specific information on population size, location, background, and needs of those groups, it seems logical that a preliminary survey should be conducted to gain that knowledge which could affect our planning and perhaps help avoid costly errors in judgment. The purpose here is to acquire answers to such questions as:

1. Who are the community members in the special population?
2. Approximately how many are there in that population?
3. Where do they live in the community?
4. What is their existing situation in terms of age, education, employment, ethnic or racial background, level of affluency, amount of unobligated time, mobility, etc.?
5. Which institutions, agencies or organizations are now offering service to that group (i.e., public health departments, mental health clinics, public social service or welfare agencies, community action agencies, vocational rehabilitation counselors and programs, youth programs—YMCA, YWCA, CYO, B'nai B'rith, Boy Scouts, Girl Scouts, churches and synagogues, city and county officials, police and corrections officials, school systems, nonpublic health agencies—local chapters of the Association for the Mentally Retarded, United Cerebral Palsy, Easter Seal Society, etc.)?
6. What specific types of service are offered?
7. What is the extent of such assistance, i.e., how many of a given population are being reached?

For some groups, such as the economically disadvantaged, racial minorities, physically disabled, visually impaired, mentally retarded, youth and aging, the above information is generally accessible although, to acquire it, some painstaking effort will be needed. In most of these cases, however, it may be difficult or impossible to gather all-inclusive information because there are still situations where individual members of some groups are "hidden" from the community and its social service agencies and professions.

Some populations, e.g., the mentally ill, ex-youthful and adult offenders, alcoholics and narcotic addicts (whether rehabilitated or not) are very difficult to assess. Public attitudes toward them are often so negative that neither the individuals having the problem nor those who provide medical or rehabilitative assistance are particularly anxious to discuss individual cases. In fact, many of these professionals and agencies refuse to divulge such information in order to protect their clients from adverse public scrutiny. This is probably as it should be—at least as long as society continues to maintain a prejudicial attitude towards these members of the community. However, by coordinating our efforts with mental health hospitals and clinics, correction agencies and alcoholic and narcotic rehabilitation programs which serve persons in a specific community, it is becoming increasingly possible to gather sufficient information about their clients or patients. We should be able to at least identify these people and encourage their participation in a recreation program. To do this, of course, would require the recreator to assume a highly professional posture that would assure the protection of the individual. This means that the community recreator should become a part of the service team doing all possible to provide a successful experience while at the same time avoiding the divulging of confidential information which could be detrimental to the client.

To further support this contention we are finding that more and more recreation specialists working in institutional settings, are attending to the question of how to develop channels of communication with community recreators to assure a continuation of recreation opportunities for discharged patients. Some correction officials are also recognizing the need for dialogue with community leaders which can help in promoting a smoother transition from prison back to the community for those persons who have paid their debt to society and in reducing the frequency of their reincarceration.

Determining Existing Leisure Opportunities

Once the etiology of a population has been reasonably well established, it is important to determine what, if any, leisure and recreation opportunities now exist in the community for that population. We should discover:

1. What recreation or leisure programs are now available to serve a special population?
2. Which agencies or groups are providing these services?
3. What is the extent of such services, i.e., who in that population are the recipients?
4. How frequently are these services offered—continuously, occasionally or rarely?
5. What types of activities are involved?

After having accumulated demographic information about a group and learning how they are currently being served, the recreator is then in a position to consider unmet needs and wants. Determining what is still needed for a given population also requires the asking of questions. Some of the answers may come from interviews with concerned agency officials and, to an extent, some may come from the professional knowledge and experience of the investigating recreator. But it is also wise to solicit the "target" population to get their individual and collective expressions of needs and desires. These answers could result in verifying, amending and/or adding to previous information. Once this has been accomplished, it is possible to ascertain:

1. Which recreational program services need to be initiated or expanded?
2. Which agencies are the logical ones to provide these services, i.e., which have the organizational objectives and resources to meet these needs?
3. Which program services can be started immediately and which ones will require longer range planning?

This is a critical point in our study. If we accept the assumptions that no single agency, including the public recreation department, can, or should, provide for *all* of the recreation needs of *all* of the people in a community, and that overlapping of services by two or more agencies should be minimized, it then seems logical that efforts to coordinate programs should be initiated. This could result in cooperative program relationships among agencies which are mutually supportive. However, even where this occurs, because of community wide limitations on facilities, leadership and funds, attempting to fill all gaps to meet all program needs for all groups would be virtually impossible. But a beginning should be made!

When considering the whole notion of cooperation and of coordinating our efforts with those of others, it should not mean the mere referral of an individual to another agency for service. Rather, it should mean an invitation to join forces— to share strengths and resources which can assure the highest quality and most relevant services possible for our citizenry. This would be especially needed in the first stages of service, i.e., where sheltered activities are appropriate. These activities often require additional facilities or facility use, more leadership and, consequently, increased finances. Probably few budgets are able to contend with a sudden or extensive expansion of programs. However, another agency might be able to offer initial funding to pay for additional professional leadership and equipment. And they might also have a ready reservoir of volunteers to assist in some aspects of the program. One critical example of this latter support is where transportation of participants is a major concern.

In the final analysis, it would be of benefit to approach any problem of service, that is within the overall objectives of our agency, with an attitude of "how can we do it?" rather than "should we do it?"

SUMMARY

Throughout this text we have consistently described recreation as a vital force in the lives of all people, especially those who suffer neglect and discrimination. Interestingly, the differences between men may either serve as an asset or limitation, depending upon society's interpretation of the difference. Save for the matter of labeling, those who have been classified by our authors as "handicapped," because of the deficiencies they suffer, might be the advantaged in another society. The only thing common to all is the human need for activity and a potential of recreation as a means to fulfill that need.

Knowledge is essential in the effective planning of services for the public. When dealing with those segments, the special populations which had been neglected in the past, it is even more important for the recreator to understand the dynamics at work. He needs to know the characteristics of the disadvantaged, the reasons they are defined as "special." Hopefully this knowledge will free him in his services to the needy; without it, he may grope in ignorance and fail to realize the potential of all those he serves. One should never make the error of thinking that because individuals suffer disabilities, they are limited in their interests or their ability to perform.

In addition to knowledge about the special populations, the recreator working with the blind, the physically handicapped, the alcoholic, etc., must be soundly grounded in a philosophy of programming and services. He needs to know recreation concepts and their relevance to the lifestyles of the people with whom he deals. He also needs to know something about the problem-solving and community analysis techniques, as these are essential to the successful development of services to the disadvantaged. It is hoped that he will utilize the materials offered as a guide for the improvement of these skills and as a reminder of the reasons for their application.

Recreation experiences are a necessary ingredient in the life process. No stage of development is without them. Their unique function may vary according to life stage, but, without satisfaction through involvement, life would be without its salt to give it savor. Much has been written about the importance of play as an educational and socializing force for the child. It is equally as important as a balancer in the daily experiences of the adult. Little, however, has been written about its importance in the development of various psychological and social diseases, the treatment of these conditions, the rehabilitation of the disadvantaged and their return to the community should they have been institutionalized. It was the purpose of this text to focus upon the role of recreation in these stages of life, particularly the rehabilitative and maintenance periods.

Although several authors spent a greater portion of their time on the disadvantaged in the institutions, in all instances the importance of recreation in the community for the special population was also cited. The majority of those labeled "disadvantaged" are not institutionalized. Programs proclaiming to remedy the conditions which contribute to social plight of the handicapped must take into consideration the recreation behaviors of these people or else they are doomed to failure. Recreation is a part of a lifestyle of all individuals and the recreation professional can significantly contribute to programs of social action. If, however, the recreator does not understand his role in this domain, he may contribute to the continuing process of neglect or the inadequate development of plans of social remediation. Recreation neglect is not the only factor in the lifestyle which contributes to the difficulties of the black, the alcoholic, physically handicapped, etc., but it is an important ingredient and should not be overlooked by the planners of social service and rehabilitation.

Finally, the success of a recreation program for the disadvantaged must be evaluated in terms of the objectives of the program. These may be in the form of specific program intentions or they may be statements of long-range goals and objectives. Both are needed in the evaluation process. It is hoped the thinking of the contributing authors has helped the reader to conceptualize some of these objectives and has offered directions for the development and implementation of meaningful experiences through recreation for America's disadvantaged populations.

Index

Addams, Jane, 7, 24
Addiction:
  recreation in, 184-190
  theories of, 178
  treatment and rehabilitation of,
    183-190
Adolescents (*see* Youth)
Adult education courses for the
    visually impaired, 271-273
Adult offenders, 3
Adult recreation programs for the
    visually impaired, 271-273
Aging, the:
  demography of, 382-384
  education level of, 383
  health of, 382
  income of, 382
  labor participation of, 383-384
  leisure and, 384, 405
  physical decline in, 391-392
  planning principles for, 401-404
  recreational services for, 382
Alcoholics Anonymous, 60
Alcohol and drugs:
  and class distinctions, 179, 180
  use of, 170
  and youth, 372
Alcohol, classification of drinkers
    of, 173
Alcoholism, 3, 18
  and alcohol addiction, 173-174
  effects of, 174
American Association on Mental
    Deficiency, 69-70, 73-77
    passim
American Park and Recreation
    Society, 158
American Psychiatric Association,
    134
American Red Cross, 140-142
American Standards Association,
    212
Amphetamines, 175, 176
Arts in youth programs for the
    visually impaired, 270

Barbiturates, 175-176
Behavior, leadership patterns in,
    37-39
Behavioral model of mental illness,
    135
Boy Scouts, 99
Bureau of Colored Work, 327
Bureau of Outdoor Recreation, 300

Charity and dependency, 2, 4
Chronic disability, 199
Civil disorders, 285, 288, 311,
    341-344
Class distinctions in alcohol and
    drug use, 179-180
Cognitive function in the visually
    impaired, 247-248
Cognitive process, 95
Committee on Statistics for the
    Blind, 239
Community Action Programs, 305
Community recreation programs,
    development of, 5-10
Congenital disability, 198
Coordinating council, establishing,
    52-53
Correctional philosophy:
  punishment in, 107-109
  rehabilitation in, 109
Corrections:
  definition of, 107
  rehabilitative approach in, 108
  work-release programs in, 110
Corrections and recreation:
  arts in, 118-119
  drama in, 119
  games, social, 121
  in half-way houses, 124-125
  innovations in, 115-116
  leisure in, 111
  mission of, 115
  movies, TV, and radio in, 120
  music in, 119
  needs of, 122-124
  photography in, 121

Corrections and recreation:
(continued)
  programming of, 117-122
  reading and writing in, 121
  and recreation programs in,
      112-115
  restrictions of, 125-126
  sports in, 111, 117-118

Delivery of recreation services:
  facilities for, 60
  knowledge of disabilities in,
      60-61
  money for, 58-59
  problems of, 57-61
  staff for, 59-60
Demography of the aging, 382-384
Demography of racial minorities,
      328-330
Dependency, treated by recreation
      programs, 46-47
Dix, Dorothea, 138, 139
Drug addiction:
  compared to habituation, 177
  World Health Organization
      definition of, 172
Drug addicts and recreation:
  counselling in, 187, 188
  individual needs in, 186
  objectives of, 186
  in prevention, 189
  roles of recreators in, 184-185,
      187
  and treatment of addicts,
      184-189
  setting of, 185
Drug use:
  and abuse, 170
  and affluence, 171
  as recreation, 170-171
  and social behavior, 181-183
  and social relationships, 171-172,
      173
  and youth, 372

Ear, the, 242-243
Easter Seal Society, 223, 224
Economically deprived (see also
      Poverty):
  description of, 284, 284

number of, 283
Economically disadvantaged, 3, 18
Emotional responsiveness, 95
Employment of the handicapped,
      212, 213
Etiology of mental retardation, 74
Etiology of poverty, 289
Eye, parts of, 241, 242

Facilities for recreational programs,
      60
4-H Club, 99
Friends Asylum, 137
"Fun and games" classification,
      235

Games, in corrections, 121
  and sports in, 111, 117-118
Games in youth programs for the
      visually impaired, 268-269
Girl Scouts, 99
Grey Ladies, 47

Half-way houses, 124-125
Hallucinogens, 176-177 (see also
      Drug use; Drug addiction)
Handicapped:
  assessment of, 55
  counselling of, 56-57
  identifying needs of, 53, 56
Health of the aging, 383, 391-392
Hemiplegia, 199
History of attitudes toward the
      mentally ill, 136-139
History of the mentally retarded,
      66-69
History of rehabilitation services,
      3-4, 14
  before 1900, 4-5
  before World War I, 4
  expansion of services, 5
  institutional recreation, 10
Hull House, 7

Identifying special population, 53,
      56
Individual needs of drug addicts,
      186
Income of the aging, 382
Industrial Revolution, 8

Innovations in corrections
    recreation, 115-116

Kennedy, Joseph P. Jr. Foundation,
    15
Kerner Commission, 307, 325
Kinesthetic sense organs, 243-244

Leaders, roles of, 97
Leadership, patterns of behavior in,
    37-39
Leisure:
    and the aging, 384-405
    in corrections, 111
Leisure and the aging, 384-405 (see
    also Recreation programs
    for the aging)
    medical factors in, 386-387
    objectives of recreation for, 385
    psychological factors in, 387-389
    settings for, 392-397
    sociological factors in, 389-391
Leisure classes, 301
    classification of, 301-302
    recreational problems in, 301-302

Medical classification of mental
    retardation, 72-77
Medical factors in aging, 386-387
Medical model of mental illness,
    134-135
Membership group, 88
Mental health practice,
    developments in, 144-145
Mental Illness and Health, Joint
    Commission on, 139
Mental illness, 3, 11, 18, 46, 47
    defined, 131, 132-136
    history of attitudes toward,
        136-139
    making choices, 47-48
    misconceptions about, 133
    new perspectives in care, in
        1960s, 149-151
    recreation in hospitals for,
        141-143
    recreation services for, after
        World War II, 145-148
Mentally ill, recreation programs
    for, 155-163

changes in mental health practices
    in 1960s, 152-154
evaluation of patient in, 155-156
programming of, 156-157
transitional activities in, 157
    in community, 157-158
community recreation services,
    159-161
recreators in, 161, 163
Mentally retarded, the, 3, 13, 18,
    57
    attitudes toward, 48
    classification of, 72-77
        in AAMD medical classification,
            75-76
        by IQ, 73
    definition of, 69-71
    etiology of, 74
    history of, 66-69
    mongolism in, 77-78
    physical, social, and mental traits
        of, 83-87
    psychological factors of, 79-81
    social factors in, 81-82
Mentally retarded and recreation,
    65-107
    activities for, 94-95
    program guides for, 96-97
    programs for, and the
        community, 98-99
    recreation needs of, 92-93
    role of leaders of, 97
    and social adjustment, 71
    social dynamics in, 87-92
Mobility in the visually impaired,
    247-248
Mongolism, 77-78

Narcotics addicts, 3, 18 (see also
    Drug addition; Drug use)
National Advisory Commission on
    Civil Disorders, 311
National Association of Retarded
    Children and Adults, 59
National Easter Seal Society, 15,
    212, 215
National Institute of Mental Health,
    131
National Mental Health Act, 150

National Multiple Sclerosis Society,
    158
Negro (*see also* Racial minorities)
    and public recreation, 325
    and public service sector, 336
    history of, 336-341
Neurosis, definition of, 134
New York Service for
    Orthopedically Handicapped
    Children, 222

Objectives of recreation for drug
    addicts, 186
Operant conditioning, 50-51
Opiates, 176

Park and recreation areas, planning
    of, 9
Park and recreation programs for
    the urban poor, 296-298
Perceptual awareness, 95
Physical fitness, 95-96
Physically disabled, the, 3, 11, 18,
    46, 52-53
    adventitious, 198
    attitudes toward, 205-210
    chronic, 199
    concepts in programs for,
        214-215
    congenital, 198
    and environment, 210-214
    handicapped, 199
    hemiplegia, 199
    paraplegia, 199
    problems of, 201-206
    quadriplegic, 199
    terminology for, 198-201
    traumatic, 198
Playground Association of America,
    6, 7, 326
Playgrounds in New York City,
    1897, 9
Poverty (*see also* Recreation
    programs for the poor)
    academic achievement in, 291
    affluence in, 288
    and civil disorders, 285, 288, 311
    emotional health in, 290, 291
    etiology of, 289

incidence of, 286-287
nature and extent of, 283-288
needs index, 308-311
OEO guidelines for recreation
    services for, 312
physical health in, 293, 294
psychological effect of, 292-293
recreation program planning for,
    302-308
in rural life, 298-300, 312
in urban life, 294-298, 311
values in, 289
President's Commission on Law
    Enforcement (Crime
    Commission), 106
Primary group, 88, 89
Problem-solving approach, 31-42
Programs for the mentally retarded,
    96-99
Psychological factors in aging,
    387-389
Psychological factors in mental
    retardation, 79-81
Psychosis, 134

Racial minorities, 3, 11
    culture forms in, 333-334
    demography of, 328-330
    socioeconomic climate of,
        329-330
    history of, 334-341
    blacks in, 336-341
    inadequacies in recreation
        programs for, 326-327
    population growth rate, 345
    in pre-riot and post-riot eras,
        341-344
    regression in recreation programs
        for, 326-327
    social organization of, 330-332
Recreation:
    among addicts, 184-190
    as agent of change, 12
    consumer spending on, 296
    definition of, 325
    and ex-prisoners, 12
    in ghetto, 325
    as government function, 9
    in leisure classes, 301-302
    needs of, among the mentally

retarded, 92-93
role of, 13
and social revolution, 234, 284
therapeutic, 230, 250, 254
Recreation programs:
assumptions in, 411-412
conflicts in, 30, 31
creation of dependency in, 46-47
evaluation of, guide for, 32,
    39-41
evaluation and research in, 61-62
factors in development of, 34-36
failure of community programs,
    195
flaws in, 11
in hospitals, 140-145
in corrections, 112-126
and needs of population, 44
nontraditional, 11, 12
objectives of participants in, 33
personalities of, 33
plan for action in, 417-421
present state of, 10
principles of, 416
problems of delivery, 57-61
problem-solving approach in,
    31-32
resources for, 35-36
responsibility of, 49
sequential planning in, 412-414
trends in, 414-416
Recreation programs for addicts,
    184-189
roles of recreators in, 184-185,
    187
setting of, 185
individual needs in, 186
objectives of, 186
counselling in, 187-188
in prevention of addiction, 189
Recreation programs for the aging,
    381-382, 384-404 (see also
    Leisure and the aging)
home care in, 400-401
institutional, 396-397
meaningful activity in, 397-400
park and recreation programs for,
    393
public or private programs for,
    394

public welfare programs for, 393
retirement communities, 394-396
settings for, 392-397
Recreation programs for the
disabled:
history of, 196-198
integrated with that for the able-
    bodied, 221-224
Recreation programs for the
mentally ill, 155-163
Recreation programs for the poor,
    312-314
future of, 319-320
guidelines for, 312
improvement and development
    of, 317-319
meeting needs in, 313-314
special programs for, 314-316
Recreation programs for racial
minorities:
expectations for, 347-348
implications for, 344-349
inadequacies in, 327
problems in delivery of, 345-347
regression in, 326-327
Recreation programs, selling of,
    50-52
Recreation programs for the visually
    handicapped, 266-271
Recreation programs for youth,
    372-374
Recreation therapy at Menninger
    Clinic, 142
Recreators:
in community recreation
    programs for mentally ill,
    162-163
as controllers, 258
as counsellors, 256-257
function of, 16
leadership in, 29, 30 (see also
    Leadership)
of mentally retarded, 97
as observers, 257
reference group, 88
role in future, 63
role in therapeutic recreation,
    255-256
as supervisors, 257
as teachers, 256

Rehabilitation Institute of Chicago,
    51-52
Rehabilitation of the visually
    impaired, 232, 275
Rural poverty, 298-300, 302-308,
    312

Segregation of the disadvantaged, 4
Senses of smell and taste, 244-245
Sensory reception, 240-245
Settlement houses, 7-8, 9
Sheltered programs for the disabled:
    funding for, 217
    outdoor recreation programs for,
        218-221
    volunteers in, 215
Social adjustment in the mentally
    retarded, 71, 81-82
Social dynamics in recreation for
    the retarded, 87-92
Social interaction, 95
Social organization of racial
    minorities, 330-332
Social revolution:
    minorities in pre-riot era, 341-342
    in post-riot era, 342, 344
    and recreation, 234, 284, 311,
        325
Socialization of youth:
    alcohol and drugs, 372
    commercial recreation, 370
    dating, 369
    the in-group, 370
    juvenile delinquency, 370
    and recreation, 372-374
    sex, 368, 372
Sports, in corrections, 111,
    117-118
Sports in programs for the visually
    impaired, 269

Technological advancement and the
    disadvantaged, 6-7
Terminology of the visually
    impaired, 232, 233, 235
Therapeutic recreation, 230, 250,
    255-256

United Cerebral Palsy Association,
    215
Urban poverty, 294-298, 311

Visually impaired, the, 3, 271-273
    adult recreation program activities

    for, 267-271
    adventitiously, 248-249
    attitudes of parents toward,
        249-250
    attitudes of society toward,
        240, 251
    and civil rights, 234
    classification by functioning,
        258-264
    congenitally, 248
    discrimination against, 252
    and loss of recreation, 231, 233
    older adult recreation programs
        for, 273-275
    physical aspects of, 236-238, 250
    and play, 229
    population of, 238-240
    psychological and social factors
        for, 234
    and recreation needs, 252
    rehabilitation of, 232
    selection of activities for, 231
    social contacts of, 249
    terminology of, 232, 233, 235
    and therapeutic recreation,
        254-258
    youth recreation programs for,
        266-271

World Health Organization, 172

Youth:
    community influences on,
        366-367
    conformity among, 363-364
    deviations in, 357-358
    excitement in, 364-365
    heredity in, 357
    and home and family, 359-361
    independence in, 362-363
    and leisure, 356
    needs of, 356-357, 361-367
    psychological aspects of, 358-359
    and recognition, 362
    and recreation, 372-374
    and school, 365-366
    socialization of, 368-372
    success in, 363
YMCA, 29, 99, 125
YMHA, 272
Youthful offenders, 3
YWCA, 99